CATALYSIS AND CHEMICAL
KINETICS

CATALYSIS AND CHEMICAL KINETICS

by

A. A. BALANDIN, A. BIELAŃSKI, G. K. BORESKOV,
S. BRETSZNAJDER, M. M. DUBININ, B. JEŻOWSKA-
TRZEBIATOWSKA, E. JÓZEFOWICZ, E. I. KLABUNOVSKII,
Z. SOKALSKI, E. TRESZCZANOWICZ, W. TRZEBIATOWSKI,
N. A. VASYUNINA, K. B. YATSIMIRSKII

ACADEMIC PRESS INC., New York
WYDAWNICTWA NAUKOWO-TECHNICZNE, Warszawa

ACADEMIC PRESS INC.
111 FIFTH AVENUE
NEW YORK, NEW YORK 10003

Library of Congress Catalog Card Number: 64-22382

PRINTED IN POLAND
by D.R.P. Warszawa

PREFACE

In the post–war years, due to considerable efforts and large financial support, many new chemical laboratories and scientific institutes have been organized in Poland. The first, and greatest, post-war difficulties have now been overcome, and the organization period has come to an end. Evidence of this is the number of papers published and the growing number of young, able scientific workers successfully developing chemical investigations at universities, in scientific institutes of the Polish Academy of Sciences, and in industrial laboratories.

With the progress of science, in many cases new research methods have been introduced and branches of chemistry developed which were not represented in Poland before. It may be stated beyond any doubt that our scientific potential in chemistry, so painfully reduced by the war, during which almost all our laboratories had been destroyed and a great part of the scientific staff exterminated, develops slowly but systematically, though still there are many serious difficulties to be overcome, the available financial means not being always sufficient.

However, there are branches of chemistry whose development in Poland should be faster and more extensive than they actually are, the more so as in the past important scientific achievements have been connected with the names of Polish scientists. I mean particularly chemical kinetics, and it is the achievements in this field in the post-war period as well as the present state that are given in this book. In the study of kinetics such Polish chemists as J. Boguski, L. Bruner, J. Zawidzki, J. Zawadzki, M. Centnerszwer, K. Jabłczyński, E. Bekier, W. Staronka, have achieved importance.

The founder of the School of Polish Kinetics was J. J. Boguski, a co-worker of Mendeleev, lecturer at the Chief High School in Warsaw and later professor of the Warsaw Technical University. The results of his classic studies on the rate of chemical reactions in heterogeneous systems were published in the first volume of "Kosmos", the periodical of the

Polish Naturalist Society, in 1876. There he formulated and proved mathematically the classic law of heterogeneic reaction rate $\dfrac{dx}{dt} = KF(a-x)$, which had been derived by him independently of western authors, and it was confirmed by W. Ostwald in the 1st edition of his "Handbuch d. allg. Chemie" in 1887 We have therefore the full right to call this equation Boguski's law. It has been established on the basis of an understanding of the kinetics of such reactions as dissolution of zinc or marble in acids.

The kinetics of chemical reactions was also the object of interest of L. Bruner, professor of the Jagiellonian University at Kraków, as well as S. Tołłoczko and K. Jabłczyński, professors of the Lwow and Warsaw Universities. Works in this field were continued for many years by M. Centnerszwer, who met his tragic death in 1942. He investigated the mechanism of dissolving metals in acids and, together with W. Heller, was the author of an original adsorption theory of this process which assumed that adsorption is the first stage in the reaction of dissolving metals in acids. It was he who took special notice of the phenomenon of passivation of metals. Besides, he was concerned with kinetics and mechanisms of dissociation of lead, thallium, silver nitrate, carbonates as well as peroxides.

J. Zawidzki, the co-worker of Walden and Ostwald (1866–1928), consequently and critically developed the principles of Van't Hoff's and Arrhenius's kinetics.

The main object of his investigations was "disturbed" reactions, which differ from the "spontaneous" ones by the substrate or product, or both of them, exerting either positive or negative catalytic influence upon the rate of the process. Autocatalytic reactions of this kind are met with more often than the spontaneous ones, which may be regarded as a particular case of autocatalytic reactions, in which neither the substrate nor the product exerts a catalytic influence upon the reaction rate.

J. Zawidzki established a general equation for autocatalytic reaction rate, breaking with the classical way of classifying kinetic equations according to the number of molecules. Analysis of this general equation enabled Zawidzki to derive eight basic types of kinetic reaction concerning autocatalysis. Zawidzki also introduced into the kinetic equations the concepts of relative concentration and reduced time, the application of which considerably facilitated the use of kinetic equations. The results of these investigations were presented in the paper "The systematics and kinetics of autocatalytic reactions", published in the Bulletin of the Polish

Academy of Sciences and Letters during 1916. Unfortunately, the war period did not favour wide distribution of these achievements.

The principal ideas of Zawidzki were presented in the monograph "Chemical Kinetics", published posthumously in 1930. It would be right, therefore, to reissue this book, which is a classical publication of Polish chemistry and, at the same time, a rarity in our libraries, the more so as the here present Professor Józefowicz, former collaborator of Professor Zawidzki, surely will not refuse his help.

Beside Boguski and Zawidzki, Professor J. Zawadzki was undoubtedly the most outstanding representative of Polish kineticists.

Many years have elapsed from the time we had the pleasure of hearing him speaking at the first post-war Congress of the Polish Chemical Society in Wrocław. Professor J. Zawadzki (1886–1950) was not only a physical chemist, but also had the ability of making use of his theoretical knowledge in application to technology.

Zawadzki's extensive works on the statics and kinetics of the thermal dissociation reaction of carbonates and sulphates, performed in co-operation with Professor Bretsznajder, were widely discussed in the scientific world. These authors found a linear dependence of the reaction rate of heterogeneous dissociation on the distance from the state of equilibrium for reactions of great importance in inorganic technology. The kinetics and mechanism of catalytic oxidation of ammonia on a contact was another sphere of interest of Professor Zawadzki in the field of fundamental research. He proposed a new reaction scheme, assuming the formation of active complex $O-NH_3$ on the surface of contact which, after splitting off water, gives an imide$=NH$, the principal intermediate product of the reaction. This scheme is superior to that in which hydroxylamine was accepted as an intermediate product formed during the oxidation of ammonia.

In this country the interest in catalysis, especially heterogeneous, was, however, limited during the inter-war period. Besides works on the reaction, mechanism of ammonia and hydrogen cyanide combustion on a contact elaborated by Zawadzki, further investigations on this subject were carried out in the laboratory of Nitrogen Compounds Works in Chorzów. Extensive investigations on the decomposition of hydrogen peroxide catalysed by amorphous hydroxides and trace elements were carried out by Professor A. Krause in Poznań, and he obtained very interesting results. (These works are continuing.)

The aim of this book is to review some investigations carried out in the fields of catalysis and kinetics during the post-war period. Besides the Poznań centre (Professor A. Krause), works on chemical kinetics and catalysis in solutions are continued by Professor E. Józefowicz at the Łódź Technical University. Professor A. Bielański from the Mining and Smelting Academy in Kraków, Professor S. Weychert from the Warsaw Technical University and Professor Z. Sokalski from the Silesian Technical University in Gliwice carry on investigations on heterogeneous catalysis. Works on the reaction kinetics of dissociation of solids are continued by Professor S. Bretsznajder (Warsaw Technical University), and on the reaction kinetics of oxidation and sulphidation of metals by Professor L. Czerski (Mining and Smelting Academy, Kraków). The works on kinetics and catalysis have also been started in the Department of Inorganic Chemistry of the Wrocław Technical University as well as in the Institute of Physical Chemistry in Wrocław. Investigations for the needs of industry are carried out by the Institute of General Chemistry and by the Institute of Organic Synthesis in Warsaw.

The further aim of this volume is to arouse wider interest in researches in the field of kinetics by reviewing the works on kinetics carried out in the post-war period. On the basis of kinetic investigations with the help of strict theoretical conclusions, detailed mechanisms of many chemical reactions have been proved; they are therefore interlinked with the phenomenon of catalysis, which constitutes a unique indicator of chemical reactions, giving them the required course. By mastering the catalysis reaction and kinetics, the required product and defined course of a chemical reaction are achieved. This proves that catalysis is of great importance for the chemical industry, in which the able application of catalysed reactions prevails.

W. Trzebiatowski

CONTENTS

[xi]

I. SOVIET ADVANCES IN CATALYSIS AND KINETICS

A. A. Balandin

The greatest contribution to the development of the chemical industry in the USSR has taken place since the October Revolution. In Czarist Russia, chemistry was developed exclusively in university and college laboratories, which were few in number. Since that time, the number of colleges and universities has been greatly increased and very many research institutes, including those of the Academy of Sciences, and branch institutes have been established—not only in the chief cities but in all parts of the country. As a result, there has been a rapid development of industrial chemistry unknown in Czarist Russia.

This intensive development of the chemical industry is one of the most important tasks in the USSR. The development of kinetics and catalysis in the USSR should be considered against this rapid advance in chemical science. The very many chemical journals appearing in the USSR publish articles dealing with catalysis and also many papers on chemical kinetics. It is, therefore, impossible in a short survey to review all the scientific material. Only the most important contributions known to the author are discussed. First the progress in kinetics and then that of catalysis will be reviewed.

Before the revolution, many prominent Russian scientists, such as Menshutkin, Bakh, Shilov, etc., were engaged with kinetics, but only few studies were dedicated to the kinetics of non-catalysed reactions. Reactions in solutions were studied exclusively.

In the post-revolution period, attention has been focussed on the kinetics of reactions in the gaseous phase, and this has been favoured by the development of vacuum techniques. The results have been applied to reactions in the liquid phase, and especially to polymerization reactions.

The majority of kinetic studies in gaseous phase have been performed by the academician Semenov and his pupils Zagulin, Zel'dovich, Koval'skii,

[1]

academician Kondrat'ev, Neiman, Sokolik, Frank-Kamenetskii, Khariton, Emmanuel', and many others.

Success has, to a large degree, been achieved by the application of new physical methods, both experimental and theoretical, to the study of chemical reaction. At present, these investigations are carried out under the direction of academician Semenov at the Institute of Physical Chemistry founded in 1927.

The most significant results are, firstly, the development of the theory of chain reactions, and, secondly, the development of the thermal theory of combustion and explosions. Investigations conducted by academician Semenov on branched chain reactions are well known, as is also the work of Hinshelwood, an English chemist, both of whom have been awarded Nobel prizes. The theory of these reactions has found wide application in the utilization of nuclear energy. The theory of combustion, developed by Soviet scientists, has contributed to the successful launching of the earth's artificial satellites. The theory of chain reactions has successfully been applied to the synthesis of polymers from monomers.

Branching of chains and their termination on walls of reaction vessels have been detected by academician Semenov and his co-workers, and simultaneously and independently by Hinshelwood and his co-workers. Initial studies have been related to the oxidation of phosphorus and sulphur by oxygen. Steadily developing studies have shown that chain reactions, hitherto known to occur in photochemistry, appear frequently in nature. Before chain reactions, academician Semenov studied physical processes of ionization of gases resulting from collisions and dielectric breakdowns, and found that these processes also occur in chain fashion. The application of these concepts, established as a result of studies of these phenomena, has proved more fruitful in the field of chemistry than in physics. The theory of chain reactions, as developed by academician Semenov, is an excellent quantitative theory and represents the most versatile aspects of phenomena, i.e. dependence of reaction rate on concentration, temperature, pressure, foreign admixtures, size of vessel, etc.

This theory includes an interesting phenomenon of degenerated explosion. It is very remarkable that this theory helped in conducting new experiments and in detecting new facts.

Academician Semenov published the results of his studies in two monographs: "Chain reactions" (1934) and "On some problems in chemical kinetics" (1954). In the first, principles of the theory of chain reactions (initiation, propagation, branching, termination of chains, effect of walls, etc.) have been formulated and the mathematical theory of these reactions has been described. Four known criteria of chain reactions have also been formulated: existence of an upper and a lower limit of pressures (or concentrations); effect of size of vessel; existence of an induction period and effect of inhibitors. All chain reactions, known at that time, have been critically considered.

In the second monograph, published 20 years later, academician Semenov pays special attention to the chemical aspects of chain reactions. He has shown that free radicals are chain transfer agents (in contrast to a previous assumption wherein excited molecules were considered to be chain transfer agents). He further considers reactions of monoradicals, such as free atoms of hydrogen, halogens, etc., free hydroxyl groups, hydrocarbon radicals, and others. He discusses addition reactions to double bonds, decay of radicals, their isomerization, and also reactions of biradicals, especially of the methylene radical, the bivalent oxygen atom and others. A very interesting linear relation between heat of reaction U and energy of activation ε has been derived for molecules and radicals:

$$\varepsilon = A - 0.75\, U$$

The second monograph contains many new problems, concerned with initiation and termination of chains, i.e. problems of dissociation and abstraction of radicals initiated by ions, ionic radicals and walls of vessels. An entirely new chapter is devoted to the discussion of the relationship between chain molecular reactions and ionic reactions. In addition, many reactions of organic compounds are discussed.

As is known, polymerization processes are divided into three types: radical, ionic and hydrolytic. Each is initiated by different substances and belongs to a different type of reaction. Soviet chemists at present pay special attention to the study of mechanisms and to the kinetics of these reactions in solution. This trend of studies was first considered separately, but recently the theory of chain reactions has won general recognition. Intensive studies are being carried out on polymerization reactions of the first type to which the theory of chain processes may be fully applied. For the first time, this has been proved by academician Medvedev and his co-workers, who have conducted many investigations in this field.

Besides academician Medvedev, many other scientists, such as Korshak, Dolgoplosk and others, have studied the problem of kinetics of polymerization processes. New interesting polymerization reactions have been discovered by academician Nesmeyanov and Freidlina. In discussing polymerization studies, the very early work of academician Lebedev should also be mentioned. Academician Arbuzow has had much success in isolating free radicals containing mainly phosphorus. In this connection, the work conducted by Razuvaev should also be mentioned.

The main problem in the thermal theory of combustion and explosion was to determine the effect of various physical factors on the kinetics of gaseous reactions, although these factors, such as thermal conductance, diffusion and others, are not directly related to the chemical reaction. The first result of studies in this field was the quantitative theory of thermal ignition, put forward by Semenov. In this theory the above factors have been considered as disturbances of thermal equilibrium due to insufficient removal of heat liberated during the reaction. New theories were advanced by Frank-Kamenetskii, Todes and, finally, Zel'dovich. The work conducted by Sokolik belongs to this group. Among works of other schools, those by Predvoditelev and his many co-workers should also be mentioned.

The theory of combustion, propagation of flame and explosion is concerned rather with physics than chemistry, and therefore it will not be discussed in detail. Bordering on the subject are the researches conducted by Kobozev, Shekhter, Balandin, Eydus and others, on kinetics of gaseous reactions during electrical discharges. A quantitative theory in this field has been developed by Vasil'ev.

In 1955, a conference on kinetics and allied subjects was held in Moscow, and attended by many scientists. Published proceedings of this conference represent the actual level of these branches of chemistry in the USSR.

Catalytic problems will now be discussed. In contrast to kinetics, much research on catalysis had already been conducted in Czarist Russia, by Zelinskii, Ipat'ev, Arbuzov, Konovalov, Kizhner, Fokin, Orlov and many others. As in other countries, some contributions to catalysis came from the field of organic chemistry, e.g. the work of Gustavson on the effect of aluminium chloride and bromide on hydrocarbons; of Kucherov on acetylene hydration; of Favorsky on acetylene–allene rearrangement occurring in the presence of potassium hydroxide; and of Chichibabin on the formation of heterocyclic compounds in the presence of alumina, etc.

Many fundamental catalytic methods have been developed in Russia and then adopted all over the world; these include a high-pressure method and hydrogenation in liquid phase (including the hydrogenation of fats). After the revolution, many scientists have worked intensively in the USSR and their work has contributed to establishing new schools and trends. The amount of research at present is large in comparison with that conducted in the past. This has been made possible by the application of up-to-date methods and techniques to studies on catalytic phenomena and catalysts. In the last decade, a very large number of new processes and catalysts have been discovered. Catalysis has found enormous practical application both in laboratories and industry, and has become one of the leading methods in modern chemical technology.

A new trend in science is now appearing, namely, the chemistry of catalysis with its three important divisions: (1) catalytic synthesis, (2) kinetics and studies of reaction mechanism, and (3) studies and preparation of catalysts. Soviet chemists have contributed much to each of these divisions. At present in the USSR the problem of the scientific selection of catalysts is dealt with by The Scientific Committee, the members of which are prominent scientists concerned with problems of catalysis. The task of the committee is to promote researches and to co-ordinate research in this field.

Some of the achievements made in the USSR on catalytic syntheses should be mentioned. Attention should, first of all, be directed to the development of the chemistry of hydrocarbons, which is concerned chiefly with catalysis. The research conducted by academician Zelinskii and his co-workers is chiefly concerned with this problem. The following are some of the reactions detected: selective dehydrogenation of many six-membered cyclic hydrocarbons over platinum, palladium and nickel by Zelinskii; dehydrogenation of hydrocarbons of other cycles and open-chain hydrocarbons over oxide catalysts by Balandin, including catalytic formation of butadiene and isoprene by dehydrogenation by Balandin, Bogdanova and others. The aromatization process of paraffin hydrocarbons detected simultaneously in the USSR by three groups of scientists (academician Kazanskii and Plate, Moldavskii and Karzhev) is of considerable importance. Recently, a five-membered cycle was closed during catalysis of saturated hydrocarbons by Kazanskii and Liberman. Of interest is a displacement reaction of hydrogen between incompletely hydrogenated aromatic hydrocarbons—the so-called non-reversible catalysis by Zelinskii and Levina.

Some Soviet chemists, interested in catalysis, have devoted their attention to hydrogenation processes (including destructive hydrogenation) and to hydrogenolysis. Reactions for the opening of six-membered cycles over platinum have been detected by Zelinskii and Kazanskii; similar opening of four- and three-membered cycles during hydrogenolysis have also recently been studied in detail by Kazanskii and Lukina. It has been found that all volatile hydrocarbons, in the presence of nickel and other catalysts, produce with water vapour carbonic acid and hydrogen. This is analogous to their combustion in oxygen under normal conditions where carbonic acid and water are formed. The reaction proceeds stepwise and may be used for obtaining aromatic compounds without branch chains, and was developed by Slovokhotova and Balandin. Isomerization reactions under the influence of aluminium chloride—mutual transitions of cycles—have been detected by Zelinskii and Turova-Polyak, as well as isomerization of open-chain hydrocarbons by Moldavskii. The research on destruction of hydrocarbons in the presence of aluminium chloride by Zelinskii and aluminosilicates by Frost should also be mentioned. This work supports the hypothesis of organic origin of petroleum and is of great practical importance; and also of interest is the hydropolymerization of unsaturated hydrocarbons by Nametkin.

An important example of the catalytic formation of compounds containing oxygen is the conversion of ethyl alcohol to butadiene by academician Lebedev. This reaction has become the basis for the commercial manufacture of rubber. This branch of chemistry was first developed in the USSR and only later developed in Germany and the USA.

At present, ethyl alcohol is not obtained from the raw materials of the food industry but as the result of catalytic reactions—hydration of ethylene or the fermentation of sugars obtained by hydrolysing wood; the mechanism of the Lebedev reaction has been studied by Gorin.

Interesting, but of little practical significance, is a reaction of alcohols developed by Dolgov and involving their conversion to esters using copper and cerium catalysts.

Of great interest are the interconversion reactions of heterocyclic compounds in the presence of aluminium oxide, chromium oxide, etc. (Yur'ev). For example, furane forms pyrrole with ammonia and thiophene with hydrogen sulphide. This reaction is of very general character, and therefore concerns a large number of heterocyclic compounds such as selenophene. Future possibilities and further applications of this reaction have not yet been exhausted. As regards studies on the mechanism of catalysis and kinetics, attention should first of all be focussed on the theories of catalysis being developed in the USSR.

The theory of intermediate compounds is based on the assumption that reacting molecules interact with catalysts to form active intermediate compounds which enable reactions to proceed according to a new mechanism ensuring fast reaction rates. Although scientists hold widely differing opinions on the exact character of intermediate compounds, this does not disprove their existence.

According to the theory of Sabatier and others, intermediate compounds are phase compounds, e.g. nickel hydride in hydrogenation, but this idea has been replaced in the USSR and abroad by the theory of chemical surface compounds.

In heterogeneous catalysis, intermediate compounds are formed on the surface of contact and, therefore, their properties are not identical with those of "volume" compounds. Furthermore, bond energies and other properties of surface compounds are very distinct and may undergo changes within definite limits depending on the proportion of catalyst surface covered. The theory of intermediate surface compounds is based on chemisorption studies of substances reacting on the surface of a catalyst under conditions similar to those occurring in the course of catalytic reactions, and also on the studies of the chemical properties of chemisorbed substances. The problem of surface compounds is very well discussed in many works by academicians Terenin, Boreskov, Lepin', Topchieva, Kiselev and others.

The studies in intermediate compounds are very important in the direct physical methods used to investigate the state of a sorbent. Very promising in this respect is the study of chemisorbed molecules by optical methods by Terenin; the determination of the electrical state of adsorbed molecules, and the detection of free atoms and radicals in an adsorption layer by means of paramagnetic resonance.

The theory of intermediate surface compounds is undoubtedly sound and is based on the assumption that catalysis proceeds under the influence of chemical forces. It is not necessary, however, to account for the whole phenomenon, as it is contradicted by the fact that chemisorbed molecules are very strongly bound to a catalyst and usually hinder the course of catalysis, as, for example, actively adsorbed hydrogen. Furthermore, although this theory does not take into account data on the structure of matter, this does not contradict the fundamental principles. The multiplet theory of catalysis, formulated and developed by academician Balandin, represents a geometrical and energetic trend in catalysis. It is based on modern concepts of the structure of matter and postulates that catalysis proceeds under the influence of chemical forces. These forces are characterized by chemical bonds of specific, closely defined length (interatomic distances) and by energy (energy of dissociation).

In accordance with the theory, owing to the short range of chemical forces, only neighbouring atoms can interact and, hence, in reactions not the whole molecule but only the individual atoms in direct contact can take part. In addition, reacting atoms should be in contact with the catalyst at some time during catalytic reaction. Based on these assumptions, the multiplet theory distinguishes, as a so-called reaction index, the atoms which form an intermediate active complex M with a catalyst:

$$
\begin{array}{ccccc}
A & D & A\text{------}D & & A\text{------}D \\
| & | \longrightarrow & | \quad\quad | & (M) \longrightarrow & \\
B & C & B\text{------}C & & B\text{------}C
\end{array}
$$

As may be seen from the above, a rearrangement of chemical bonds occurs during the reaction. The active centres marked with a dotted line do not appear in all reactions.

Substituents may be attached to atoms A, B, C and D, and although these remain unchanged during the reaction, they have an effect on bond length and energy within the index, and therefore also on the rate and equilibrium constant. It is not necessary, according to this theory, for all index atoms to be in contact with the catalyst at the same time; it is a gradual process the character of which may be ascertained experimentally using labelled atoms.

The multiplet theory of catalysis has been used to determine an accurate classification based on chemical features—kind of atoms and bonds in an index. The symbols A, B, C and D may be replaced in an index by the actual symbols of atoms in reacting parts of molecules. The multiplet classification has enabled scientists to systematize experimental data and to predict reactions hitherto unknown, and many of these reactions have subsequently been detected. The important fact is that, by utilizing such a classification, an appropriate catalyst may be ascribed to every type of reaction. In a physical sense a duplet reaction is as follows: a reaction proceeds more easily if reacting atoms arrange themselves on the surface of a catalyst entering cavities of the surface layer of a crystalline lattice. These cavities play the role of free valencies, since here atoms may arrange themselves during a crystallization process, and it is, therefore, important that the reacting atoms are in contact with several lattice atoms. If an atom enters a cavity too deeply, a constant state of activated adsorption will follow which very frequently hinders catalysis. The complete disruption of a bond into free radicals would be the limiting case.

It may be seen from the above that, during catalysis, initial molecules should collect as a monomolecular layer on the surface of the catalyst.

This has actually been proved as reacting parts of molecules are directed towards the surface. This also is in agreement with experimental data on reaction kinetics. The selectivity of catalysis depends on the orientation of molecules, and the multiplet theory enables scientists to formulate from all these considerations the structure and energy correspondence principles in catalysis.

The structure correspondence principle is associated with the fact that modern knowledge of the shape and dimensions of molecules and of crystallographic lattices enables models of multiplet complexes to be constructed. Dehydrogenation of cyclohexane and its derivatives over a metallic catalyst may be described on the basis of the multiplet theory by a sextet model wherein a six-membered ring arranges itself flatly on a face of platinum.

It may be seen from this model that, in this case, the catalysts can only be metals which crystallize in a cubic (face-centred cubes, Al lattice) or a hexagonal system (A3 lattice), since only on the octahedral faces of the first or on the base faces of the second may the required arrangements of atoms be found. In addition, the mutual distances between atoms of metal catalysts should have definite values, otherwise the hydrogen atoms in cyclohexane would be too distant from the attracting atoms of the catalyst or a ring would not superimpose itself on the lattice. Experimental data are available to give full support to this theory and to explain why Pt, Pd or Ni are catalysts for the reactions in question and why Ca, Ce or Fe show no catalytic activity. It was found recently that benzene may be hydrogenated on rhenium and this had previously been predicted by the theory. According to the sextet model, benzene may be hydrogenated on mixed catalysts with increasing content of one of the metals, but only if the required structure is preserved. This is supported by X-ray measurements on mixed crystals of Ni, Co, Fe, Pd and Ag.

Dehydrogenation proceeds on oxides according to the edge mechanism, which has been extensively studied.

Angles between valencies in a multiplet complex tend to retain their value, and therefore an optimum $K-K$ distance should exist in a duplet for a given reaction.

Using X-ray and kinetic methods, Rubinshtein studied the activity of catalysts containing MgO in dehydrogenation and dehydration reactions of butyl alcohol. Depending on the manner of preparation, the parameter of the MgO lattice, i.e. the interatomic distance, undergoes changes. Rubinshtein has found that, for equal degrees of dispersion, there exists an optimum parameter for catalysis, and this is an important verification of the multiplet theory.

In addition, it appears that for dehydrogenation the optimum parameter is smaller than for dehydration; this agrees with the fact that the interatomic distance for an O—H bond (1.01Å) is shorter than that for a C—O bond (1.45 Å), while the distances for the remaining bonds remain the same. Similarly, alcohols are dehydrated over Nb and Ta oxides ($R = 1.47$ and 1.49 Å, respectively), whereas they are chiefly dehydrogenated over oxides with shorter interatomic distances ($R = 1.36$ Å) (Balandin, Egorova).

The duplet dehydrogenation of open-chain hydrocarbons has recently been studied, since the compounds formed are of such importance in the synthesis of rubber from petroleum.

The energy correspondence principle is based on the following assumptions: according to the multiplet theory, the energy barrier of a reaction is equal to the energy of formation E' or decomposition of a multiplet complex M. Disruption of A—B and C—D bonds is facilitated by the formation of bonds between atoms A, B, C and D and the catalyst K:

$$E' = -Q_{AB}-Q_{CD}+(Q_{AK}+Q_{BK}+Q_{CK}+Q_{DK})$$

Correspondingly, for decomposition of M we obtain

$$E'' = Q_{AD}+Q_{BC}-(Q_{AK}+Q_{BK}+Q_{CK}+Q_{DK})$$

where Qs are bond energies.

Bond energies may be estimated on the basis of thermodynamic, adsorptive and optical experimental data. In the case of the energy correspondence, the condition $E' = E''$ should be satisfied. Energy barriers are correlated to energy of activation by a linear relation, the same as that found by Semenov and mentioned above:

$$\varepsilon = A-0.75\,E$$

The multiplet theory has also been used in developing two methods for estimating bond energies between reacting atoms and a catalyst, the first one being mainly applied to oxides by Tolstopyatova and the second to metals by Kiperman. Experimental data on bond energies are now being collected.

Data available at present (and most extensive for Ni) enable the sequence, according to rate, of various heterogeneous catalytic reactions, calculated by means of the above relations, to be compared with the actual experimental results.

For example, it follows from experiments that decomposition over nickel and accompanied by C—C bond rupture (e.g. hydrogenolysis of cyclopentane at $E' = -48.5$) is more difficult than dehydrogenation of cyclohexane ($E' = -33$). This proceeds almost as fast as dehydrogenation of amines ($E' = -28$) and disproportionation of the latter, e.g. of aniline to diphenylamine and ammonia. Similarly, and in order of their rates, the dehydration of alcohols ($E' = -26$), the dimerization of ethylene to butylene, the migration of a double bond in a chain ($E' = -25$) and the dehydrogenation of alcohols ($E = -23.5$) may be accomplished. The bond between nitrogen and oxygen is very easily reduced ($E'' = 18.5$), but the C—Cl bond is more difficult ($E' = -6$).

Many calculations have been carried out for hydrogenolysis reactions over nickel, actually some hundreds of reactions, and, in the majority of cases, these calculations have been confirmed by experimental data. Bond energies within a molecule are affected by substituents lying outside the index. On the other hand, bond energies with the catalyst are affected by the nature, number and arrangement of atoms of a catalyst adjoining an active centre. Hence, it follows that energy barrier and reaction rate are dependent on the manner in which a catalyst has been prepared and on the presence of admixtures, defects, etc. These effects are taken into account by a sublimation term in the relation expressing energy of activation.

Thus, bond energies are variable quantities. The equations of the multiplet theory have resulted in the so-called method of volcano-shaped curves which are applied to many problems. Very recently, this method of calculation has been confirmed experimentally in over a hundred hydrogenation reactions of furane derivatives such as tripticene, organic peroxides, and even monosaccharides and polyhydric alcohols. An entirely new approach is the application of structure and energy correspondence principles to enzymatic reactions. The multiplet theory is now applied abroad and by many scientists in the USSR, such as Balandin, Rubinshtein, Tolstopyatova, Bork, Bogdanova, Klabunovskii, Ponomarev, Vasyunina, Dankov and others.

The electron theory of catalysis shows a very promising trend. This theory was initiated in the 1920s in the USSR by Pisarzhevskii, Roginskii and Shul'ts. It was, however, only developed recently, after the Whitmore theory of carbonium ions had been advanced, and it became of paramount importance when the physical theory of solids, in which semiconductors play such an important role, was applied to heterogeneous catalysis. This trend is very intensively studied in the USSR by Roginskii, Terenin, Vol'kenshtein, Bonch-Bruevich and others, and many of these investigations are more advanced than those abroad. Of real importance in the development of the electronic theory and the chemical trend of catalysis, is the classification of catalytic reactions with respect to the nature of primary activation processes occurring during the chemisorption of reacting molecules on the surface of a catalyst (Roginskii). According to the electron theory of catalysis, two kinds of reaction are most important in modern applied catalysis, namely: the electronic or oxidation–reduction reactions and the ionic or acid–base reactions. In the initial stages of the oxidation–reduction catalysis, often homolytic in character, valence defects, electrons and "electron holes" of a catalyst take part, and partial or complete transitions of electrons between the substrate and the catalyst occur. In the initial stages of the acid–base catalysis, often heterolytic in character, the ions of a catalyst are involved and transitions of protons between the substrate and the catalyst occur. More infrequent are the transitions of other ions to form acceptor—donor heteropolar bonds of the Lewis type in which no protons take part. Active transition forms are positive molecular ions with the excess of one proton, or negative ions lacking one proton; in a particular case these may be carbonium ions and carbanions, respectively.

The primary stage of catalysis is the ability for specific adsorption exhibited by solids. The electron theory of catalysis correlates this ability for specific adsorption with the type of electron structure, i.e. its surface and the particular electronic (colour, electrical conductance, unfilled internal electronic orbitals) and ionic (presence of acidic groups) properties exhibited by the solid.

Typical catalysts for reactions of the first electronic class are solids with metallic conductance: metals, e.g. Pt, Pd, Ag, Pu, Ni and others, and semiconductors, e.g. Cr_2O_3, V_2O_5, MoO_3, WS_2, NiS and others. On raising the temperature to the range corresponding to the conductivity of a semiconductor, characteristics of a solid become decisive. At low temperatures, these properties in the case of semiconductors are structurally sensitive and are determined by changes in the ideal order and perfectness of a lattice (defects).

In catalysis of this type, the oxides and sulphides of transition elements, as well as the transition elements in the form of simple solids or alloys, are of great importance. According to Roginskii, it is evident that there exists a special widely spread semiconductor catalysis with its own characteristic mechanisms, electronic kinetics and a number of secondary regularities, which are absent in solid catalysts of other types. Of special interest in this case is the effect of admixtures of atoms with valence differing from that of the basic atoms of the catalyst. Systematic studies concerning the relation between volume and surface electronic properties of semi-conductors, the conductivity and conductance of admixtures and catalytic properties, as well as changes in their properties during chemisorption and catalysis, become important projects for research. Of increasing importance is the mechanical and electronic quantum theory of chemisorption and the theory of the boundary layer developed by Vol'kenshtein in the USSR, and among others by Hauffe and Engels in West Germany. These theories allow a proper explanation of kinetic relations and a proper investigation of admixtures, but they involve intricate mathematical calculations.

In semiconductor catalysis, surface ionic radicals, radicals and molecules are produced as primary labile forms and are attached to the surface by means of odd-electron bonds. That these forms take part in catalysis has been shown by isotopic methods. It is probable that flat chains participate in heterogeneous catalysis, as such chains have been detected by means of isotopic methods in the synthin process and the contact oxidation of hydrocarbons (Roginskii, Sakharov, Margolis).

In ionic reactions, the catalytic process often begins with the transition of hydrogen, in the form of a proton (rarely as H-ion), between the catalyst and the substrate, resulting in the formation of labile ionic radicals. In this the heterolytic mechanism of cleavage and formation of bonds is predominant.

The electronic and acid–base characteristics of a solid are dependent on the kind of elements forming the crystal lattice and on the type of the lattice itself. Electronic and acid–base properties of a solid are very sensitive to certain lattice defects, and especially defects dependent on a change in chemical composition. This makes it possible to adjust catalytic properties by means of admixtures, and to correlate electronic and acidic properties to catalytic activity. Very frequent defects are associated with specific processes of preparation. These processes also determine the secondary structure of a catalyst (spatial disposition of constituents) on which the area of surface and the porosity depend. Therefore, the catalytic properties of a solid are sensitive to processes of preparation and to the conditions under which they take place. Active centres are related to lattice defects, resulting in a heterogeneous surface. Heterogeneity and interactions of adsorbed molecules lead to changes in the heat of adsorption and in the energy of activation of catalytic and adsorptive processes achieved by changing the area of the surface covered. This fact imparts a new physical sense to the static theory of processes on heterogeneous surfaces and provides prerequisites for developing the electronic theory of catalytic reactions.

The chemical theory of intermediate surface compounds, the structure and energy multiplet theory and the electron theory are all similar in principle and supplement one another. Attraction of molecules by a solid lattice in adsorption, and then in catalysis, results from the electrostatic and quantum mechanical interactions of electrons and nuclei. As is known, distance is taken into account in all equations representing these interactions. Thus, of importance to the electron theory is the structural factor which is fundamental to the structural part of the multiplet theory. And conversely, the above-mentioned interactions, considered in the light of the electron theory, determine the value of bond energies sensitive to various effects, and this knowledge is necessary in applying the energy considerations of the multiplet theory. Bond energies are also important in the theory of intermediate compounds. Thus advance made in any of these theories has its effect on the related theories.

In connection with the theories of catalysis developed in the USSR, mention should be made of the first application to heterogeneous catalysis by Tomkin of the theory of transition state, and later connected with the multiplet theory. In addition, Semenov, Voevodskii and Vol'kenshtein developed the chain theory of catalysis on surfaces, Kobozev the theory of assemblies and Roginskii the theory of supersaturation.

Many studies have been dedicated to the kinetics of catalytic reactions. At present, however, only basic conclusions resulting from them will be outlined.

Tomkin and co-workers, on the one hand, and Roginskii and co-workers, on the other hand, have shown that the rate of some heterogeneous catalytic reactions may be expressed by means of exponential equations. Such equations have been derived for ammonia synthesis by Temkin, for oxidation of sulphur dioxide by Boreskov, for CO conversion and oxidation and many other reactions.

Two explanations have been suggested to account for deviations from the simple Langmuir adsorption. They are due to interactions of molecules on a smooth surface or due to heterogeneity of a surface. As shown by studies on the gradual adsorption of hydrogen with increasing proportions of deuterium on nickel, the subsequent desorption gives the same distribution of hydrogen and deuterium, thus affording strong support for the second explanation by Roginskii and Keir.

On the other hand, in many cases (over a hundred systems studied) of dehydrogenation reactions of hydrocarbons, alcohols and amines, and dehydration and catalytic cracking, partial pressures appear in the kinetic equation similar to those in the Langmuir isotherm (Balandin, Frost and co-workers). This apparently indicates the homogeneity of active centres. In addition, experiments on the catalysis of compounds with intricate structure, which do not superimpose on a surface (Balandin, Klabunovskii), as well as the observance of a logarithmic relation between coefficients of the Arrhenius equation, the so-called compensation effect, indicate a heterogeneous surface as supported also by studies of Roginskii and Temkin. The solution to this controversy has been provided by the theory of quasi-homogeneous surfaces (by Balandin). In this case, the ratio of adsorption coefficients of different compounds is independent of the degree of unsaturation of active centres. This theory makes it possible to evaluate the change in free energy, enthalpy and entropy in adsorption on active centres from adsorption coefficients, and their changes with temperature.

Adsorption coefficients are calculated from a kinetic equation similar to the Langmuir isotherm. The assumption that coefficients appearing in this equation are indeed adsorption coefficients, has been proved by means of a radioisotopic kinetic method developed by Balandin, Neiman, Isagulyants, Bogdanova and others.

Beginning with the classical work of Lebedev, who established definite relations between the rate of reaction and the number of substituents, much has been achieved on the kinetics of catalytic hydrogenation. This investigation has been continued by Kazanskii, Zal'kind, Freidlin, Taipale, Markman and others, and especially by Sokol'skii from Alma-Ata, who developed an entirely new method for investigating hydrogenation processes based on the measurement of electrical potential of a catalyst during a reaction.

Kinetic equations have been derived by Balandin, Frost and others for studying kinetics in flow systems. Many extensive and successful studies have been conducted on macrokinetics, a problem of great importance in carrying out commercial catalytic processes in which diffusion and heat exchange play a considerable role. All this work mentioned is directly concerned with catalytic processes, but special attention has also been given to the study of catalysts.

The many different physical methods for studying catalysts have been developed and improved, namely, the method of labelled atoms by Roginskii and Neiman; the adsorption method by academician Dubinin, Roginskii,

Kiselev, Boreskov and others; the X-ray and structural method by Rubin-shtein; the electronographic method by Dankov; the electronic and micro-scopic method by Shekhter; the optical method by Terenin; the thermographic method by Balandin and Rode; the magnetic method and others. Much systematic work has been conducted in this field and valuable results have been obtained.

In this short review the author has endeavoured to show how varied and extensive is the knowledge of kinetics and catalysis developed in the USSR.

REFERENCES

1. Semenov N. N.: Tsepnye reaktsii. ONTI. Leningrad, 1934.
2. Semenov N. N.: O nekotorykh problemakh khimii, kinetiki reaktsionnoi sposobnostsi. Izd. Akad. Nauk SSSR. Moscow, 1954.
3. Materials: Sovetskaya Khimiya za 25 let. Izd. Akad. Nauk SSSR. Moscow, 1942.
4. Materials: Voprosy khimicheskoi kinetiki, kataliza i reaktsionnoi sposobnostsi. Izd. Akad. Nauk SSSR. Moscow, 1935.
5. Zelinskii N. D.: Sobranie Trudov. Vol. 3. Izd. Akad. Nauk SSSR. Moscow, 1955.
6. Balandin A. A., *Uch. Zap. Mosk. Gos. Univ.*, **175**, 97 (1956); *Zh. Fiz. Khim.*, **31**, 745 (1957).
7. Kazanskii B. A., *Usp. Khim.*, **17**, 641 (1948).
8. Boreskov G. K.: Kataliz v proizvodstve sernoi kisloty. Goskhimizdat. Moscow — Leningrad, 1954.
9. Sbornik pod red. Roginskogo S. Z.: Probl. Kinetiki i Kataliza, *Akad. Nauk SSSR*, **1-8**.
10. Roginskii S. Z.: Adsorptsiya i kataliz na neodnorodnoi poverkhnosti. Izd. Akad. Nauk SSSR. Moscow—Leningrad, 1945; *Khim. Nauka i Promy.*, **2**, 138 (1957).
11. Kobozev N. I., *Usp. Khim.*, **25**, 545 (1956).
12. Rubinshtein A. M., *Usp. Khim.*, **21**, 1287 (1952); *Izv. Akad. Nauk SSSR, Otd. Khim. Nauk*, 929 (1958).

II. THE POTENTIAL THEORY OF THE ADSORPTION OF GASES AND VAPOURS ON ADSORBENTS WITH ENERGY-HETEROGENEOUS SURFACES

M. M. DUBININ

This paper summarizes results of theoretical and experimental studies conducted mainly by E. D. Zaverina, L. V. Radushkevich, D. P. Timofeeva E. G. Zhukovskaya, K. M. Nikolaev, and B. N. Vasil'ev. The conclusions have contributed to the development of the potential theory of adsorption wherein dispersion forces are of predominant importance. The ideas formulated may, first of all, be applied to the physical adsorption of gases and vapours on carbon adsorbents consisting of a non-polar substance, i.e. carbon. They are also important to other adsorbent–adsorbate systems if the predominant factor in adsorptive interactions is dispersion forces.

Active carbons are adsorbents with energy-heterogeneous surfaces resulting from both the random arrangement of elementary carbon crystallites on the surface of the adsorbent, which assumes some sort of mosaic character, and the effect of the increase in energy of adsorption (adsorption potentials) in very fine pores—micropores—of carbon due to the superposition of forces of the opposite capillary walls.

In Fig. 1, the curve *1* representing the dependence of the heat of adsorption, calculated per 1 mole of adsorbed hexane vapour, on the amount of the adsorbate for finely porous active carbon is located higher than the similar curve *2* for non-porous carbon black adsorbent (1). This difference is due to the increase in energy of activation in carbon micropores of dimensions comparable to the size of the molecules adsorbed.

The hexane vapour, adsorbed preferentially on surfaces of the micropores, liquefies due to compression. It follows from equilibrium conditions that the surface of the adsorbed liquid layer becomes equipotential. The volume of liquid, as a sufficiently good approximation, expresses the volume of filled adsorption space.

The basic characteristic feature of the field of adsorption forces is the distribution of the filled adsorption volume with respect to adsorption potentials. Since the adsorption potential expresses the work of dispersion forces independent of temperature, the distribution curve mentioned above or the characteristic curve is independent of temperature. This basic assumption of the adsorption theory has been previously formulated and experimentally proved by Polanyi (2,3).

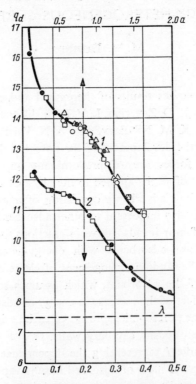

Fig. 1. Curves of differential heats of adsorption for hexane vapour at 20°C:
1 — on active carbon, 2 — on heat-treated carbon black.

With vapours of different substances the forces of the attraction of molecules to the adsorbent surface are of course different. According to the theory of dispersive interactions, their ratio approximately corresponds to the ratio of the polarizabilities, α, of vapour molecules. The same ratio applies to work done by dispersion forces, or to adsorption potentials. Thus, for equal degrees of filling of the volume of adsorption space, W, for two different vapours, the ratio of adsorption potentials remains constant:

$$\frac{\varepsilon}{\varepsilon_0} = \frac{\alpha}{\alpha_0} = \beta \tag{1}$$

The constant, β, in this relation is called the affinity coefficient (adsorption activity coefficient) (4). The basic task of the adsorption theory is to derive the distribution function of the volume of adsorption space, W, with respect to adsorption potentials, ε,

$$W = f\left(\frac{\varepsilon}{\beta}\right) \tag{2}$$

i.e. according to the equation of characteristic curve. Since the nature of vapour has already been taken into account and temperature, as may be seen from considerations given above, does not influence the shape of the curve, to every adsorbent may be ascribed an inherent characteristic curve describing its field of adsorption forces.

It has been established in our investigations that, due to the effect of the increase in adsorption potentials within carbon micropores, the characteristic curve of an adsorbent represents its porous structure (5, 6). L. W. Radushkevich attempted to justify theoretically the equations of characteristic curves for limiting structural types of adsorbents (7).

The first structural type of adsorbent includes active carbons with very fine micropores with inherent increased adsorption potentials resulting from the superposition of forces of the opposite capillary walls. The equation of characteristic curve for carbons cf this type is as follows (6):

$$W = W_0 \cdot e^{-K\frac{\varepsilon^2}{\beta^2}} \tag{3}$$

where W_0 is the limiting volume of the adsorption space expressing the volume of micropores of the active carbon. Parameter K expresses the distribution function of pore volumes with respect to their size.

The linear form of this equation is as follows:

$$\log W = \log W_0 - 0.434 \frac{K}{\beta^2} \cdot \varepsilon^2 \tag{4}$$

Figure 2 represents the results of experiments conducted by K. M. Nikolaev illustrating the applicability of the equation of the characteristic curve (1) to the adsorption of nitrogen, krypton, xenon, tetrafluoroethylene and hexafluoropropylene for various degrees of filling of the adsorption space

$\dfrac{W}{W_0}$ ranging from 0.06 to 0.94 (8). Experimental points have been calculated according to adsorption isotherms at temperatures ranging from $-195°C$ (N_2) to $50°C$ (C_2F_4 and C_3F_6) for two samples of active carbons belonging to extreme members of a series of adsorbents of the first structural type.

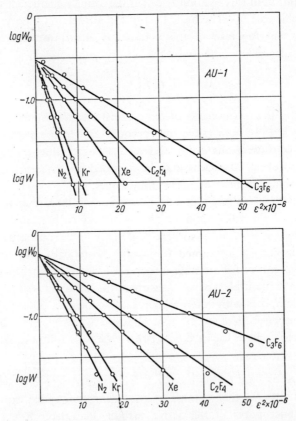

Fig. 2. Linear characteristic adsorption curves calculated from Eq. (4) for AU-1 (top) and AU-2 (bottom).

For each sample of the active carbon, all straight lines intersect the axis of ordinates practically at the same point. This proves the constancy of the limiting volumes of the adsorption space for each sample of carbon. Average values are as follows:

for AU-1 $W_0 = 0.32 \pm 0.01$ cm³/g,

for AU-2 $W_0 = 0.53 \pm 0.01$ cm³/g.

Affinity coefficients, β, of characteristic curves (Table 1) may easily be calculated from slopes of the straight lines.

TABLE 1

AFFINITY COEFFICIENTS, β, OF CHARACTERISTIC CURVES

Substance	Affinity coefficient		Average values of β
	AU-1	AU-2	
Nitrogen	1.00	1.00	1.00
Krypton	1.11	1.10	1.11
Xenon	1.50	1.47	1.49
Tetrafluoroethylene	1.80	1.75	1.78
Hexafluoropropylene	2.31	2.29	2.30

The value for nitrogen vapour has been accepted as a standard value ($\beta = 1$). It may seen from the data tabulated in Table 1 that affinity coefficients, β, are practically independent of the sample of carbon.

The second structural type of adsorbent comprises active carbons with large micropores wherein there is no superposition of fields of opposite capillary walls, and therefore no increase in adsorption potentials. To the second type, of course, belong also non-porous carbon adsorbents, e.g. carbon black.

The equation of the characteristic curve for adsorbents of the second type is as follows (6):

$$W = W_0' \cdot e^{-m \frac{\varepsilon}{\beta}} \tag{5}$$

where W_0' is the limiting volume of adsorption space. The above equation agrees with experimental data over a wide range of pore filling to varying degrees.

The equation of adsorption isotherm may easily be derived from the equation of characteristic curve. This will be shown by taking an adsorbent belonging to the first structural type (5, 6) as an example. By substituting the equation

$$W = a \cdot v \tag{6}$$

where v is the volume of 1 millimole of condensed vapour, and the Polanyi adsorption potential equation

$$\varepsilon = 2.30 \cdot RT \log P_s/P \tag{7}$$

into the equation of the characteristic curve (3), we obtain the adsorption isotherm equation:

$$a = \frac{W_0}{v} \cdot e^{-B\frac{T^2}{\beta}(\log P_s/P)^2} \tag{8}$$

The linear form of this equation is as follows:

$$\log a = c - D(\log P_s/P)^2 \tag{9}$$

As may be seen from the graph in Fig. 3, the equation may be used over a wide range of relative equilibrium pressures from 1×10^{-5} to 0.1.

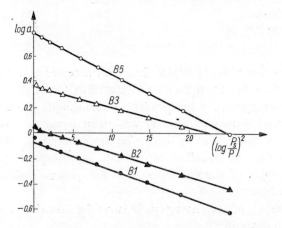

Fig. 3. Linear adsorption isotherms for benzene vapour calculated from Eq. (9).

The adsorption isotherm equation (8) permits the calculation of values of adsorption for various temperatures, if use is made of the values of saturation pressures, P_s, given in available tables.

Recently, the author and K. M. Nikolaev have shown the applicability of the adsorption isotherm equation (8) up to the critical temperature, T_c, of the adsorbate if a more accurate value of its molar volume near T_c (8) is used. A more accurate determination of the molar volume under these conditions has been based on the following premises.

On approaching the critical temperature, the density of a liquid in a phase of increasing volume drops rapidly. For instance, Fig. 4 represents the dependence of the density of liquid tetrafluoroethylene on temperature. For temperatures lower than the boiling temperature of the liquid under the atmospheric pressure (−76.3°C), i.e. along AB, the density of the liquid drops slowly with the change in temperature (approximately linearly). The considerable drop of liquid density shown is characteristic for *BC*, i.e. for a temperature range near the critical temperature (+33.3°C).

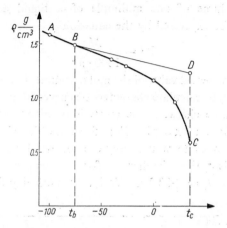

Fig. 4. Dependence of the density of liquid tetrafluoroethylene on temperature.

The liquid adsorbate is considerably compressed in the field of adsorption forces. But, since the compressibility of a liquid quickly increases on nearing the critical temperature, the use of density values of liquids, taken from available tables, to calculate the filled adsorption space is permissible only for temperatures differing considerably from the critical temperature (practically below the boiling temperature). Otherwise, the use of these values becomes unjustified.

It has been shown that the temperature-dependence of the density of an adsorbate over a temperature range from t_b to t_c may be expressed by means of a linear relation, i.e. by *BD*, assuming for the boiling temperature, t_b, the density value of the liquid taken from a table and for the critical temperature, t_c, the density, ρ_m, equal to four times the volume of molecules, i.e. the constant b from the van der Waals equation (8)

$$\rho_m = \frac{M}{1000 \cdot b} \qquad (10)$$

where M is molecular weight, b is a constant expressed in cm³/millimole.

Thus, the corrected value of the density of a liquid adsorbate, ρ^*, may be expressed as follows:

$$\rho^* = \rho_b - n(t - t_b) \qquad (11)$$

where

$$n = \frac{\rho_b - \rho_m}{t_c - t_b} \qquad (12)$$

Then, the volume of one millimole of a liquid adsorbate, V^*, at $t_b < t < t_c$ may be expressed by the equation

$$V^* = \frac{M}{1000 \cdot \rho^*} \qquad (13)$$

By using the corrected value of the molar volume, V^*, over a temperature range from t_b to t_c to calculate characteristic curves from vapour adsorption isotherms, the same characteristic curve is obtained for each sample of active carbon. As an example, Fig. 5 shows the characteristic curve for the adsorption of tetrafluoroethylene on AU-1 calculated from five experimental adsorption isotherms for a temperature range from $t_b = -76.3°C$ to $t_c = +33.3°C$. Variously marked points fit the same curve well.

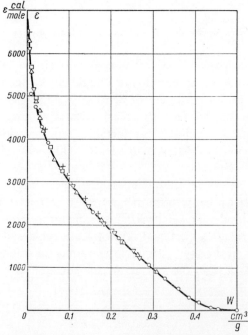

Fig. 5. Characteristic curve for the adsorption of tetrafluoroethylene on AU-1 calculated from adsorption isotherms for temperatures

+	33.3°C	(critical)	▽ −28°C
□	0°C		
△	−40°C		○ −76.3°C

In addition it has been shown that, with substances at temperatures higher than the critical temperature, i.e. with gases adsorbed on active carbons belonging to the first structural type, filled volumes of the adsorption space may be represented by the equation

$$W = a \cdot b \tag{14}$$

where a is the value of adsorption and b is the constant from the van der Waals equation.

The adsorption potential equation (15) may be derived by assuming that, at the critical temperature, adsorption potentials for a substance considered as a vapour or gas should be equal:

$$\varepsilon = 2.30 \cdot RT \log\left(\tau^2 \frac{P_c}{P}\right) \tag{15}$$

$$\tau = \frac{T}{T_c} \tag{16}$$

where τ is the reduced temperature and P_c is the critical pressure.

Figures 6 and 7 show characteristic curves for the adsorption of various substances calculated from adsorption isotherms over a wide range of temperatures, including critical regions, by means of Eqs. (6), (7) and (13) for a substance in the vapour state and Eqs. (14) and (15) for substances in the gaseous state. As a good approximation, one characteristic curve corresponds to each adsorbent–adsorbate system.

By using the equation of the characteristic curve (3) for an active carbon of the first structural type and the above-mentioned equations for filled volumes of adsorption space and for adsorption potentials, an adsorption isotherm equation will be obtained for a substance in the vapour state (17) and the gaseous state (18) when values of adsorption are expressed in millimoles per gram.

For vapours $T \leqslant T_c$

$$a = \frac{W_0}{V^*} \cdot e^{-B \frac{T^2}{\beta^2}(\log P_s/P)^2} \tag{17}$$

and for gases $T \geqslant T_c$

$$a = \frac{W_0}{b} \cdot e^{-B \frac{T^2}{\beta^2}\left(\log \tau^2 \frac{P_c}{P}\right)^2} \tag{18}$$

where the volume of one millimole of the liquid, V^*, for temperatures $t < t_b$ may be taken from available tables (Eq. (17) is then equal to

Eq. (8)), and for temperatures $t_b < t < t_c$ is calculated from Eq. (13). These equations may be applied for various degrees of filling of the adsorption space $\dfrac{W}{W_0}$ ranging from 0.06 to 0.94 with a substance in gaseous state, at the usual range of relative equilibrium pressures from 1×10^{-5} to 0.1 (8).

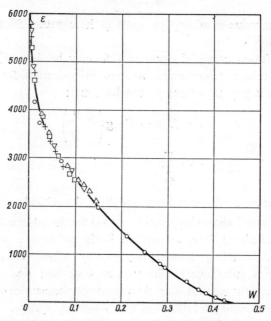

Fig. 6. Characteristic curve for the adsorption of xenon on AU-1 calculated from adsorption isotherms for temperatures

+ 50°C □ 30°C
▽ 16.6°C (critical)
△ 0°C ○ −107°C

B. N. Vasil'ev investigated (in our laboratory) the adsorption isotherms of carbon dioxide vapour on silica gel belonging to the second structural type (9) over a wide range of temperatures and pressures including also critical regions. The characteristic curve for the adsorption of carbon dioxide has been calculated from adsorption isotherms—molar volumes having been derived from Eq. (13), which takes into account the increase in the density of the substance in an adsorbed layer at temperatures near the critical temperature. As may be seen from Fig. 8, calculated points fit the same characteristic curve with sufficient accuracy. Therefore, the ideas presented are of general character and embrace adsorbents of the two limiting structural types.

The equation of the characteristic curve (5) for adsorbents of the second structural type may also be written in the linear form:

$$\log a = \log W_0' - 0.434 \frac{m}{\beta} \cdot \varepsilon \qquad (19)$$

Figure 9 shows the results calculated from experiments conducted by B. N. Vasil'ev which prove that the equation of the characteristic curve

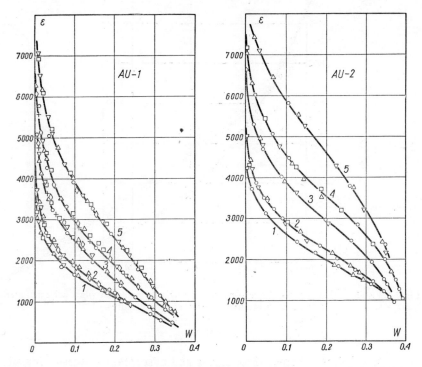

Fig. 7. Characteristic curves for the adsorption of various substances on AU-1 (left-hand graph) and AU-2 (right-hand graph):
1 — for N_2, 2 — for Kr, 3 — for Xe, 4 — for C_2F_4, 5 — for C_3F_6.

(3) may be applied to the adsorbent–adsorbate system in question over a sufficiently wide range for varying degrees of filling of the volume of the adsorption space.

The application of the equation of the characteristic curve (5) to adsorbents of the second structural type, similar to the adsorbents of the first structural type, permits the derivation of an adsorption isotherm equation for gaseous substances:

$$a = \frac{W_0'}{V^*} \cdot e^{-A \frac{T}{\beta} \log P_s/P} \qquad (20)$$

The volume of one mole of liquid, V^*, at temperatures $t < t_b$ has been taken from tables and for $t_b < t < t_c$ has been calculated from Eq. (13).

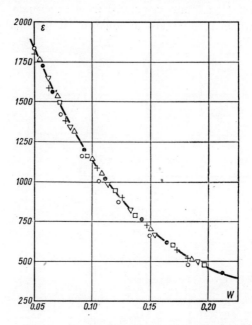

Fig. 8. Characteristic curve for the adsorption of carbon dioxide on silica gel calculated from adsorption isotherms at temperatures

○ +25°C	+ 0°C	△ −20.4°C
● −30°C	▽ −41°C	□ −51.1°C

Figure 10 shows characteristic curves and adsorption isotherms for adsorbents of the first and second structural types. The isotherm rises quite steeply for active carbons of the second structural type. The lower the constant B, the steeper is the isotherm curve.

Since the molecular polarizability of a substance is approximately proportional to the volume of its molecule or to the molar volume of the liquid substance, the results of the investigations conducted together with D. P. Timofeev (10) have justified the conclusion that the relation between the affinity coefficients, β, of characteristic curves and the molar volume, V, of a substance is directly proportional. Then, as an approximation, the adsorption isotherm equation (8) will take the form:

$$a = \frac{W_0}{V} \cdot e^{-k \frac{T^2}{v^2}(\log P_S/P)^2} \tag{21}$$

In addition to the constants W_0 and K, which may be derived from the adsorption isotherm of the standard vapour, e.g. benzene vapour, this

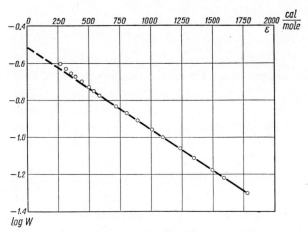

Fig. 9. Linear characteristic curve for the adsorption of carbon dioxide on silica gel calculated from Eq. (19).

equation contains only physical constants, V and P_0, of the adsorbate. It expresses the dependence of adsorbability on physical properties of the

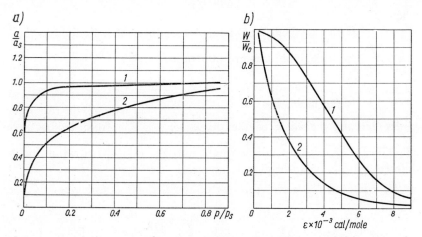

Fig. 10. General form of characteristic curves *a)* and adsorption isotherms *b)* for active carbons of the first and second structural types:
1 — for the first structural type, *2* — for the second structural type.

substance and allows quite accurate calculations of the value of adsorption for any vapour.

A similar method for calculating the affinity coefficient, β, has been developed by B. A. Vas'kovskii (11), who has shown that the coefficient may more accurately be expressed by the ratio of parachors, P, of substances according to the Sagden equation:

$$\beta = \frac{P}{P_0} \tag{22}$$

As is known, parachors are equal to molar volumes of liquid substances when the values of their surface tensions are near unity. Under these conditions, intermolecular forces of attraction would cause the same compression of liquids and a more accurate proportionality between their molar volumes and volumes of molecules would be maintained. Equation (22) has been justified in a series of investigations (12, 13).

The potential theory of adsorption allows the calculation of differential heats of adsorption from constants appearing in adsorption isotherm equations for adsorbents of the first and second structural types. G. P. Bering and W. W. Serpinskii have shown on thermodynamic grounds that from the independence of the equation of characteristic curve of temperature follows the following differential equation of heat of adsorption, φ:

$$\varphi = \alpha R T^2 \left(\frac{\partial \ln h}{\partial \ln a}\right)_T - RT \ln h + \lambda \tag{23}$$

where:

     α is the coefficient of thermal expansion of a liquid adsorbate,

$h = \dfrac{P}{P_s}$ is the equilibrium pressure ratio,

     a is the value of adsorption,

     λ is the latent heat of condensation.

By deriving the value of the derivative $\left(\dfrac{\partial \ln h}{\partial \ln a}\right)_T$ from the isotherm equation (8) or (20) and substituting it into Eq. (23), the equation for the differential heat of adsorption is obtained.

An equation for active carbons of the first structural type:

$$q = 1510 \frac{\alpha \beta T}{\sqrt{B \cdot \log \dfrac{W_0}{a \cdot v}}} + 6930 \beta \sqrt{\frac{\log \dfrac{W_0}{a \cdot v}}{B}} + \lambda \left[\frac{cal}{mole}\right] \tag{24}$$

and for active carbons of the second structural type:

$$q = 2300\frac{\alpha\beta}{A}RT - 5300\frac{\beta R}{A}\log\left(\frac{av}{W_0}\right) + \lambda \left[\frac{cal}{mole}\right] \qquad (25)$$

Equations (24) and (25) express the dependence of differential heats on the value of the adsorption of vapours in the range of temperatures T for which the adsorption isotherm equation is valid.

Thus, the theoretical ideas presented allow a quantitative description of the physical adsorption of gases and vapours on real adsorbents over a wide range of temperatures including the region of critical temperature. Furthermore, they correlate the adsorption process to the porous structure of adsorbents, and permit the estimation of the adsorbability of substances from their physical constants and the calculation of the dependence of the differential heat of adsorption from the value of adsorption from adsorption isotherm equations.

REFERENCES

1. Avgul' N. N., Berezin G. I., Kiselov A. W., Lygina I. A., *Zh. Fiz. Khim.*, **30**, 2106 (1956).
2. Polanyi M., *Verh. Dtsch. Phys. Ges.*, **16**, 1012 (1914).
3. Polanyi M., *Trans. Faraday Soc.*, **28**, 316 (1932).
4. Dubinin M. M., Zaverina E. D., *Acta Physicochim. SSSR*, **4**, 647 (1936).
5. Dubinin M. M., Zaverina E. D., Radushkevich L. V., *Zh. Fiz. Khim.*, **21**, 1351 (1947).
6. Dubinin M. M., Zaverina E. D., *Zh. Fiz. Khim.*, **23**, 1129 (1949).
7. Radushkevich L. W., *Zh. Fiz. Khim.*, **23**, 1410 (1949).
8. Nikolaev K. M., Dubinin M. M., *Izv. Akad. Nauk SSSR, Otd. Khim. Nauk* (in press).
9. Vasil'ev B. N.: O svoistvakh veshchestva v adsorbirovannom sostoyanii po dannym issledovaniya adsorbtsii dvuokisi ugleroda v shirokom intervale temperatur i davlenii. Dissertatsiya Inst. Fiz. Khim. Akad. Nauk SSSR. Moscow, 1957.
10. Dubinin M. M., Timofeev D. P., *Zh. Fiz. Khim.*, **22**, 113 (1948).
11. Dubinin M. M., Zaverina E. D., *Dokl. Akad. Nauk SSSR*, **72**, 319 (1950).
12. Dubinin M. M., Zaverina E. D., Timofeev D. P., *Izv. Akad. Nauk SSSR, Otd. Khim. Nauk*, 670 (1957).
13. Dubinin M. M., Zhukovskaya E. G., *Izv. Akad. Nauk SSSR, Otd. Khim. Nauk* (in press).

III. NEW DATA ON THE MULTIPLET THEORY OF CATALYSIS

A. A. BALANDIN

1. KINETICS OF HOMOGENEOUS AND HETEROGENEOUS CATALYTIC REACTIONS

It is known that in order to study the kinetics and mechanism of a homogeneous reaction, the reaction rate $\bar{\bar{v}}$ should be measured as a function of the concentrations or partial pressures P_r of the reagents:

$$\bar{\bar{v}} = f(P_r) \tag{1}$$

The order of a reaction, i.e. the number of molecules forming an active complex, determined in this, way enables the calculation of the reaction rate constant k. Calculations are correspondingly more complex in the case of composite reactions, but the principle of these calculations remains the same—the application of the law of mass action. Thus, for composite reactions several rate constants (of individual reactions) are determined. The next step requires the relationship between the temperature and the rate constant:

$$k = f_2(T) \tag{2}$$

Applying the Arrhenius equation, therefore, the activation energy ε and he so-called action constant k_0 are calculated and then used in the theory of the structure of matter. The study of the kinetics of heterogeneous catalytic reactions in a flow system of reactants presents another problem. The principle of procedure remains the same as in homogeneous reactions, the manner of performing the measurements and calculations, however, is changed. In addition, it is necessary to measure some new quantities not occurring in the kinetics of homogeneous reactions. Due to complex relationships, the reactions selected for study are those for which simpler relationships may be predicted on the grounds of the atomic and molecular theory.

With this in mind, such reactions as dehydrogenation, dehydration and some cracking reactions (e.g. decomposition of isopropyl benzene to benzene and propylene) are suitable, since these are unimolecular reactions. Although the reacting molecules are frequently complex in structure, the reaction, however, involves a small group of atoms inside the molecule. According to the nomenclature used in the multiplet theory, these are unimolecular duplet reactions. In these instances Langmuir's absorption isotherm is used, which is valid for homogeneous as well as for quasi-homogeneous surfaces. Therefore, the concept of a quasi-homogeneous surface should be explained (1). If, for individual types of surface areas (numbered $n = 1, 2, 3 \ldots$), the adsorption coefficients of a given substance (numbered 1) are arranged in the sequence given in Eq. (3), and of another substance (numbered 2) in the sequence given in Eq. (4)

$$r = 1 \quad a_1, a_2, a_3 \ldots. \tag{3}$$

$$r = 2 \quad a_1', a_2', a_3' \ldots. \tag{4}$$

then

$$a_1 = a_2 = a_3 \quad a_1' = a_2' = a_3' \tag{5}$$

and the surface is said to be homogeneous. If values of a do not satisfy these equations, the surface is heterogeneous.

If

$$\frac{a_1}{a_1'} = \frac{a_2}{a_2'} = \frac{a_3}{a_3'} = \text{const.} \tag{6}$$

the surface is quasi-homogeneous. The theory of quasi-homogeneous surfaces has been developed by the author in detail (1).

The author has derived a general kinetic equation (2) for these cases, which takes into account the adsorption of reaction constituents, change of volume with reaction, change of rate and the effect of foreign additives. In simple cases met in practice, where practically the whole surface is taken up and a pure original substance is passed over a catalyst, the equation is as follows:

$$(z_2 + \nu_3 z_3) \ln \frac{A_1}{A_1 - m_0} - (z_2 + \nu_3 z_3 - 1)\, m = k\nu \tag{7}$$

where:

A_1 — flow rate of original substance (in moles),

m_0 — rate at which the reaction products leave the reaction zone (in moles),

ν — volume of reaction zone taken up by catalyst,

v_3 — stoichiometric coefficient of one of the reaction products (e.g. in the dehydrogenation reaction of alcohols v_3 for hydrogen is 1, in the dehydrogenation reaction of cyclohexane to benzene $v_3 = 3$),

z_r — relative adsorption coefficients, i.e. coefficients a for a given substance in relation to the value of a_1 of the first original substance, $z_r = a_r/a_1$.

This equation is solved for the constants z and k in the following manner (1, 2): first the rate m, at which the reaction products are liberated, is determined as a function of the composition of the mixture, i.e. partial pressure P_r:

$$m = f(P_r) \tag{8}$$

Hence, one may determine z_r. It is best to apply the binary mixture method for this purpose. If the percentage of the reaction is low (up to approximately 12%), the value of z is found according to a simple equation derived by the author:

$$z_r = \frac{\dfrac{m_0}{m} - 1}{\dfrac{100}{p} - 1} \tag{9}$$

where:

m_0 — as above, designates the rate at which reaction products leave the reaction zone, when a pure original substance is passed through,

m — the same rate, but for the case when a mixture containing p per cent of the original substance is passed through,

z — quantities required.

Since the symbols a are equilibrium constants of adsorption and the symbols z are equilibrium constants of desorption, the corresponding values of the change of free energy, ΔF, may be calculated by introducing the above quantities into known thermodynamic equations.

Knowing z, the reaction rate constant k may be calculated from Eq. (7). If the specific surface area of a catalyst has been measured by the BET method, the value of k may be referred to the unit of area and the specific (unit) reaction rate constant is thus obtained.

The next step is to establish the temperature relationship between z and k:

$$z = f_3(T) \tag{10}$$
$$k = f_4(T) \tag{11}$$

The heat of adsorption, ΔH, is derived from the temperature relationship of z. It was shown in practice that ΔH is practically constant under the conditions studied. Therefore, the log z vs. $1/T$ plot gives a straight-line relationship. The plot of the log z vs. $1/T$ relationship for the dehydrogenation reaction of isopropyl alcohol on a manganous oxide catalyst is illustrated in Fig. 1.

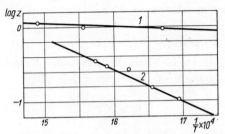

Fig. 1. Graph showing that the heat of desorption $(-\Delta H)$ is not dependent on the temperature of the MnO_2:

1—isopropyl alcohol—acetone, 2—isopropyl alcohol—hydrogen.

With known values of ΔP and ΔH, the change of entropy for adsorption or desorption, respectively, may also be calculated.

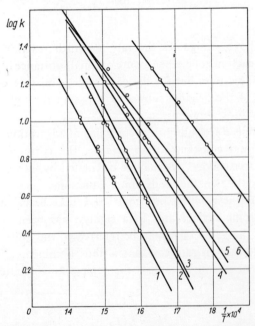

Fig. 2. Arrhenius straight lines for the dehydrogenation of alcohols on an oxide catalyst:
1 — allyl alcohol, 2 — ethyl alcohol, 3 — furylethyl alcohol, 4 — n-butyl alcohol, 5 — n-propyl alcohol, 6 — isoamyl alcohol, 7 — isopropyl alcohol.

The equations given below are used for calculating ΔF, ΔH and ΔS:

$$\Delta F = -4.57\ T \log z \tag{12}$$

$$\Delta H = 4.57\ T^2\,\mathrm{d}\log z/\mathrm{d}T \tag{13}$$

$$\Delta S = \frac{\Delta H - \Delta F}{T} \tag{14}$$

As regards the relation between the temperature and the k value, the Arrhenius equation, as a rule, is satisfied, thus enabling the real energy of activitation ε' to be calculated. As an example, the $\log k$ vs. $1/T$ plot for the dehydrogenation process of alcohols of various constitution on oxide catalyst is illustrated in Fig. 2. As may be seen from this graph, all the points lie on straight lines. Hence, the action constant k_0 may be calculated. It is of practical importance that the apparent energies of activation ε, i.e. energies calculated directly, using the percentage reaction, and real energies ε', calculated in the manner given above, with the coefficients z taken into account, are approximately equal, $\varepsilon \approx \varepsilon'$.

It should be especially pointed out that all the quantities (z, ΔF, ΔH, ΔS, k, ε, k_0), determined by the kinetic method described above, do not refer to a total surface but to the active centres of the catalyst. Hence the difference between the method given above and other methods, e.g. purely adsorptive methods, where the average properties of both the active centres and the large ballast presented by the non-active surface of the catalyst are determined.

The study of the kinetics of heterogeneous systems, in contrast to homogeneous systems, allows one to take another step forward. In heterogeneous catalysis there appears the so-called compensation effect, i.e. the linear relationship between ε and $\lg k_0$:

$$\lg k_0 = a\varepsilon + b \tag{15}$$

This relationship probably results from the exponential character of the arrangement of the active centres on a surface. In the reactions studied, this relation was always observed for related reactions and catalysts. This relationship is illustrated in Fig. 3, taking as an example the hydrogenation reaction of isopropyl alcohol on a ZnO contact catalyst prepared by different methods. This reaction has been studied in the Soviet Institute of Organic Chemistry by A. E. Agronomov (1). The quantity k here refers to the unit of surface.

We have found that the resorption process follows an analogous relationship between ΔH and ΔS. Figure 4 illustrates a parallel arrangement of the ΔH and ΔS curves, calculated on the basis of the z value at various temperatures, for the dehydrogenation process of various alcohols on an oxide contact catalyst. With this in mind, approximately a hundred systems of various catalysts and reactions of this type were studied in the author's laboratory (1).

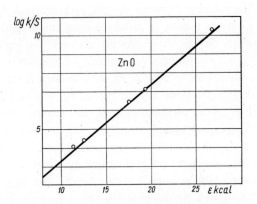

Fig. 3. Compensation effect in the dehydrogenation of isopropyl alcohol on ZnO prepared by different methods.

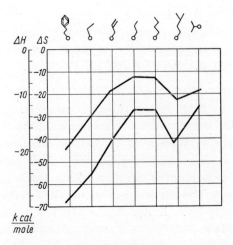

Fig. 4. Parallelism of entropy and heat of desorption. Dehydrogenation of alcohols on an oxide catalyst.

The occurrence of the compensation effect and the fact that, in practice, the value of ε depends very little on the z value, impart a great significance to the activation energy (the priority principle of the energy of activation). Actually, knowing the value of ε from the linear relationship (Eq.(15)), the rate constant k of a catalytic reaction, i.e. the activity of a given catalyst in a given reaction, may be evaluated. Values of a for certain types of reactions and catalysts (3) are given in Table 1, the value of b usually being near unity.

It appears that by applying the multiplet theory to studies, one may proceed one step further (4).

TABLE 1

MEAN VALUES OF a FOR DEHYDROGENATION REACTIONS

Groups of substances and catalysts	$a \times 10^{-3}$
Alcohols and amines on metals	2.3
Hydrocarbons on metals	2.7
Alcohols on oxides	2.8
Hydrocarbons on oxides	3.5

2. APPLICATION OF THE MULTIPLET THEORY TO CATALYSIS

According to the multiplet theory, the activation energy is a complex quantity and may be resolved into simple components. The magnitude of some components, in the first approximation, depends only on the nature of the reacting bonds; for other components, it depends on the nature of the catalyst and the reacting atoms. As a further approximation, the effect of substituents in a molecule and the influence of atoms adjacent to the active centres of a catalyst should be taken into account. For the sake of explanation, consider the course of the dehydrogenation reaction of butyl alcohol by the formation of a multiplet (Fig. 5).

The dehydrogenation reactions of other alcohols, amines and aliphatic hydrocarbons may be similarly represented. A molecule is oriented in such a way that its reacting atoms contact the catalyst, and bonds are rearranged forming an intermediate complex (M):

$$
\begin{array}{ccc}
\begin{array}{cc} C{-}O \\ | \quad | \\ H \quad H \end{array}
\longrightarrow
\begin{array}{c} C \cdots O \ (M) \\ \cdot \quad \cdot \\ \cdot \quad \cdot \\ H \cdots H \end{array}
\longrightarrow
\begin{array}{c} \uparrow C = O \\ \downarrow H{-}H \end{array}
\end{array} \qquad (16)
$$

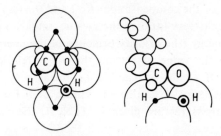

Fig. 5. Model for the dehydrogenation of alcohols. Surface of the catalyst—111 face.

This is a duplet type of reaction and the reacting atoms form an index group which characterizes a given reaction. Generally, the index of a duplet reaction takes the form of

$$
\begin{array}{cc}
A & D \\
| & | \\
B & C
\end{array}
\tag{17}
$$

Owing to the small distance over which chemical valence forces act, these atoms should be in contact with those on the surfaces of the catalyst. The multiplet theory (4) considers various mutual positions of atoms, taking into account real dimensions and the arrangement of the atoms, the principle of preservation of valence angles in the intermediate complex M being observed as far as possible. According to the above, it is desirable that catalysts of optimum action possess a definite quantitative ratio between the geometric arrangements of atoms and the interatomic distances in reacting molecules, and the catalyst lattice. This is the basis of the structure correspondence principle of the multiplet theory. An analogous geometric principle has also been adopted in crystallography, the theory of alloys, the study of epitaxy and other fields. Discussion of the many applications of the geometry correspondence principle (4,5), however, exceeds the scope of this article.

In addition to the structure correspondence principle, the multiplet theory also considers the energy correspondence principle. According to this theory, E', the heat of formation of the complex M from products, and E'', the heat of disruption of the complex M to the reaction products, are expressed by the following equations:

$$
E' = (-Q_{AB}+Q_{AK}+Q_{BK})+(-Q_{CD}+Q_{CK}+Q_{DK})
\tag{18}
$$

$$
E'' = (Q_{AD}-Q_{AK}-Q_{DK})+(Q_{BC}-Q_{BK}-Q_{CK})
\tag{19}
$$

where:

Q — bond energy of atoms,

K — catalyst,

A, B, C, D — reacting atoms.

Activation energy, ε, is linked to E' and E'' by the following relationship (6):

$$\varepsilon = A - \gamma E \qquad (20)$$

where:

γ and A — constants,

E — minimum value of E' and E''.

The coefficient γ is approximately 0.75 for endothermic processes and approximately 0.25 for exothermic processes. The value of A is nearly zero.

Thus, the value of E may be calculated from the algebraic sum Q, and, hence, the value of the activation energy ε from E. Conversely, the values of ε, determined experimentally, may be resolved into individual values of Q.

By introducing new variables, which are functions of Q, namely, the heat of reaction $u = -Q_{AB} - Q_{CD} + Q_{BC} + Q_{AD}$, the adsorption potential $q = Q_{AK} + Q_{BK} + Q_{CK} + Q_{DK}$ and the number of bonds split and formed $\bar{\bar{s}} = Q_{AB} + Q_{CD} + Q_{AD} + Q_{BC}$, the equations interrelating values E and q will be obtained, which, when given graphically, represent characteristic curves, the so-called "volcano-shaped" curves. This method is discussed in more detail in another paper (6) by the author, as well as in a paper by Z. Sokalski (7). It will not, therefore, be discussed in detail here.

The maximum on the volcano-shaped curves corresponds to the most active complex. It follows, therefore, that the condition for the maximum specific activity of a catalyst is expressed by the equation

$$\frac{Q_{AB} + Q_{CD} + Q_{AD} + Q_{BC}}{2} = Q_{AK} + Q_{BK} + Q_{CK} + Q_{DK} \qquad (21)$$

which defines the energy correspondence principle for duplet catalytic reactions. The assumption made here is that the structure correspondence principle is also satisfied. These considerations emphasize the great significance of the bond energies Q in the catalyst selection theory, and the importance of their experimental determination. Knowing the value of Q, one may use the multiplet theory equations (Eqs. (18) and (19)) in definite cases.

3. BOND ENERGY WITH THE CATALYST. METHODS FOR ITS DETERMINATION AND REGULARITIES OBSERVED

Among the methods used in the determination of the bond energy with the catalyst, the thermochemical method should first be mentioned, according to which the bond energies are calculated using the heat of formation U (under standard conditions) of compounds considered in space. The term "thermochemical" should be understood in its broader sense, since the value of U may be determined either by a purely thermochemical method or by a spectroscopic method. The calculations, however, are performed using the Hess thermochemical law and the additivity principle:

$$Q_{AB} = D_{A_2}/m + U_{AB} + D_{B_2}/n \qquad (22)$$

$$Q_{AK} = D_{A_2}/m + U_{AK} \qquad (23)$$

$$Q_{BK} = D_{B_2}/n + U_{BK} \qquad (24)$$

where:

U_{AB}, U_{AK}, U_{BK} — heats of formation of compounds AB, AK and BK from elements,

m and n — valencies,

D_{A_2} and D_{B_2} — energies of dissociation of A_2 and B_2 (or, generally, D/m and D/n — energies of atomization of A and B).

It follows, therefore, that the magnitude of the energies of atomization of elements D does not affect the magnitude of the energy barriers for the reaction E, since the value of D becomes eliminated. For a duplet adsorption with the AB bond we obtain

$$E_{AB} = -Q_{AB} + Q_{AK} + Q_{BK} \qquad (25)$$

Thus, after substituting suitable values of D from Eqs. (22), (23) and (24), the following equation is obtained:

$$E_{AB} = -U_{AB} + U_{AK} + U_{BK} \qquad (26)$$

where the value of D does not appear.

The property E, represented above, is of great importance, since it allows us to apply the values of E irrespective of the fact that the numerical values of the energy of atomization of some elements have not been very accurately established and from time to time are subject to correction, e.g. carbon and nitrogen (Pauling, Cottrell, Kondrat'ev).

The next method for determination of the bond energy with the catalyst is the method of adsorption equilibria in which the bond energy is already determined on a surface, but not yet for equilibria, nor for reaction kinetics. By studying the adsorption equilibrium for the gas XY at different degrees of surface coverage [K] and by combining the data obtained with the corresponding heat of chemical reaction from Eq. (28), the heat of formation $U_{[K]X}$ on the surface is obtained:

$$[K]+XY_{(gas)} = [K]X+Y_{(gas)} \qquad (27)$$
$$X_{(gas)}+Y_{(gas)} = XY_{(gas)} \qquad (28)$$
$$[K]+X_{(gas)} = [K]X \qquad (29)$$

This method has already been applied to some cases, mainly in the Soviet Institute of Organic Chemistry (8).

A third, comparative, method has been proposed by the author. This method takes kinetics into account, since it compares the rates of different reactions occurring on a given catalyst. Relative rates of reactions of different bonds in the same molecule are compared. Given a large collection of such molecules and bonds, and applying multiplet theory equations of the type (18), on the basis of experimental results the relative energy levels of a bond with a catalyst may be determined within quite narrow limits, accurate to within a few kilocalories. If one of the values of the bond energy for this system, e.g. Q_{HNi}, is combined with the corresponding value determined according to the thermochemical method, a system of equations is obtained and a system of bond energies with a catalyst is arrived at using the comparative method (9). The last line in Table 2 gives such a system for nickel. The data in the remaining columns of Table 2 refer to the bond energies between atoms of reacting molecules and are taken from a compilation made by Cottrell (10). As was mentioned previously, any correction of the value of the energy of atomization has no effect on the E values calculated according to Eqs. (18) and (19). In the next part of the paper, the numerical values taken from Table 2 will be used.

TABLE 2

BOND ENERGIES Q_{AB} AND Q_{AK} (KCAL/MOLE)

	C	N	O	Cl	Br	C=	H
C	66.2					46.7	
N	55.5	60				56.5	
O	77.1	44	47			83.4	
H	90.6	84.3	110.6				104.2
Cl	73	37	52	57.9			103.1
Br	60	58	48	60.5	50.6		135
Ni	6	18	48.5	67	54	$Q_{=CNi}=19$	55

Next, there are two variants of a kinetic method for the experimental determination of bond energies of atoms reacting with a catalyst, developed in the Soviet Institute of Organic Chemistry. The first variant of this method, developed jointly with A. A. Tolstopyatova (11), is more suitable for oxide catalysts. It involves the determination of the activation energy on a given catalyst for the same number of reactions as the number of kinds of atoms in the duplet index. These reactions include (other reactions have also been studied): dehydrogenation of hydrocarbons (I) and alcohols (II), and dehydration of alcohols (III). Reactions II and III usually occur simultaneously on oxide catalysts. The indexes are as follows:

$$
\begin{array}{ccc}
\text{C—C} & \text{C—O} & \text{C—C} \\
| \quad | \ (\text{I}) & | \quad | \ (\text{II}) & | \quad | \ (\text{III}) \\
\text{H H} & \text{H H} & \text{H O}
\end{array}
\tag{30}
$$

The volcano-shaped curves (in a suitable scale) for these reactions are illustrated in Fig. 6. Perpendicular lines between the volcano-shaped

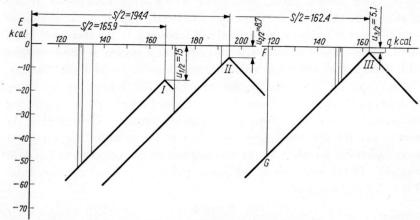

Fig. 6. Volcano-shaped curves for dehydrogenation on Cr_2O_3 prepared by different methods:
I — hydrocarbons, *II* — alcohols, *III* — dehydration of alcohols.

curve and the axis of abscissae represent values of E. From the system of equations, compiled according to the equation of the type (18), the bond energies are calculated for reactions I, II and III:

$$
Q_{HK} = \frac{1}{3}\,(-\varepsilon_1 - 2\varepsilon_2 + 2\varepsilon_3) + 62
\tag{31}
$$

$$
Q_{CK} = \frac{1}{3}\,(-\varepsilon_1 + 2\varepsilon_2 - 2\varepsilon_3) + 28.5
\tag{32}
$$

$$
Q_{OK} = \frac{1}{3}\,(3\varepsilon_1 - 2\varepsilon_2 - 2\varepsilon_3) + 48.6
\tag{33}
$$

In addition (see above),

$$\varepsilon = -0.75E \qquad (34)$$

These equations enable the bond energies of H, C and O with a catalyst to be calculated from the energy of activation.

TABLE 3

BOND ENERGIES WITH THE CATALYST (KCAL). KINETIC METHOD OF DETERMINATION
(VARIANT I)

Catalyst	Manner of preparation	Bond energies			Substances
		Q_{HK}	Q_{CK}	Q_{OK}	
TiO_2	on asbestos, prepared oxide	56.4	10.1	68.6 ⎱	C_6H_{12}; C_2H_5OH
TiO_2	from $TiCl_4$	53.0	16.6	64.8 ⎰	
ZrO_2	from zirconium nitrate precipitated with ammonia	53.0	9.1	55.6	C_6H_{12}; iso-C_3H_7OH
ThO_2	from thorium nitrate precipitated with ammonia	65.2	10.8	52.5 ⎱	$CH_3C_6H_{11}$;
ThO_2	on asbestos, prepared oxide	61.2	11.0	47.1 ⎰	iso-C_3H_7OH
Cr_2O_3	precipitated with sodium carbonate	54.7	11.0	71.8	$CH_3C_6H_{11}$; iso-C_3H_7OH
MoO_2	on asbestos, prepared oxide	43.2	23.2	65.6	C_6H_{12}; iso-C_3H_7OH HCOOH
WO_3	on asbestos, prepared oxide	47.0	21.3	55.7 ⎱	$CH_3C_6H_{11}$;
WS_2		59.0	21.4	53.4 ⎰	iso-C_3H_7OH
Ni		55	6	48.5	

Table 3 gives a comparison of results obtained in the Soviet Institute of Organic Chemistry during joint studies undertaken with A. A. Tolstopyatova. Elements are arranged in the table according to their consecutive numbers in the Periodic Table (but not according to valencies in the given oxide).

As was shown experimentally, the activation energies for the same index groups with different substituents on the same catalyst are practically the same. This supports the view that, according to the multiplet theory, molecules orientate during a reaction with their index groups towards the catalyst. The order of magnitude of the energies obtained for bonding with a catalyst is acceptable, as there are no unsuitable values — negative, too large or, conversely, nearing zero.

More important is that the average values of the bond energies with different oxides are comparable to the corresponding bond energies for nickel, obtained by the comparative method (see last line in Table 3).

As has been found in our experiments, hydrocarbons, under the most commonly used conditions, are not dehydrogenated on oxides of group II elements of the Periodic Table (Mg, Ca, Sr, Ba), whereas alcohols are dehydrogenated to aldehydes and ketones and dehydrated to unsaturated hydrocarbons. This may possibly be accounted for in the following manner: the bond energies of the catalyst with hydrogen and carbon are low here and, hence, insufficient to lower the energy barrier, which is necessary to effect the dehydrogenation of hydrocarbons. Conversely, the bond energies with oxygen are high, which allows these oxides to catalyse the dehydrogenation and dehydration of alcohols with an oxygen atom in the index group. The large affinity of alkaline-earth metals to oxygen supports this view.

The review of experimental data is as follows: the oxides studied by us may be divided into two groups according to their action. The first group catalyses dehydration reactions and the second one catalyses both dehydration and dehydrogenation reactions.

Table 4 gives a list of oxides arranged in these two groups.

TABLE 4

DEHYDRATION CATALYSTS

Bond energies of atoms of elements H, C, O reacting catalyst atoms Q_{AK}, kcal	Kind of catalyst		
	Al_2O_3	MoO_3	WO_3
Q_{HK}	45.7	40.2	50.2
Q_{CK}	26.2	23.2	22.3
Q_{OK}	37.7	65.6	40.5

DEHYDRATION AND DEHYDROGENATION CATALYSTS

Bond energies of atoms of elements H, C, O reacting with catalyst atoms Q_{AK}, kcal	Kind of catalyst					
	BeO	CeO_2	TiO_2	ZrO_2	ThO_2	Cr_2O_3
Q_{HK}	49.8	57.6	65.9	53.0	65.2	54.7
Q_{CK}	11.3	11.5	11.9	9.1	10.8	11.0
Q_{OK}	66.8	49.9	45.4	55.6	52.5	71.8

It appears that oxides may be divided into the same two groups with respect to bond energy. Bond energies with hydrogen ($Q_{HK} = 30 - 50$ kcal) in the group of catalysts which catalyse dehydration reactions $Al_2O_3-WO_3$ are lower than those in the group of catalysts with a mixed action TiO_2 $-Cr_2O_3$ (where Q_{HK} ranges from 53 to 65 kcal). Here, the exception is BeO, which indicates the presence of additional factors with a weaker action. Bond energies with carbon in the group of catalysts used in de- hydration are higher, ranging from 22 to 33 kcal, whereas in the group of catalysts with a mixed action, they only vary from 9 to 12 kcal. Bond energies with oxygen differ much more. Values of Q_{OK} obtained indicate that the active centre in oxides does not consist of oxide atoms, otherwise a peroxide bond would be present, which is weaker ($Q_{O-O} = 47$ kcal). The bond energy of nitrogen with thorium oxide (catalyst) was determined by an analogous method (22.8 kcal). Thus, a series $Q_{CK} < Q_{HK} < Q_{OK}$ is obtained, which is in agreement with other chemical data.

The effect of differences in valencies frequently masks the relationship existing between the value of the bond energy and the position of a given metal in the Periodic Table. A similar situation also exists in analytical chemistry.

Knowing the activation energy and by making use of a volcano-shaped curve, the adsorption potential q may also be determined. For cyclohexane and chromic trioxide, Cr_2O_3, $q = 130.4$ kcal, the value of q differs con- siderably from the optimum adsorption potential, which corresponds to the maximum on the volcano-shaped curve, and in this case (according to Eq. (21)) is 165.3 kcal. Of course, according to the theory, it is possible to improve the properties of a catalyst by changing the manner of its preparation.

A more detailed discussion in the light of the multiplet theory indicates (12) that bond energies contain a sublimation term, dependent on the microroughness of the surface. Therefore, the values of Q obtained should be dependent on the manner in which the catalyst has been prepared (as well as on the nature of its carrier), since the number, and sometimes the nature, of the catalyst atoms adjoining an active centre is changed at the same time. Actually, this has been supported experimentally. Table 5, for example, gives the results obtained for chromic trioxide.

Experimental results also indicate that substituents at the atoms of an index group, which considerably change the bond energy between the atoms of the group, also have an effect on the magnitude of the bond energy with the catalyst. These substituents are chiefly groups in which

TABLE 5

EFFECT OF THE MANNER OF PREPARATION AND THE NATURE OF THE CARRIER
ON THE NUMERICAL VALUE OF BOND ENERGY Q

Cr_2O_3 catalyst	Bond energy Q, kcal		
	Q_{HCr}	Q_{CCr}	Q_{OCr}
From $Cr(NO_3)_3$ precipitated with sodium carbonate	54.7	11.0	71.8
From $Cr(NO_3)_3$ precipitated with sodium carbonate on asbestos	60.7	11.9	44.9
From $(NH_4)_2Cr_2O_7$	60.8	8.8	45.2
From $(NH_4)_2Cr_2O_7$ on asbestos	57.7	14.8	35.1

multiple bonds are conjugated with multiple bonds within an index group during its reaction, e.g. a phenolic group in dehydrogenation. This has also been found to be in agreement with the multiplet theory. The effect of molecular structure on the bond energy with the catalyst has been studied in more detail in one of the recent works on cerium oxide (13).

For the case when a catalyst is more selective and it is impossible to match several reactions with it, analogous to the reactions expressed by Eq. (30), the author, jointly with S. L. Kiperman, has developed the second variant of the kinetic method for the determination of bond energies. This variant also involves the application of multiplet theory equations (18) and (19). It is best suited to metallic catalysts. According to this method, Q_{HK} for the ortho–para conversion of hydrogen is determined first. This reaction may be treated as a duplet reaction (14); its index consists of only one kind of atom, i.e. hydrogen:

$$\begin{array}{cc} H & H \\ | & | \\ H & H \end{array}$$

If the activation energy ε is determined experimentally, this reaction alone is sufficient to calculate the hydrogen–catalyst bond energy.

In Eq. (18), H is substituted for A, B, C, D and Ni for K. Since $\varepsilon_1 = 5910$ kcal and $Q_{H-N} = 104.2$ kcal, then, having also taken into account Eq. (34), we obtain

$$Q_{H-Ni} = \frac{1}{2} Q_{H-N} - \frac{1}{3} \varepsilon_1 = 50.1 \text{ kcal} \tag{35}$$

Similarly, $Q_{D-Ni} = 50.1$ kcal is obtained for the ortho–para conversion of deuterium. The values of Q_{H-Ni} and Q_{D-Ni} obtained are then used to calculate the bond energies between the nickel catalyst and other elements.

The next step is the calculation for the reaction containing two kinds of atoms in its duplet, also including hydrogen, for which Q_{H-Ni} has previously been calculated. An example of such a reaction is the hydrogenation of ethylene with an index

$$\begin{array}{cc} C & H \\ \| & | \\ C & H \end{array}$$

A procedure similar to the one shown above will give

$$Q_{=C-Ni} = \frac{1}{2}(Q_{C=C} + Q_{H-H}) - Q_{H-Ni} - \frac{2}{3}\varepsilon_3 \qquad (36)$$

where:

$\varepsilon_3 = 8200$ kcal — activation energy,

$Q_{C=C} = 46.7$ kcal — energy for disrupting one of the C=C bonds,

$=C =$ carbon atom at a double bond.

Substituting the values of $Q_{H-H} = 104.7$ and Q_{H-Ni}, found previously, we obtain $Q_{=C-Ni} = 19.9$ kcal. Using other data, however, a value $Q_{=C-Ni} = 18.6$ kcal is obtained, i.e. 19.2 kcal on the average.

For the reaction of the ethylene–deuterium isotopic exchange, we obtained $Q_{=C-Ni} = 23.2$ kcal, which only differs slightly from the value obtained above.

Proceeding in the same manner, i.e. considering reactions in the index of which further new atoms gradually appear, the bond energies between nickel and various elements of organic compounds may be calculated. Such calculations have been carried out for the hydrogenation of acetone, the isotopic exchange between methyl alcohol and deuterium, ammonia and deuterium, and others. The results obtained are given in Table 6.

TABLE 6

BOND ENERGIES BETWEEN A CATALYST AND VARIOUS ELEMENTS, IN KCAL. KINETIC METHOD
OF DETERMINATION (VARIANT II)

Catalyst	Kind of element					
	H	D (deuterium)	−C	=C	O	N
Ni	50.1	50.1	7.7	19.9	54.2	18.6

It is very interesting to note that the bond energies calculated by the kinetic method are very similar to the values obtained in a quite independent manner, namely, by the comparative method (see above), which is concerned with more complex organic compounds (cf. data in Tables 2 and 6). The fact that identical results are obtained, using two quite different methods, proves the validity of the theory.

Adsorption potentials q, calculated on the basis of the activation energies for almost all nickel contacts, are very near the maximum value $s/2$, and, hence, the activity of these nickel catalysts approaches the maximum.

Recently, similar kinetic data have also been obtained for the bonds between some elements and iron, palladium and platinum.

4. THEORY OF CATALYST SELECTION AND BOND ENERGY

Work has been carried out on the determination of bond energy in order to make use of it in the development of the theory of catalyst selection, i.e. the basic problem of catalysis. This problem has two aspects: first, which substances will catalyse a given reaction, and second, for which reactions a given catalyst will be active. The answer to the second question, if the relative ease with which a given reaction proceeds may be determined, will also solve the problem of the selectivity of a given catalyst. Of course, the complete solution of this problem will involve considerable time and recent studies of catalysis aim at approaching the final solution. The multiplet theory, however, allows us even now to predict, under definite conditions, the course of reactions of complex organic compounds on contacts. Nickel in particular belongs to these catalysts, since in this case the necessary bond energies have been more accurately determined than those for other substances.

Table 7 contains the indices of various duplet-type reactions on Ni, and below them are given their respective energy barriers $(-E)$, calculated from Eq. (18), and the bond energies (Table 2). The higher the value of E, the more easily a given reaction should proceed.

A definite sequence of reactions follows from the data in Table 7, which is in agreement with the experimental results obtained for most of

TABLE 7

INDICES OF VARIOUS DUPLET-TYPE REACTIONS ON NICKEL AND THEIR ENERGY BARRIERS

Ni	$\begin{matrix}C-C\\ |\ \ |\\ H\ \ H\end{matrix}$	$\begin{matrix}N=C\\ |\ \ |\\ H\ \ N\end{matrix}$	$\begin{matrix}C-N\\ |\ \ |\\ H\ \ H\end{matrix}$	$\begin{matrix}C-C\\ |\ \ |\\ H\ \ O\end{matrix}$	$\begin{matrix}C\ \ C\\ |\ \ \|\\ H\ C\end{matrix}$	$\begin{matrix}C-C\\ |\ \ \|\\ H\ \ C\end{matrix}$	$\begin{matrix}C-O\\ |\ \ |\\ H\ \ H\end{matrix}$	$\begin{matrix}C\ H\\ \|\ |\\ N\ H\end{matrix}$	$\begin{matrix}C\ H\\ \|\ |\\ O\ H\end{matrix}$
$E' =$	-33	-30	-28	-26	-25	-25	-23.5	-12.6	-7
	$\begin{matrix}C\ \ H\\ |\ \ |\\ C\ \ H\end{matrix}$	$\begin{matrix}C\ \ H\\ |\ \ |\\ H\ \ H\end{matrix}$	$\begin{matrix}N\ \ H\\ |\ \ |\\ N\ \ H\end{matrix}$	$\begin{matrix}C\ \ H\\ |\ \ |\\ O\ \ H\end{matrix}$	$\begin{matrix}C\ \ H\\ |\ \ |\\ Br\ H\end{matrix}$	$\begin{matrix}C\ H\\ |\ \ |\\ Cl\ H\end{matrix}$	$\begin{matrix}H\ \ O\\ |\ \ |\\ O\ \ H\end{matrix}$	$\begin{matrix}O\ H\\ |\ \ |\\ O\ H\end{matrix}$	$\begin{matrix}N\ H\\ |\ \ |\\ O\ H\end{matrix}$
$E' =$	-48.5	-25.5	-18	-17	6	6	$14(E')$	$18.5(E')$ kcal	

the reactions studied. As the temperature rises, the easier reactions proceed first, and are followed by the more difficult ones.

As an example of the calculations, consider the decomposition reaction of acetamide on nickel. After the C=O double bond is hydrogenated, acetamine is first decomposed to ethyl amine and water, then ethyl amine decomposes to give ammonia and ethane, the latter being finally converted to methane (Scheme 1).

A second example may be furnished by a gradually proceeding hydro-genolysis (reaction of destructive hydrogenation) of *n*-chloronitrobenzene, studied at the Soviet Institute of Organic Chemistry (15). If the above-mentioned regularities did not exist, nitrobenzene, for example, would be obtained if the C—Cl bond were disrupted first, or chlorobenzene, if the C—N bond were disrupted first, etc. In accordance with the predictions of the theory (Table 7), however, experimental results indicate that the nitro-gen—oxygen bond is disrupted first, then the carbon—chlorine, then the carbon—nitrogen, and finally the carbon—carbon bond (Scheme 2).

Simultaneously with the rise of temperature, *n*-chloronitrobenzene is gradually converted to *n*-chloroaniline and water, aniline and HCl, benzene and ammonia, and finally methane. It follows from the data contained in chemical literature (15) that, for the hydrogenolysis reaction over nickel, under the conditions of hydrogenation as suggested by Sa-batier, the calculations based on the multiplet theory (second horizontal row of indices, Table 7) are in agreement almost without exception with the experimental data obtained during the study of a hundred substances. These substances belong to various groups of organic compounds, such as: acid amides, nitro derivatives of saturated hydrocarbons, esters of nitric acid, ketoximes, amines, aromatic alcohols, chlorine derivatives of aromatic compounds, esters of chlorine-substituted acids, bromine deri-vatives of aromatic amines, etc. Many reactions of this type have been studied at the Soviet Institute of Organic Chemistry.

Recently, the multiplet theory has been successfully applied to the study of hydrogenation processes, cyclization and hydrogenolysis of furane compounds over nickel (16). Table 8 gives the sequence of reactions established from Eq. (18) and the data are set out as in Table 7. Figure 7 gives the corresponding volcano-shaped curves. Using this sequence of reactions (Table 8), it may be predicted, for example, that 1-(alpha-furyl)-pentene-1-one-3 over nickel in an atmosphere of hydrogen should undergo gradually proceeding conversions (Scheme 3).

TABLE 8

SEQUENCE OF REACTIONS DURING HYDROGENATION OVER NICKEL

No. of reaction	Reaction	Scheme	u	s	E'
1.	Hydrogenation of an olefinic bond	$\begin{matrix} C & H \\ \| & \| \\ C & H \end{matrix}$	30.1	331.9	−2.9
2.	Hydrogenation of a carbonylic bond	$\begin{matrix} C & H \\ \| & \vdash \\ O & H \end{matrix}$	13.5	388.7	−10.1
3.	Hydrogenation of the first double bond in a furane ring	$\begin{matrix} C & H \\ \| & \| \\ C(F)H \end{matrix}$	14.1	347.9	−10 9
3a.	Hydrogenolysis of an ether bond in a furane ring	$\begin{matrix} C & H \\ \| & \| \\ O(F)H \end{matrix}$	3.8	398.4	−11.8
4.	Formation of spirane from furane alcohol	$\begin{matrix} C & O \\ \| & \| \\ C & H \end{matrix}$	10.3	324.9	−15.8
5.	Hydrogenolysis of a carbon–oxygen bond	$\begin{matrix} C & H \\ \| & \| \\ O & H \end{matrix}$	19.8	382.4	−16.8
6.	Hydrogenolysis of a carbon–carbon bond	$\begin{matrix} C & H \\ \| & \| \\ C & H \end{matrix}$	10.6	351.4	−48.4

Almost without any exception, this theory is valid for nearly a hundred conversions of furane compounds (16). Table 9 shows the beginning of such a sequence of conversions. Steps 1 and 2 denote that in this instance reaction 1 has already taken place (Table 6), but reaction 2 has not yet started. The same happens in other cases.

Attention should be drawn to two important facts as seen in Table 9: first, the ordinal numbers of the reactions are actually consecutive (this means that the sequence of reactions, as required by the theory, has been preserved), and second, still in conformity with the theory, the mean temperature of the reaction increases with the consecutive number of the reaction (25°C for steps 1 and 2, etc.).

The author and E. I. Klabunovskii have studied the kinetics of the hydrogenation of tripticene derivatives on nickel (18). These compounds are of complex spatial structure and do not arrange themselves in a plane, but nevertheless the dehydrogenation proceeds under moderate conditions. It may be seen from a model prepared to a suitable scale that the active

TABLE 9

SEQUENCE OF HYDROGENATION REACTIONS OF FURANE COMPOUNDS OVER NICKEL. COMPARISON OF EXPERIMENTAL AND THEORETICAL DATA. DESIGNATION: F = ALPHA-FURYL

No. of conversion	Original substance	Product A		Temperature, °C
	Conversions reaching step 1,2 (average temp. 25°C)			
1	$\diagup\!\!\!\diagdown_O\diagup$—CH=CH—CH=O	$\diagup\!\!\!\diagdown_O\diagup$—CH$_2$—CH$_2$—CH=O	1.236	23
	F—CH=CH—(C=O)—R	F—CH$_2$CH$_2$—C(C=O)—R		
2	R=CH$_3$	R=CH$_3$	1.236	20
3	R=iso-C$_6$H$_{13}$	R=iso-C$_6$H$_{13}$	1.236	20
4	F—(CH=CH)$_2$—(C=O)—CH$_3$	F—(CH$_2$—CH$_2$)$_2$—CO—CH$_3$	1.236	20
5	F—CH=CH—CO—F	F—CH$_2$—CH$_2$—CO—F	1.236	42
6	(F—CH=CH)$_2$C=O	(F—CH$_2$—CH$_2$)$_2$C=O	1.236	20
	Conversions reaching step 1,3 (average temp. 40°C)			
7	$\diagup\!\!\!\diagdown_O\diagup$—CH=CH$_2$	$\diagup\!\!\!\diagdown_O\diagup$—CH$_2$—CH$_3$	{1.36 / 1.36	65 / 15
8	F—CH=CH—CH$_2$OH	F—CH$_2$—CH$_2$—CH$_2$OH	1.356	—

centres of dehydrogenation are located on protrusions on the surface of the catalyst. Space models to a suitable scale may be prepared.

In the course of these studies the following problem arose: it was known from preliminary studies that on hydrogenation compound I

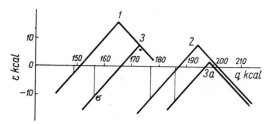

Fig. 7. Volcano-shaped curves for the reactions of furane derivatives. The numbering is the same as in Table 8.

converts to compound IV; it was necessary to establish whether the hydrogenation passes through stage A or stage B (Scheme 4). In accordance with predictions of the theory, as may be seen from Table 7, the reaction should pass through stage A, and not B. This has actually been supported by the results of detailed experimental studies (17).

TABLE 10

HYDROGENATION OF PEROXIDES ON RANEY SKELETAL NICKEL

Peroxide	Structural formula of peroxide	Solvent	Order of re-action	Hydrogenation rate constant for $-O-O-$ at 20°C per 1 kg of catalyst	Apparent activation energy, kcal/mole (at 5–25°C)
1	2	3	4	5	6
Isopropylbenzene hydroperoxide	CH_3 / $C-O-O-H$ / CH_3	ethyl alcohol	zero	25.3 ml/min	5.0
Ethylphenyl-isopropyl peroxide	CH_3 / $C-O-O-C_2H_5$ / CH_3	ethyl alcohol	zero	29.0 ml/min[a]	5.4
Tetralin hydro-peroxide	$O-O-H$	benzene	zero	5.2 ml/min	—
Cyclohexene hydroperoxide	$-O-O-H$	ethyl alcohol	zero	6.4 ml/min	5.0
3-Methyl-1-bu-tyl hydroper-oxide	CH_3 / $CH\equiv C-C-O-O-H$ / CH_3	ethyl alcohol	zero	15.8 ml/min[a]	5.5
Benzoyl peroxide	O O / $-C-O-O-C-$	benzene	first	0.35 ml/min	6.5
p-Nitrobenzoyl peroxide	O O / NO_2 $-C-O-O-C-$ NO_2	toluene	first	0.17 ml/min[a]	
tert-Butyl per-benzoate	O CH_3 / $-C-O-O-C-CH_3$ / CH_3	ethyl alcohol	first	0.32 ml/min	9.4
tert-Butyl per-oxide	CH_2 CH_3 / $CH_3-C-O-O-C-CH_3$ / CH_3 CH_3	ethyl alcohol	no hydrogenation takes place		

[a] Rate constant determined at 25 °C.

Interesting results have been obtained in further studies on the kinetics of the hydrogenation of organic bifunctional peroxides and hydroperoxides. These results have been given in the paper by the author, N. W. Nikiforova and L. Kh. Freidlin (19).

The phenomenon itself of the hydrogenation of peroxides over nickel has not hitherto been described in the literature. Since the value of E in this case is very large and is equal to 14 kcal, the multiplet theory predicts that compounds containing a peroxide link should easily undergo hydrogenolysis over nickel, forming the corresponding alcohols (Table 7). Therefore, the real activation energy should be nearly zero. Studies carried out by us have actually shown that organic peroxide and hydroperoxide compounds may easily be hydrogenated over nickel, even at low temperatures and under atmospheric pressure, which is in agreement with the predictions of the theory. The results obtained are shown in Table 10.

The apparent activation energy is low (approx. 5 kcal). The facts that peroxide links easily undergo hydrogenolysis on nickel, and that the activation energy observed is low, furnish new support for the multiplet theory. Further and more detailed support for the predictions of the theory is obtained by studying the sequence of reactions of the effect of hydrogen on various functional groups and bifunctional peroxides. Some examples are given below. Table 11 shows the sequences of reactions for some of the peroxide compounds studied, which were established by means of the multiplet theory equations. The same sequence is observed experimentally, as may be seen in Scheme 5 below, in which the sequence of the reactions observed is illustrated.

It is interesting to note that a change in the nature of a catalyst brings about a change in this sequence, as predicted by the multiplet theory, since different catalysts have different bond energies.

The equations of the multiplet theory have also been successfully applied to reactions of more complex compounds, namely, to the catalytic hydrogenation of simple sugars, which involves several types of reactions. The sequence of the reactions, which has been determined theoretically, is valid for approximately 30 tested conversions. This problem is discussed in more detail by N. A. Vasyunina in her paper (cf. paper on pp. 75–83).

Still more complicated are the reactions of asymmetric catalysis, i.e. the action of chemical models of enzymes, and even more so, the action of the enzymes themselves. Recently, however, thanks to the multiplet theory, these problems have also been successfully explained to some

TABLE 11

Ni	N H	O N	C H	C H	C H	C H	C H
	$\mid$ $\mid$	$\mid$ $\mid$	$\parallel$ $\mid$	$\mid$ $\mid$	$\parallel$ $\mid$	$\mid$ $\mid$	$\mid$ $\mid$
	O H	O H	C H	C H	O H	O H	C H
$E' =$	18.4	14.2	6.4	-2.9	-10	-17	-48 kcal

SCHEME 1

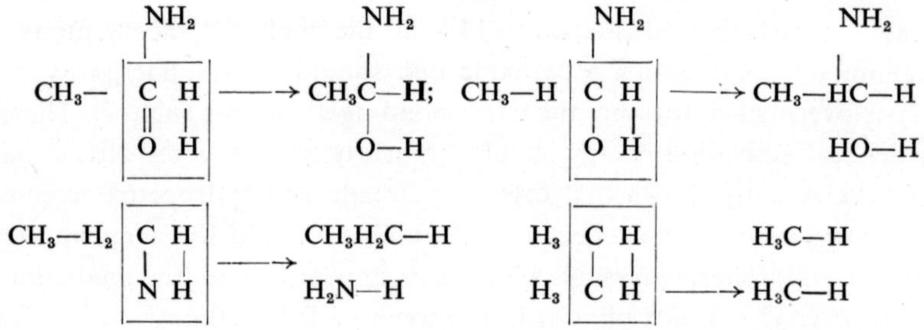

SCHEME 2

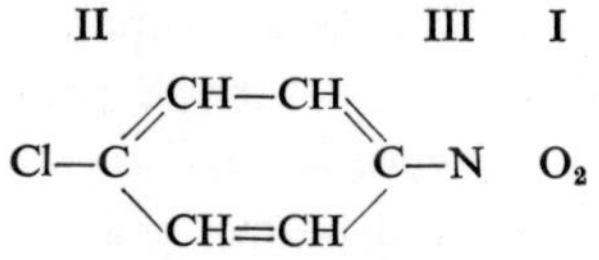

SCHEME 3

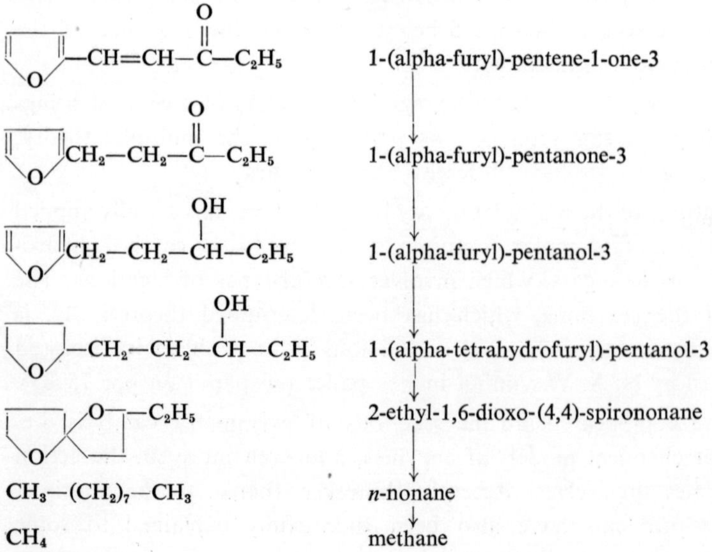

SCHEME 4

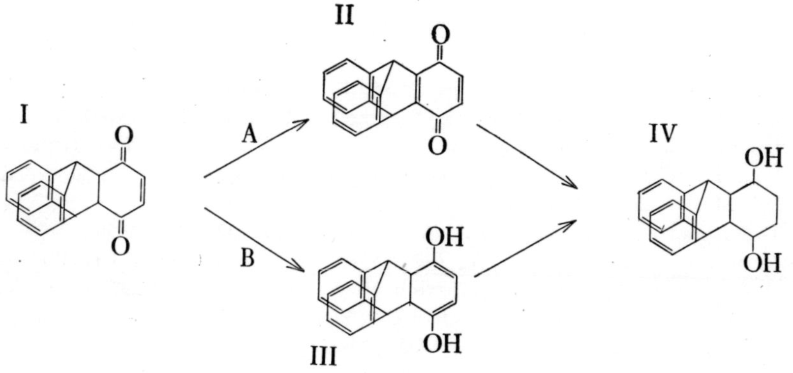

SCHEME 5

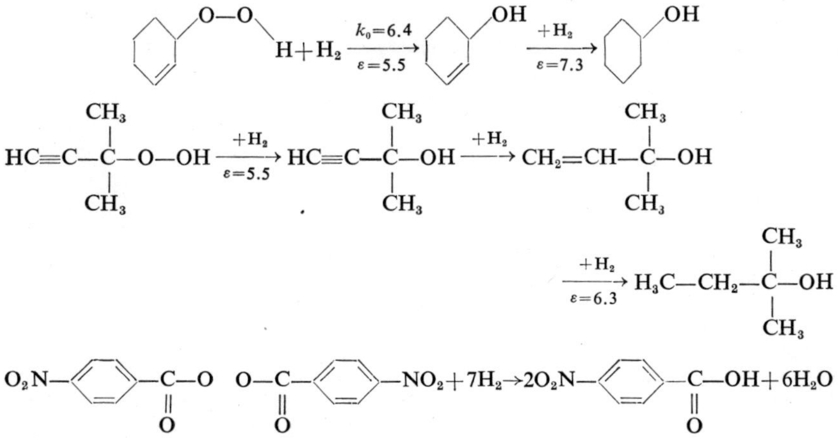

degree and are the subject of a paper by E. I. Klabunovskii (cf. paper on pp. 85-91). The application of the multiplet theory in chemistry has recently been discussed in detail by the author.

REFERENCES

1. Balandin A. A., *Zh. Fiz. Khim.*, 31, 745 (1957); *Advances in Catalysis*, **10**, 96 (1958)
2. Balandin A. A., *Vestn. Mosk. Univ.*, No. 4, 137 (1957).
3. Balandin A. A., *Izv. Akad. Nauk SSSR, Otd. Khim. Nauk*, 624 (1955).
4. Balandin A. A., *Uch. Zap. Mosk. Gos. Univ.*, **175**, 97 (1956).
5. Trapnell B. M. W., *Advances in Catalysis*, **3**, 1 (1951).
6. Balandin A. A.: Trudy konferentsii po katalizu i khimicheskoi kinetike vo Vroclave, (1958).

7. Sokalski Z.: Najnowsze kierunki w katalizie. Nowa technika. **119**. PWT. Warszawa, 1957.
8. Kiperman S. L., Balandin A. A., Davydova I. R., *Izv. Akad. Nauk SSSR, Otd. Khim. Nauk*, 1129 (1957).
9. Balandin A. A., *Dokl. Akad. Nauk SSSR*, **107**, 85 (1956).
10. Cottrell T.: Prochnosti khimicheskikh svyazei. Izd. In. Lit. Moscow, 1956.
11. Balandin A. A., Tolstopyatova A. A., *Zh. Fiz. Khim.*, **30**, 1367, 1636 (1956).
12. Balandin A. A.: Poverkhnostnye khimicheskie soedinenya i ikh rol v adsorptsii. Izd. Moskovskogo Universiteta. Moscow, 1957.
13. Tolstopyatova A. A., Balandin A. A., *Zh. Fiz. Khim.*, **32**, 1831 (1958).
14. Kiperman S. L., Balandin A. A., *Dokl. Akad. Nauk SSSR*, **113**, 335 (1957).
15. Dowden D. A., Mackenzie N., Trapnell B. M. W., *Proc. Roy. Soc.*, A237, 245 (1956).
16. Balandin A. A.: Voprosy khimicheskoi kinetiki, kataliza i reaktsionnoi sposobnosti. Izd. Akad. Nauk SSSR. Moscow, 1955, p. 461.
17. Balandin A. A., Ponomarev A. A., *Zh. Obshch. Khim.*, **26**, 1146 (1956).
18. Balandin A. A., Klabunovskii E. I., *Dokl. Akad. Nauk SSSR*, **113**, 585 (1957).
19. Balandin A. A., Nikiforova N. W., Freidlin L. Kh., *Dokl. Akad. Nauk SSSR*, **112**, 649 (1957).
20. Balandin A. A., *Biokhimiya*, **23**, 475 (1958).

IV. SOME PROBLEMS OF THE THEORY OF CATALYST SELECTION

G. K. BORESKOV

In view of the leading role of catalysis in modern chemical industry and the wide development of studies of the preparation and improvement of catalysts for various reactions, particular importance is attached to the search for the generalizations which would allow even a partial prediction of the course of catalysis. These generalizations, of course, should result from the mechanism of catalytic action.

As is known, catalysis is associated with the intermediate chemical interaction between reactants and catalyst, thus providing a new path of reaction which is more complex with respect to the number of steps, but easier with respect to the height of energy barriers in individual steps. The catalyst participates in the formation of an active complex in all or some steps of the new path of reaction. Consequently, the sufficiently accurate and general definition of a catalyst would be: *a catalyst is a substance which alters the rate of a chemical reaction, takes part in the formation of an active complex in the given reaction and returns to its original state after completion of the chemical change.*

This definition is valid for both homogeneous and heterogeneous catalysis. In heterogeneous catalysis, the active complex may contain a large number of atoms which form a crystal or a complex polymerized molecule of the catalyst.

The increase in the rate, caused by the fact that the reaction follows the path of intermediate interactions with the catalyst, has been made possible by the following factors:

1. Omission of the endothermic steps of interaction which require a high activation energy.

2. Decrease in activation energy due to a more favourable form of the bonds between the reacting atoms.

3. Increase in the probability of the necessary orientation of molecules during the formation of an active complex as a result of the multiple bonds with the catalyst being formed at definite distances from one another (1).

4. Occurrence of the chain mechanism, which would be impossible in the absence of a catalyst (2).

The effect of water on the oxidation of carbon monoxide is an example of the origin of a chain reaction in the presence of a catalyst. Apparently, the chain mechanism of acceleration of reaction does not occur frequently in heterogeneous catalysis.

The rate of a catalysed reaction, characteristic of the activity of the given catalyst, is determined by the entropy and enthalpy of formation of active complexes in the individual steps of the new path of reaction and, first of all, in the slowest rate-determining step. It appears that it is essentially possible to calculate the probability of formation of such complexes and, therefore, to predict the catalytic action. At present, however, this is practically impossible and a search for simplifications and partial solutions is necessary to develop the theory of catalyst selection.

The interaction between reagents and a catalyst, like any chemical interaction, is associated with electron transfers. Although in heterogeneous catalysis the intermediate interaction occurs on the surface of the catalyst, the interaction energy, nature and probability of the formation of bonds are determined by the electronic structure of both the surface and deeper layers of the solid catalyst.

In providing a scientific basis for the selection of catalysts it is therefore important to gather data concerning the relation between the specific catalytic activity and electronic structure of various groups of solid catalysts.

In this paper some data concerning this problem, obtained at the Karpov Institute of Physical Chemistry for metallic and oxide catalysts for reduction and oxidation reactions, will be discussed.

1. CATALYTIC ACTIVITY OF METALS

It is particularly important to know the catalytic properties of metals due to their very high catalytic activity for certain reactions, the chemical purity of element metals and the considerable practical significance of metallic catalysts. Approximately one-third of industrial catalysts are the catalysts containing various metals as basic active components.

Metallic catalysts are used in many oxidation and reduction reactions: hydrogenation (Pd, Pt, Ni, Cu), dehydrogenation (Pt, Pd and others), oxidation (Pt, Ag), isotopic exchange of hydrogen (Ni, Pt), syntheses based on carbon monoxide and hydrogen (Co, Fe, Ni and others), synthesis of ammonia (Fe), catalytic purification (Ni, Pt, Pd, Fe) and many others.

With respect to catalytic activity, metals considerably exceed other catalysts for many reactions. For instance, the reactions of isotopic exchange of hydrogen in the presence of platinum, nickel and certain other metallic catalysts take place at a high rate at the temperature of liquid nitrogen.

From now on, solid catalysts of which the active component is in the metallic state will be called metallic catalysts.

The metallic state does not determine the catalytic activity, since there also are active non-metallic catalysts and the specific catalytic activity considerably varies with individual groups of metals. The electronic structure, characteristic of certain metals, is particularly significant for catalytic properties.

It may be stated on the basis of many experimental data that, generally with respect to both the number of catalysed reactions and the value of activity, the catalytic properties are characteristic of the metals of the long periods of the Periodic Table, particularly of Groups VI, VII, VIII and I B.

To illustrate this problem, the results of determinations of the specific catalytic activity (i.e. activity referred to the unit area of a catalyst) of a series of metals will be given for the isotopic exchange reactions in molecular hydrogen (3), hydrogen–oxygen interaction (4), synthesis and decomposition of ammonia (5) and the isotopic exchange reactions in molecular nitrogen (6).

It has been shown that, if the effect of substance and heat transfers is eliminated and the attainment of a constant catalyst composition under the conditions of a given reaction is ensured, the specific catalytic activity of the catalyst of the given composition is practically constant and independent of the method of its preparation and heat treatment (7).

The principal results of the determinations of specific catalytic activity are given in Fig. 1.

A distinct maximum of the specific catalytic activity of the metals of Group VIII is observed for the isotopic exchange in molecular hydrogen and for the hydrogen–oxygen reaction. A rapid drop in the catalytic activity is observed when passing from nickel to copper and from platinum to gold.

A weak catalytic activity for the isotopic exchange in molecular hydrogen is also shown by other elements with the completely filled d-level.

For instance, the specific catalytic activity of germanium (8) is orders higher than that of nickel and the activation energy is higher by 9 kcal/mole (Table 1). It should be pointed out here that the difference in the rate of exchange on germanium and nickel is due to the difference in activation energies, and the pre-exponential coefficients are practically constant.

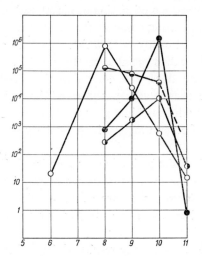

Fig. 1. Specific catalytic activity of the metals of Period 4 for various reactions:

● — $H_2 + D_2 \rightleftharpoons 2HD$
◑ — $2H_2 + O_2 \rightarrow 2H_2O$
○ — $N_2 + 3H_2 \rightleftharpoons 2NH_3$
◓ — $^{14}N_2 + ^{15}N_2 \rightleftharpoons 2\ ^{14}N\ ^{15}N$

TABLE 1

SPECIFIC CATALYTIC ACTIVITIES AND ACTIVATION ENERGIES OF GERMANIUM AND NICKEL
FOR THE ISOTOPIC EXCHANGE IN MOLECULAR HYDROGEN

Property	Germanium	Nickel
Specific catalytic activity, at 25°C	2×10^{-6}	6
at 300°C	1.5	3500
Activation energy, kcal/mole	17	8

The view has been put forward many times that there is a relation between the catalytic activity and semiconducting properties of solid catalysts. It would therefore be interesting to find the degree to which the catalytic activity of germanium is altered by introducing the additives changing its electrical conductance. Consequently, the catalytic activity of the specimens of germanium with gallium (*p*-type) and antimony (*n*-type) added and of pure germanium of low electrical conductance has been investigated for the isotopic exchange of hydrogen. In spite of the change in the concentration of free electrons and holes in the specimens under investigation of the order of 7–9, the rate of adsorption of hydrogen and that of isotopic exchange are similar for all the specimens. It may be concluded therefrom that the adsorption of hydrogen on germanium takes place without any contribution by free electrons and holes, i.e. without charging of surface. Apparently, the adsorption of hydrogen on germanium occurs due to a two-electron covalent bond to which contribute the electrons from the surface of germanium (28).

The specific catalytic activity of metals for the hydrogen–oxygen reaction changes within Period 4 in the same way as for the isotopic exchange in molecular hydrogen. It may be concluded therefrom that, for this reaction also, the governing factor is the bond energy between hydrogen and the catalyst surface. A similar arrangement of catalysts by their specific catalytic activities results from the data obtained by Beeck (9) on ethylene hydrogenation (Cr < Fe < Ni, Ta < W < Pt) and by Kemball (10) on ammonia–hydrogen isotopic exchange (Fe < Ni ≫ Cu). A similar relation, characterized by the maximum activity of cobalt, has been found by Katz and Kistiakowsky (11) for the recombination of hydrogen atoms:

$$Cr < Fe < Co > Ni > Cu > Zn$$

For the isotopic exchange of ethane and propane with hydrogen (12), the maximum of the specific catalytic activity is shifted towards Group VI and the metals of Group VIII give products of a more complete exchange: iron, cobalt and nickel bring about the cracking to methane. In all cases, when passing to Group I B, a rapid drop in the activity is observed.

For the synthesis of ammonia from nitrogen and hydrogen, where the step determining the over-all rate is the nitrogen chemisorption, the maximum of the catalytic activity is shifted towards the first elements of Group VIII, and in Period 4 it involves iron. The specific catalytic activity of nickel for the same exchange is three times lower than that of iron.

Figure 1 also includes the specific catalytic activities of various metals for the isotopic exchange in molecular nitrogen. They drop in the order iron–cobalt–nickel, but very much more slowly than the activities for the synthesis of ammonia. The catalytic activity of copper was so low that it was non measurable.

If it is assumed that the isotopic exchange in molecular nitrogen follows the adsorption-desorption mechanism, the adsorption and desorption rates near the adsorption equilibrium may be determined on the basis of the exchange rate. Thus, it is possible to explain the nature of the step limiting the synthesis of ammonia.

The Japanese authors—Enomoto, Horiuti and Kabayshi (13)—arrived at the conclusion that the slowest step of the synthesis of ammonia is the hydrogenation of the adsorbed nitrogen, but, for this to be true, both the rate of nitrogen sorption and that of isotopic exchange should be higher than the rate of synthesis.

It has been shown on the basis of data obtained that, at equal coverages of the surfaces of the iron catalysts by the adsorbed nitrogen, the rate of the isotopic exchange in molecular nitrogen is not higher but lower than the rate of synthesis. This supports the mechanism of Temkin and Pyzhev (14), who have assumed that the synthesis step determining the over-all rate is the adsorption of nitrogen. The exchange rate, lower than the synthesis rate, points to the limited mobility of the nitrogen atoms adsorbed.

It is very important in the theory of catalyst selection to show a relation between the specific catalytic activity of metals and the properties of their electronic structures.

As is known, the d-shell of the metal atoms of the long periods of the Periodic Table is gradually filled. In the crystalline state of the elements at the beginning of a long period, both the s- and d-electrons take part in the metallic bond. This manifests itself by the increase in the bond strength with the increase in the ordinal number. With a large number of electrons, however, as shown by magnetic measurement, some of d-electrons remain in the atomic shells and does not participate in the bond. This manifests itself by the appearance of a maximum for such properties of the metals of long periods as compressibility, heat of sublimation, melting point, etc.

Pauling (15) believes that the number of electrons taking part in the bond increases for the first long period, attaining approximately the value of 6 for chromium, next remains constant to nickel and then decreases, beginning from copper. On the other hand, Hume-Rothery, Irving and Williams (16) believe that immediately after the maximum number of the bond electrons in Group VI is reached their number in the atoms of the next metals begins to decrease, this being more rapid in the first long period than in the next ones.

The number of electrons participating in the bond between the metal atoms in the solid phase agrees with the valence of these metals appearing in chemical transformations. For example, the maximum number of electrons taking part in the chemical bond of the metals of Period 4 increases initially, attains a maximum for chromium and manganese, drops when passing to iron and diminishes gradually until the d-shell is completely filled. The decrease of the maximum valence in the first long period occurs more rapidly than in the next ones. Also interesting is the change in the nature of the bond when passing along this period. The metals at the beginning of Period IV are capable of forming a hydrogen bond with hydrogen, while, as the d-shell becomes more and more filled, the reaction with hydrogen leads to the formation of the positive hydrogen ion.

The inherent chemical properties of the metals of the groups considered manifest themselves by a considerable number of valence states, which is associated with a large number of the electrons capable of taking part in the chemical bond and with the ease with which the metals pass from one valence state to another. In the solid state this corresponds to a high density of electronic levels.

The comparison of the electronic structure of metals with their catalytic activities shows that at the beginning of a period the catalytic activity increases with the increase in the ordinal number and manifests itself most distinctly for the metals with the total number of s- and d-electrons (the number of electrons outside the shell of the preceding noble gas) exceeding the number of electrons participating in the metallic bond. As may be seen, the strength of the bond ensuring the stability of the metallic phase and the presence of unbound electrons in the atomic shells present many possibilities for the surface interactions which are very important for catalytic processes.

Under these conditions, the bond energy is critical for the surface interactions between the reactants and the catalyst. Fully determined and not very high bond energies favour a high rate of the catalysed reaction, which passes along a new path, and through intermediate interactions with the catalyst. In individual cases, particularly in the catalytic processes occurring at low temperatures, only the chemisorption with a very low bond energy is important. This is supported by the data obtained in the USSR in the laboratories of the Karpov Institute of Physical Chemistry by the author and A. A. Vasilevich for the reactions of the isotopic exchange in molecular hydrogen on platinum (17).

The rate of the isotopic exchange between hydrogen and deuterium, and also the rate of the exchange between the adsorbed and gaseous hydrogen, have been measured on the layer of platinum obtained by cathode spraying *in vacuo*. In order to increase the accuracy of measurements in the latter case, an exchange between the tritium adsorbed on the platinum surface and gaseous protium has been performed and the rate of exchange has been determined as a function of the increase in the activity of the gas.

The measurements have been made under a pressure of 0.01 mm Hg and at temperatures of 78 and 90°K (Figs. 2 and 3). It has been found that the homogeneous molecular exchange between protium and deuterium at 78°K occurred 4000 times more quickly than that between the adsorbed tritium and the gaseous protium.

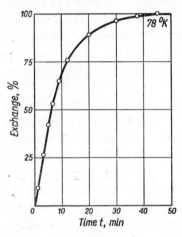

Fig. 2. Homomolecular isotopic exchange between protium and deuterium on platinum at 78°K.

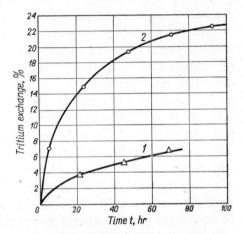

Fig. 3. Isotopic exchange between the adsorbed tritium and the gaseous protium on platinum: 1—at 78°K, 2—at 90°K.

The results obtained support the view that the main portion of the chemisorbed hydrogen does not take part in the homomolecular exchange. Of course, the isotopic exchange between hydrogen molecules occurs through the less strongly bound hydrogen, the amount of which lies at the limit of the error of the sorption measurements.

The above data on the change in the specific catalytic activity of metals of the long periods in the reactions of the isotopic exchange of molecular hydrogen may be accounted for by the effect of the electronic structure of the metals on the nature and energy of the surface interaction with hydrogen. The adsorption of hydrogen on the metals with unfilled d-shells occurs at a high rate and, even under low pressures, corresponds to the coverage of a larger part of the surface.

For the adsorption–desorption mechanism of exchange, the reaction reaches the maximum rate at the coverage of almost half of the catalyst surface with the chemisorbed hydrogen. Therefore, the decrease in the bond energy between hydrogen and the metal surface with a decrease in the number of unpaired electrons in the d-shell for the iron–cobalt–nickel series brings about an increase in the specific catalytic activity.

When passing to the next metal, i.e. copper, with a filled d-shell, the bond energy between hydrogen and the metal surface and the rate of chemisorption rapidly decrease. Hydrogen is not chemisorbed on copper at a considerable rate until the temperature is high (above 400°C). Consequently, the catalytic activity of copper for the exchange reaction of hydrogen atoms is very low.

For the synthesis of ammonia, the maximum of the specific catalytic activity is shifted towards the smaller number of d-electrons, and in Period 4 it falls to iron. The value of the bond energy between nitrogen and the iron surface is apparently the nearest to the optimum value for the synthesis of ammonia. It is too high on chromium and, therefore, the successive hydrogenation steps of the adsorbed nitrogen are very slow; on the other hand, the chemisorption energy of nitrogen on nickel is too small and the sorption is very slow. These assumptions are in agreement with the kinetic data concerning the synthesis of ammonia on different metals.

It may be concluded from the review of data concerning the specific catalytic activity of metals that for the transition metals it changes markedly, depending upon the degree of filling of the d-shell, the maximum for various reactions corresponding to the various degrees of filling. The principal reasons for this difference are the specificities of the structure and the properties of the active complexes of the various reactions. Furthermore, an essential effect may be exerted by the action of the reaction mixture on the catalyst, which manifests itself in the dissolution of individual reaction components and results in a change of the electronic structure. In consequence, the metallic properties of the catalyst are also altered. Such changes in composition, usually uncontrolled and frequently unnoticeable, may very strongly affect the electronic structure and the catalytic activity of metals (28).

The explanation of the dependence of the catalytic activity of metals on the degree of filling of the d-shell presents many possibilities of controlling the properties of the metallic catalysts by changing their electronic structure through the introduction of various additives. The metal alloys with a sufficiently developed surface are sure to find a wide application as catalysts for many industrial processes.

2. OXIDE CATALYSTS

Oxides, like metals, are the most common active components of industrial catalysts. Since oxygen is a component of all oxides, their properties, including the catalytic ones, may be considered dependent only upon the cation. Therefore, it is worth dealing with the explanation of the dependence of the catalytic activity of oxides on the position of the metal involved in the Periodic Table. This problem, in comparison with that when element catalysts are involved, is complicated by the various stoichiometric compositions of oxides, since a number of metals each form several oxides of a different composition and structure. Apart from that, it is possible to change the oxygen content in the given oxide within definite, often wide, limits without any phase transformation. Finally, the composition of oxide catalysts may also undergo changes under the influence of the reaction mixture.

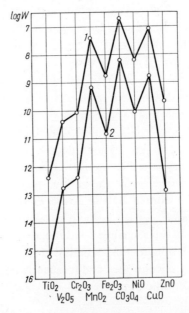

Fig. 4. Specific catalytic activities of oxides of metals of Period 4 for the oxidation of hydrogen:
1—at 300°C, *2*—at 150°C.

A definite and constant composition of an oxide catalyst, dependent on the ratio of the rates of interaction between the individual components and the catalyst (28), corresponds to each temperature and composition of the reaction mixture. Only when the rate of this interaction is sufficiently high and the catalyst attains quickly a constant composition may the specific catalytic activity of the oxide be unequivocally determined for a given reaction. On the other hand, if the rate of the interaction between reactants and the catalyst is low, the actual composition of the catalyst and, therefore, its specific catalytic activity will depend on the conditions under which it has been prepared, and may change within wide limits. This should be taken into consideration when comparing the specific catalytic activities of the oxides of various metals.

The catalytic activities of oxides of a number of metals of Period 4 for the hydrogen–oxygen reaction (Fig. 4) has been investigated in the USSR in the Karpov Institute of Physical Chemistry laboratory by V. V. Popovskii (19). The investigations have been conducted under atmospheric pressure in a stationary circulation apparatus permitting direct measurement of reaction rate at constant composition of the reaction mixture, the unfavourable effect of mass and heat transfer being avoided. All the oxides have been previously subjected to the action of oxygen at 400°C and the catalytic activity has been measured at a large excess of oxygen; the hydrogen content of the reaction mixture did not exceed 1%. The results of the measurements are given in Fig. 2 and Table 2.

The characteristics of the catalytic activity correspond to the composition of the oxides after preliminary treatment.

TABLE 2

CATALYTIC ACTIVITY OF VARIOUS OXIDES FOR THE OXIDATION OF HYDROGEN

Catalyst	Specific area, m^2/g	Reaction rate, moles of $H_2/hr \cdot cm^2$ Temperature, °C		Order of reaction with respect to hydrogen	Activation energy, kcal/mole	Pre-exponential coefficient
		300	150			
TiO_2	66.8	4×10^{-13}	6.3×10^{-16}	0.8	21	1.5×10^1
V_2O_5	2.3	4.2×10^{-11}	1.8×10^{-13}	0.8	18	1.1×10^2
Cr_2O_3	2.9	8.9×10^{-11}	4.8×10^{-13}	1	18	6.0×10^3
MnO_2	130	3.9×10^{-8}	7.4×10^{-10}	1	14	8.0×10^4
Fe_2O_3	27.2	1.7×10^{-9}	1.4×10^{-11}	0.6	15	1.3×10^1
Co_3O_4	7.7	2.0×10^{-7}	6.5×10^{-9}	1	11	3.0×10^4
NiO	7.1	2.7×10^{-9}	2.6×10^{-10}	1	8	3.0×10^1
CuO	17.7	8.0×10^{-8}	1.6×10^{-9}	1	13	2.1×10^4
ZnO	4.5	2.0×10^{-10}	1.3×10^{-13}	0.7	24	2.1×10^4

The specific catalytic activity of the oxides of the elements at the beginning of Period 4 is very low and increases rapidly when passing from titanium to manganese; for manganese oxide it is 10^6 times higher than for titanium dioxide. When passing to iron oxide, it decreases almost 1000 times, and increases again for Co_3O_4. The activity of nickel oxide is considerably lower than that of Co_3O_4. It again increases when passing to copper oxide. The specific catalytic activity of zinc oxide is almost 1000 times lower than that of copper oxide.

It follows that after the preliminary treatment with oxygen at 400°C the most active for the oxidation of hydrogen are oxides of metals, for which the filling of $4s$ and $3d$ electron shells exceeds half the possible number of electrons, but is not yet complete.

The maximum of the catalytic activity is shown by the oxides with the varying charge of the metal cation (manganese oxide, cobaltous-cobaltic oxide, copper oxide). The oxidation of hydrogen on these oxides is characterized by the lowest activation energy.

It would be interesting to attempt a correlation between the specific catalytic activity and other properties of oxides.

This problem has now been coped with successfully by many authors (21–24, 30).

The oxidation–reduction catalytic reactions consist of a number of intermediate surface interactions usually involving electron transfer between reactants and the catalyst. The electron transfers are accompanied by the formation of active complexes through which pass the intermediate stages. The energy of the active complex should therefore be dependent upon the electronic structure of the catalyst.

This dependence is determined by the values of the two component energies of the active complex: the emission work of the electron and the interaction energy between the ion formed and the catalyst. The latter quantity may vary at various spots of the surface and it is difficult to predict its dependence on the catalyst properties. Therefore, the prediction of the catalytic action limits the effect of the emission work of the electron under the assumption that the remaining quantities, which determine the activation energy, remain constant. When the formation of a complex in the stage determining the over-all rate of the reaction is associated with an electron transfer from the catalyst to the reactant, it may be assumed that the activation energy of the reaction will increase with the increase in the emission work. On the other hand, if during the formation of an active complex

TABLE 3

CONTACT POTENTIAL DIFFERENCE BETWEEN GOLD AND THE OXIDES (V)

TiO$_2$	V$_2$O$_5$	Cr$_2$O$_3$	MnO$_2$	Fe$_2$O$_3$	Co$_3$O$_4$	NiO	CrO	ZnO
−1.36	−0.75	−0.10	—	−0.74	−0.13	1.02	−0.03	0.0

an electron is transferred from the reactant to the catalyst, the reverse dependence is apparently true.

Table 3 gives the values of contact potential differences between gold and the oxides of the elements of Period 4. The measurements have been conducted by I. Morozova and V. V. Popovskii by the vibrating electrode method in a metal chamber at 22°C and under an oxygen pressure of 10 mm Hg on the oxides for which the catalytic activity has been investigated.

The comparison of the data above and the catalytic activity of the same oxides does not show a sufficiently regular dependence. This proves that, when passing from one oxide to another, the change in the emission work is not the principal factor determining the change in the activation energy of the catalytic reaction.

The oxygen bonding energy under the conditions of the catalytic reaction may more fully characterize the oxides. With other conditions being the same, the oxygen bonding energy should determine both the activation energy for bonding oxygen by the catalyst and the activation energy for the interaction between oxygen and the substances being oxidized.

The bond energy may be estimated from the mobility of oxygen in oxides due to the isotopic exchange with molecular oxygen. Therefore, it may be expected that for a number of oxides there is a definite relation between the change in the rate of the isotopic exchange and the catalytic activity for the oxidation by molecular oxygen.

In Fig. 5 data concerning the isotopic exchange between molecular oxygen and some oxides of the metals of Period 4 at 300°C and under an oxygen pressure of 10 mm Hg are given. A comparison with the corresponding curve shows that the relation mentioned above actually occurs for the oxidation of hydrogen at a large excess of oxygen. The differences in the catalytic activities of oxides are less marked than they are at the rate of the isotopic exchange of oxygen, but the general nature of changes, except for copper oxide, shows a similarity.

It should be pointed out that the relation between the rates of the oxygen exchange and a catalysed reaction should manifest itself only when the course of the catalytic reaction does not essentially alter the stationary oxygen content in oxides, since the oxygen bonding energy in oxides changes markedly in many cases even at minute changes in the stoichiometric composition of the oxide.

A valuable method of controlling the activity of oxide catalysts is the introduction of promoters. In many cases their action is probably associated

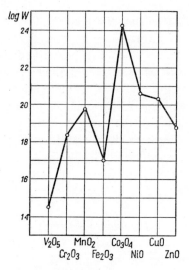

Fig. 5. Activity of the oxides of the metals of Period 4 for the isotopic exchange with molecular oxygen at 300°C and under a pressure of 10 mm Hg.

with a shift of the chemical potential level of the solid catalyst. Recently, a number of studies have been carried out to explain the relation between the change in the electrical conductance and the catalytic activity when introducing promoters into oxide catalysts.

Interesting results concerning this problem have been obtained by the Polish authors, A. Bielański, I. Dereń, I. Haber and co-workers (25). The attempts made by Hauffe to justify theoretically this relation did not give satisfactory results. It has been found in many cases that there is no agreement between theoretical conclusions and experimental results (26, 27).

The author has put forward the view (31) that these discrepancies result from the arbitrary assumption that a change in the value of chemical potential corresponds to a change in the activation energy of electrical conductance (24).

Actually, the introduction of additives at considerable concentrations may cause profound changes in the electronic structure, especially a shift of the valence zone limits, and this may affect the correspondence of the changes in chemical potential and in the activation energy of electrical conductance.

In most cases, however, the discrepancy between the expected and observed relations of the catalytic activity and the semiconducting properties of oxides is probably to be found elsewhere. During the changes in the composition of oxide catalysts the change in the emission work of the electron is accompanied by a change in the second component of the activation energy (the interaction energy between reactants and catalyst during the formation of an active complex). This change may be predominant.

REFERENCES

1. Balandin A. A.: Voprosy khimicheskoi kinetiki, kataliza i reaktsionnoi sposobnosti. Izd. Akad. Nauk SSSR. Moscow, 1955, p. 461.
2. Semenov N. N., Voevodskii V. V.,: Sbornik. Geterogennyi kataliz v khimicheskoi promyshlennosti, Moscow, 1955, p. 233.
3. Avdeenko M.A., Boreskov G. K., Slin'ko M. G.: Sbornik. Problemy kinetiki i kataliza IX. Izotopy v katalize. Izd. Akad. Nauk SSSR. Moscow, 1957, p. 61.
4. Boreskov G. K., Slin'ko M. G., Filippova A. G., Gur'yanova R. N., *Dokl. Akad. Nauk SSSR*, **94**, 713, (1954).
5. Shcheglov O. F., Boreskov G. K., Slin'ko M. G., *Dokl. Akad. Nauk SSSR*, **105**, 123 (1955).
6. Gorbunow A. I., Boreskov G. K., *Dokl. Akad. Nauk SSSR* (1958).
7. Boreskov G. K.: Sbornik. Geterogennyi kataliz v khimicheskoi promyshlennosti. Goskhimizdat. Moscow, 1955, p. 5.
8. Boreskov G. K., Kuchaev V. L., *Dokl. Akad. Nauk SSSR* (1960).
9. Beeck O., *Discussions Faraday Soc.*, **8**, 118 (1950).
10. Kemball C., *Proc. Roy. Soc.*, **A214**, 413 (1952).
11. Katz S., Kistiakovsky G. B., Steiner R. F., *J. Am. Chem. Soc.*, **71**, 2258 (1949).
12. Kemball C., *Proc. Roy. Soc.*, **A223**, 361, 377 (1954).
13. Enomoto, Horiuti, Kabayshi J., *Res. Inst. Catalysis Hokkaido Univ.*, **3**, 185 (1955).
14. Temkin M. I., Pyzhev V. A., *Zh. Fiz. Khim.*, **13**, 851 (1939).
15. Pauling L., *Proc. Roy. Soc.*, **A196**, 343 (1949).
16. Hume-Rothery W., Irving H. M., Williams R. P., *Proc. Roy. Soc.*, **A208**, 431 (1951).
17. Boreskov G. K.: Sbornik. Problemy kinetiki i kataliza. X. Fizika i fiziko-khimiya kataliza. Izd. Akad. Nauk SSSR, 1960, 128.
18. Boreskov G. K., *Zh. Fiz. Khim.*, **32**, 2739 (1958); *ibid.*, **33**, 1969 (1959).
19. Popovskii V. V., Boreskov G. K.: Sbornik. Problemy kinetiki i kataliza. X. Fizika i fizicheskaya khimiya kataliza. Izd. Akad. Nauk SSSR, 1960, str. 67; *Kinetika i Kataliz*, **1**, 566 (1960).
20. Boreskov G. K., Slin'ko M. G., *Khim. Prom.*, **19** (1955).
21. Vol'kenshtein F. F.: Problemy kinetiki i kataliza. USh 1955, p. 68.

22. Roginskii S. Z., *Khim. Nauka i Promy.*, **2**, No. 2. 138 (1957).
23. Dowden D. A., Mackenzie N., Trapnell B., *Proc. Roy. Soc.*, **A237**, 245 (1956).
24. Hauffe K., *Angew. Chem.*, **68**, 776 (1956); Hauffe K., Schlosser E. G., *Z. Elektrochem.*, **61**, 506 (1957).
25. Bielański A., Dereń I., Haber I., *Bull. Acad. Polon. Sci., Classe III*, **3**, 221,491 (1955); *ibid.*, **4** 103, 523 (1956); *ibid.*, **5**, 197, 673 (1957).
26. Keier N. P., Roginskii S. Z., Sazonova I. S., *Dokl. Akad. Nauk SSSR*, **106**, 859 (1956).
27. Keier N. P., Kutseva L. N., *Dokl. Akad. Nauk SSSR*, **117**, 259 (1957).
28. Kuchaev V. L., Boreskov G. K., *Kinetika i Kataliz*, **1**, 356 (1960).
29. Boreskov G. K., Vasilevich A. A., *Kinetika i Kataliz*, **1**, 69 (1960).
30. Boreskov G. K., *Dokl. Akad. Nauk SSSR*, **127**, 591 (1959).
31. Boreskov G. K., *Probl. Fiz. Khim.*, **1**, 101 (1958).

V. HYDROLYTIC HYDROGENATION OF POLYSACCHARIDES AND THE MULTIPLET THEORY OF CATALYSIS

N. A. VASYUNINA

The importance of polysaccharide hydrolysis has been realized for over 30 years, since the time of Bergius.

One of the applications of the hydrolysis products—monosaccharides—is their hydrogenation to form, for example, polyhydric alcohols.

Polyhydric alcohols are produced in many industrial plants by hydrolysing polysaccharides and subsequent hydrogenation of the monosaccharides. The hydrolysis of polysaccharides by dilute inorganic acids is, however, always accompanied by considerable loss due to the fact that the hydrolysis is a consecutive reaction, i.e. it does not stop at the stage of monosaccharide formation but proceeds further and causes their decomposition. The separate execution of both hydrolysis and hydrogenation processes is also accompanied by the formation of free monosaccharides, a fact which both complicates and increases the cost of their manufacture.

A new general method for hydrolytic hydrogenation has been developed in the USSR permitting hydrolysis and hydrogenation to proceed in the same operation, and this has considerably simplified polyhydric alcohol production and reduced manufacturing costs.

Polyhydric alcohols, from ethylene glycol to sorbitol, find many applications and various uses in different branches of industry. They are used as moisture stabilizers, plasticizers and antifreezes, as well as starting materials in the manufacture of alkyd resins and other polymers.

The hydrolytic hydrogenation is carried out in the presence of an inorganic acid and a solid hydrogenation catalyst, as two processes—hydrolysis and hydrogenation—quickly follow one another.

At elevated temperatures, a polysaccharide is hydrolysed by an acid to monosaccharides which are quickly subjected to hydrogenation to

[75]

the corresponding polyhydric alcohols in the presence of a hydrogenation catalyst. The equations for the reaction are as follows:

$$(C_6H_{10}O_5)_n \xrightarrow{\text{H}_2\text{O, H}_2} n\,C_6H_{14}O_6$$

$$(C_5H_8O_4)_n \xrightarrow{\text{H}_2\text{O, H}_2} n\,C_2H_{12}O_5$$

The combination of two such processes is of considerable importance, since it achieves the efficient conversion of polysaccharides difficult to hydrolyse, e.g. cellulose, to polyhydric alcohols. A combination of both hydrolysis and hydrogenation processes has hitherto not been investigated. In the technical literature there is only one case mentioned, namely, that of starch, which may be hydrolysed and hydrogenated in the presence of sulphuric acid and Raney nickel to sorbitol.

This reaction, however, can only take place during the first moments, since the two catalysts—sulphuric acid and Raney nickel—readily interact, especially at elevated temperatures, to form nickel sulphate, which is inactive for hydrogenation.

If, instead of free acid, nickel sulphate is used with the required addition of metallic nickel, easily hydrolysable polysaccharides such as chemicellulose and starch may be subjected to hydrolytic hydrogenation. This, however, is another method developed in detail in the USSR but not included in this paper, which is limited to presenting the results of studies conducted by the author jointly with A. A. Balandin, S. W. Chepigo and G. S. Barysheva (1, 2, 3, 4).

The object of the investigation has been the determination of the optimum conditions for the hydrolytic hydrogenation of cellulose. Therefore, the rate and yield of the process have been systematically investigated with special reference to the following factors: pH of the medium, properties of the inorganic acid, amount of the heterogeneous catalyst, concentration of the polysaccharide, temperature and pressure.

The hydrolytic hydrogenation process required an acid-insoluble catalyst capable of operating in the medium of an inorganic acid. After investigating a variety of catalysts, it was found that the required conditions are best fulfilled by a specially prepared ruthenium catalyst. The technique adopted in the laboratory experiments was as follows: the polysaccharide—sulphite or cotton cellulose—in a 1.5% aqueous solution of phosphoric acid was placed in an insulated autoclave and the ruthenium catalyst containing 0.1% Ru, based on the polysaccharide, was added. The hydrolysis stage determines the over-all rate of the reaction, since the hydrogenation takes place very quickly and occurs under more moderate conditions than those required for hydrolysis.

For example, glucose (10 g) in the presence of a ruthenium catalyst and an inorganic acid undergoes total hydrogenation within 10–15 minutes at 110°C under a hydrogen pressure of 20 25 atm.

It was found that the optimum conditions for the hydrogenation of cellulose in the presence of phosphoric acid and a ruthenium catalyst are as follows: temperature, 180°C, hydrogen pressure, 50–100 atm, and the total time for the process, 40–50 minutes. The required concentration of phosphoric acid is 1.5%. At a lower acidity (about 1%), the hydrolysis of cellulose under the above conditions proceeds slowly, thus slowing down the course of the whole reaction. A higher concentration of the acid (about 2–3%) speeds up the process only slightly and there is, therefore, no advantage in increasing the acidity, as it necessitates the removal of excess acid from the final product.

At a temperature below 180°C, even at 170°C, the hydrolysis of cellulose, under conditions of the experiment, proceeds very slowly and, therefore, the whole process is retarded. At a higher temperature, 180–200°C, the decomposition of reaction products takes place, which may be recognized by development of a yellow colour and characteristic odour of the solution. In addition, at increased temperature, the acid causes dehydration of the polyhydric alcohols to form the corresponding anhydrides.

Investigations have shown that the required hydrogen pressure is 50–60 atm, since at lower pressures and observing the above conditions of temperature and concentration of the acid, the hydrogenation does not take place even after 2 hours. Increased pressure, up to about 100 atm, has no effect on the rate of hydrogenation.

Only small amounts of the ruthenium catalyst are used, 0.1% Ru being quite sufficient in relation to the weight of the initial polysaccharide. The hydrogenation takes place in the presence of even 0.02% Ru, but under these conditions the catalyst is quickly fouled.

Concerning the nature of the acid, phosphoric acid should be used to obtain sorbitol from cellulose. It is true that, in the presence of sulphuric acid, the hydrolytic hydrogenation occurs under even milder conditions—at 150–160°C within 30–40 minutes—but| in addition to sorbitol 25–40% of sorbitan is also formed. In this case, sorbitan is the product of the third consecutive reaction, namely, the removal of one water molecule from sorbitol. If the time factor is increased to 1 hour and the temperature increased to 180°C, sorbitan is almost exclusively formed during the hydrogenation. Usually, the reaction products are colourless and odourless solutions from which, upon settling, the catalyst may be easily removed. No gaseous by-products are formed during this process.

The hydrogenation product is isolated by evaporation of the aqueous solution *in vacuo* after removal of the mineral acid by means of synthetic ion exchangers. If phosphoric acid is used, the evaporated product is sorbitol, the yield being 90–95% of the cellulose used. The purity of the product was estimated by elementary analysis, the determination of the molecular weight and the percentage content of hydroxyl groups by acetylation, as well as by two-dimensional paper chromatography.

As mentioned, sorbitan is formed if sulphuric acid is used. It was analysed similarly to sorbitol and the yield was 90–95%.

It should be noted that sorbitan is similar in physico-chemical properties to polyhydric alcohols, such as glycerol, and, therefore, may find application in industry.

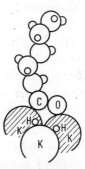

Fig. 1. Space model representing the index for the hydrogenation reaction of mono-saccharides.

It is interesting to apply the multiplet theory to the process under discussion. This theory is applied to heterogeneous catalytic reactions and the hydrogenation of monosaccharides is a reaction of this type.

On the basis of the multiplet theory, this reaction is of the duplet character with reacting atoms and bonds as illustrated in the following index:

$$
\begin{array}{cc}
>\text{C} & \text{H} \\
\| & | \\
\text{O} & \text{H}
\end{array}
\tag{1}
$$

The multiplet theory is concerned not only with structure factors but also with energy factors. The index for the hydrogenation reaction of mono-saccharides may be represented by a space model (Fig. 1), where the catalyst atoms are represented by large circles. The magnitude of the radii of these atoms is of great importance in catalysis. Metal catalysts used in hydrogenation reactions may be arranged in a series and in order of increasing values of their radii:

Metal:	γ-Fe	Ni	Co	Cu	Ru	Os	Rh	Ir	Pd	Pt
Radius:	1.239	1.244	1.254	1.275	1.332	1.335	1.342	1.355	1.372	1.385
	A2	A1	A1	A1	A3	A3	A1	A1	A1	A1

In the above arrangement, it should be noted that ruthenium occupies a position between nickel and the noble metals, and it was found that Pd and Pt are less active catalysts for this reaction than Ru.

The hydrogenation reaction of monosaccharides differs from other hydrogenation reactions, in that a monosaccharide molecule contains many hydroxyl groups which have an effect on the energy of the reacting bonds.

Energy factors, considered according to the multiplet theory, are concerned with the bond energy between the catalyst and the reacting atoms. Unfortunately, these values have not been determined for ruthenium; on the other hand, they are well known for nickel.

Therefore, it would be interesting to consider a reaction similar to the above but using nickel as the catalyst. Such a reaction would be one of hydrogenation and hydrogenolysis (destructive hydrogenation) of monosaccharides in the presence of nickel and in an inert medium. These reactions have been thoroughly investigated and, according to data in the literature, have found industrial application.

In an aqueous solution, with nickel and a hydrogen pressure of 150–300 atm, the following reactions take place:

1. At 120–130°C monosaccharides undergo almost complete hydrogenation to the corresponding polyhydric alcohols—xylase to xylitol, glucose to sorbitol, etc.
2. At higher temperatures, hydroxyl groups beginning with the terminal ones are split off from the alcohols. Thus, glycerol is first converted to propylene glycol -1,2 and then to isopropyl alcohol. Higher alcohols lose their hydroxyl groups less readily than the lower ones.
3. More difficult, in a shortage of hydrogen (due to insufficient mixing), monosaccharides produce gluconic acids (up to several per cent) and cause an acidic reaction of the medium.
4. These reactions are partially competitive with the splitting of C—C bonds, usually at the middle of a molecule, but generally occurring at higher temperatures. Thus, under certain conditions, α-propylene glycol and glycerol are formed from sorbitol.

The sequence of these reactions may undergo certain changes depending on the structure of the molecules, but nevertheless there is a general regularity apparent from the experimental data. The multiplet theory of catalysis may be applied to the equations of the reactions in question and, accordingly, a duplet reaction occurs, the more easily, the lower the energy barrier $(-E)$, i.e. the higher the value associated with the heat of formation of the intermediate multiplet complex:

$$E = Q_{AB} - Q_{CD} + (Q_{AK} + Q_{BK} + Q_{CK} + Q_{DK}) \qquad (2)$$

where: Q = the bond energy,
K = the catalyst,
A, B, C, D = reacting atoms of a molecule.

The index (1) may be used as an example.

Thus, the higher the value of E, the higher is the rate of reaction, and, as should be pointed out, E is a kinetic quantity—the energy of formation of an active multiplet complex (equal to 3/4 of activation energy of opposite sign), but not the heat of reaction appearing in the Bertholet principle or ΔF, according to some authors.

By taking indices of the reactions applicable to this process, and by substituting the known values of Q into equation (2), the results shown in Table 1 are obtained for a nickel catalyst.

TABLE 1

CALCULATED RELATIVE EASE, E, AT WHICH THE REACTION OCCURS OVER Ni (THE EFFECT OF THE NATURE OF ATOMS IN THE INDEX)

Ser. No.	Type of reaction	Reaction index	E_{calc}, cal/mole
1	Hydrogenation of a carbonyl group in monosaccharides	$>$C H $\parallel$ $\mid$ O H	$-10,000$
2	Reduction of an alcoholic group, hydrogenolysis of C—O bond	$\geqslant$C H $\mid$ $\mid$ O H	$-17,000$
3	Cannizzaro's reaction, formation of gluconic acids	$>$C H $\parallel$ $\mid$ O C$\leqslant$	$-32,000$
4	Rupture of carbon chain of alcohols, hydrogenolysis of C—C bond	$\geqslant$C H $\mid$ $\mid$ $\geqslant$C H	$>-48,000$

It is apparent, therefore, that the sequence of reactions shown in Table 1 is in agreement with the experimental data.

At the same time, it follows from the data in Table 1 that, in the case of monosaccharides, the open-chain form containing a carbonyl group of $E = -10,000$ cal/mole should more easily undergo hydrogenation than cyclic forms predominant in an aqueous solution for which the value of E is lower ($E = -17,000$ cal/mole).

The effect of the structure of a compound on the rate of reaction of the given type is due to the effect of substituents situated outside the index group. For example, the introduction of a substituent at the atom A in formula (1) influences the value of Q_{AB} and Q_{AK} in equation (2). Thus, the value of E is changed and, consequently, the rate of reaction is also changed. By changing quantities containing A in the equation for the heat of reaction $U = Q_{AD} + Q_{BC} + Q_{AB} + Q_{CD}$ (see formula (1)) and in the known thermodynamic equation $\Delta F = -U - T\Delta S$, where $S = $ entropy, we obtain

$$\delta E = \delta Q_{AK} - \delta Q_{AB}$$
$$\delta U = \delta Q_{AD} - \delta Q_{AB} \tag{3}$$
$$\delta F = -\delta U - T\delta\Delta S$$

It follows from equation (3) that the introduction of a substituent at A will give

$$\delta E = -\delta\Delta F - (T\delta\Delta S - \delta Q_{AD} + \delta Q_{AK}) \tag{4}$$

For condensed systems (i.e. solid and liquid) the value of $\delta\Delta S$ should be small; quantities δQ_{AD} and δQ_{AK} also are slight in comparison to quantity $\delta\Delta F$ and, in addition, they appear in equation (4) with opposite signs. Therefore, if there is no evolution of gases during a reaction, the value of the sum inside brackets in equation (4) should not be large. Hydrogen is contained in the system in all cases. Therefore, it follows:

$$\Delta E \cong -\delta\Delta F \tag{5}$$

Thus, the reaction should proceed more quickly for a larger drop in the free energy of formation, $\delta\Delta F$, due to substitution.

Tables 2 and 3 contain values of $\delta\Delta F$ calculated from free energies of formation according to data by Parks and Hoffman. The average value between the extreme values found in the relevant table has been assumed at the outset of the calculation of $\delta\Delta F$. Actually, the values of δE taken from Tables 2 and 3 should be added to the value of E taken from Table 1.

The sequence of reactions, calculated from $\delta\Delta F$, is in agreement with experimental data.

Actually, the preferential rupture of the hydrocarbon chain occurs at the middle (see Nos. 1, 4 and 12 in Table 3), which is accounted for by the fact that the values of Q_{C-C} are smallest at this point and increase towards the chain ends. The primary hydroxyl groups are split off more readily

TABLE 2

CALCULATED RELATIVE EASE, δE, AT WHICH THE HYDROGENOLYSIS REACTIONS OF C—O
BONDS IN POLYHYDRIC ALCOHOLS OCCUR OVER Ni (THE EFFECT OF SUBSTITUENTS ON
REACTION 2, TABLE 1)

Ser. No.	Reaction	$\delta E = -\delta \Delta F_{calc}$, cal/mole
1	Hexitol → methylpentitol + H_2O	2600
2	Pentitol → methylerythritol + H_2O	2600
3	Erythritol → methylglycerol + H_2O	2700
4	Erythritol → butene-3-ol-(1, 2, 4) + H_2O	−300
5	Glycerol → propylene glycol-(1, 2) + H_2O	2100
6	Glycerol → propylene glycol-(1, 3) + H_2O	−1300
7	Propylene glycol → n-propyl alcohol + H_2O	−1600
8	Propylene glycol → isopropyl alcohol + H_2O	2500
9	Ethylene glycol → ethyl alcohol + H_2O	−2700

TABLE 3

CALCULATED RELATIVE EASE, δE, AT WHICH THE HYDROGENOLYSIS REACTIONS OF C—C
BONDS IN POLYHYDRIC ALCOHOLS OCCUR OVER Ni (THE EFFECT OF SUBSTITUENTS ON
REACTION 4, TABLE 1)

Ser. No.	Reaction	$\delta E = -\delta \Delta F_{calc}$, cal/mole
1	Hexitol → two glycerol molecules	1200
2	Hexitol → erythritol + ethylene glycol	400
3	Hexitol → methyl alcohol + pentitol	160
4	Methylpentitol → glycerol + propylene glycol	700
5	Methylpentitol → methylglycerol + ethylene glycol	500
6	Methylpentitol → methylerythritol + methyl alcohol	−1060
7	Pentitol → ethylene glycol + glycerol	1100
8	Pentitol → erythritol + methyl alcohol	−40
9	Methylerythritol → ethylene glycol + propylene glycol	600
10	Methylerithritol → ethyl alcohol + glycerol	−600
11	Methylerithritol → methyl alcohol + methylglycerol	−40
12	Erythritol → two ethylene glycol molecules	1200
13	Erythritol → glycerol + methyl alcohol	200
14	Methylglycerol → ethyl alcohol + ethylene glycol	−1200
15	Methylglycerol → methyl alcohol + propylene glycol	200
16	Glycerol → ethylene glycol + methyl alcohol	−40

than are the secondary hydroxyl groups (see Nos. 3 and 5 in Table 2). In
reaction 4, Table 1, the total effect of hydroxyl groups has been taken
into account by pointing out that $E > -48,000$ cal/mole.

It is clear, however, that the greater the number of hydroxyl groups, the more C—C bonds should be weakened. This condition explains the fact that for higher alcohols—hexitols and pentitols—the rupture of C—C bonds precedes the splitting off of hydroxyl groups, whereas for lower alcohols—glycerol and ethylene glycol—the situation is reversed. Thus, the formation of propylene glycol-(1,2) from glycerol (No. 5, Table 2) corresponds to the general order, that the 1,2-isomer is formed instead of the 1,3-isomer (Nos. 5 and 6, Table 2), and this is in agreement with experimental data. This also accounts for the fact that a propylene glycol–glycerol mixture of varying composition is obtained from the hydrogenolysis of sorbitol.

Some authors—Schmidt (5), Natta, Rigamonti and Beati (6)—previously established certain regularities concerning the ease with which the reactions in question occur, and established their sequence. The application of the multiplet theory reveals more general regularities, as shown in Tables 1, 2 and 3, and, therefore, the multiplet theory may find many applications in investigations on the hydrogenation of monosaccharides and polyhydric alcohols.

REFERENCES

1. Chepigo S. W., Balandin A. A., Vasyunina N. A., Sergeev A. S., *Khim. Nauka i Promy.*, **2**, No. 4, 416 (1957).
2. Balandin A. A., Vasyunina N. A., Barysheva G. S., Chepigo S. W., *Izv. Akad. Nauk SSSR, Otd. Khim. Nauk*, No. 3, 392 (1957).
3. Balandin A. A., Vasyunina N. A., *Dokl. Akad. Nauk SSSR*, **117**, No. 1, 84 (1957)
4. Balandin A. A., *Uch. Zap. Mosk. Gos. Univ.*, **175**, 97 (1956).
5. Schmidt O., *Z. Physik. Chem.*, **A125**, 337 (1932).
6. Natta G., Rigamonti R., Beati E., *Ber.* **76**, 641 (1943).

VI. THE THEORY OF ENZYMATIC AND ASYMMETRIC CATALYSIS

E. I. KLABUNOVSKII

Practically all processes important to life are influenced by enzymes or asymmetric substances. The mechanism of their stereospecific action is in most cases unexplained. Therefore, in seeking an explanation of the complex manner in which these catalysts operate, the attempts to obtain asymmetric inorganic and organic catalysts—chemical models of enzymes—play a particularly important role. The problem is important not only in providing an explanation for the stereospecific action of enzymes but also in elucidating the mechanism of asymmetric catalysis which played an important role in the appearance and development of the asymmetry of the organic world. Recently, stereospecific catalysis has acquired great practical importance in the work of Natta on stereospecific polymerization. In this connection, the application of the theory of catalysis is interesting in providing both a classification and an explanation of the stereospecific action of enzymes and their chemical models.

The multiplet theory of catalysis, developed by A. A. Balandin (1), characterizes the atoms or groups of atoms which form an intermediate adsorption complex with a catalyst—a multiplet. Also, the multiplet theory may successfully be applied to the study of enzymatic reactions, since enzymes are microheterogeneous catalysts, and, in a number of cases concerned with chemical models of enzymes, they are fully heterogeneous catalysts. In addition, the multiplet theory permits the systematization of reactions occurring under the influence of enzymes or their chemical models.

The review of asymmetric enzymatic reactions, resulting in the formation of optically active compounds, shows that these reactions may be divided into two groups: addition to C=C bonds or to C=O bonds (2). They include the asymmetric cyanhydrin synthesis occurring under the influence of hydroxynitrilase, the formation of ketoalcohols in the presence

[85]

of carboligase, the reduction of a carbonyl group to an alcohol group in the presence of reductase, and syntheses occurring under the influence of ketoaldomutase.

Table 1 gives enzymes and starting substances, as well as the reaction index characteristic of the enzyme.

TABLE 1

Enzyme	Starting substance	Reaction index
Hydroxynitrilase	Aldehyde + HCN	C C ≡N ‖ | O H
Carboligase	Aldehyde	C C ‖ | O H
Ketoaldomutase (aspartase, fumarase)	Aldehyde, acids	C H ‖ | C O
Reductase	Hydroxy compounds	C H ‖ | C H

In addition to natural enzymes, the action which causes asymmetry in chemical reactions is exhibited by optically active catalysts relatively simple in structure. The ability to cause asymmetry is shown even by optically active solvents. For example, the asymmetric course of the reaction between α-phenylethylamine and phenylisocyanate takes place in (−)-α-pinene (3), as well as certain Grignard reactions in (+)-dimethoxybutane (4).

Only by the application of optically active catalysts is it possible to attain certain asymmetric effects. For example, in the decarboxylation of camphoric acid by alkaloids, the difference between rates of decomposition of optical antipodes may be as much as 17% (5). Pratesi (6) has thoroughly studied the effect of the structure of organic catalysts such as various optically active bases and amino acids on the efficiency of the asymmetric decomposition of camphoric acid. In these cases, the action of the catalysts resembles that of carboxylase.

The action of alkaloids is of interest in the reduction of β-methyl-and β-(α-naphthyl)-cinnamic acids in the presence of hydrocinchonine (7), and in the bromination of a cinchonine salt of cinnamic acid or of glucosamine cinnamate (8).

The catalytic action of alkaloids corresponds more closely to that of enzymes, if the possibility of forming individual chemical compounds, i.e. salts, as in the previous case, is excluded. Many examples can be given of the action of brucine and strychnine in the formation of one of the ester antipodes in excess in the acylation or benzoylation of racemic variants of secondary alcohols and in the esterification of racemic variants of acid chlorides (9).

In addition, this group of reactions should include the dehydration of methylphenylcarbinol (10) in the presence of 2% camphorsulphonic acid to form an optically active ester, as well as the asymmetric dehydration of an unsaturated alcohol to form a substituted allene (11).

In all these reactions, in spite of their diversity, there is an identity of index, and they therefore belong to the same group of reactions as those catalysed by esterase.

The application of asymmetric camphorsulphonic acid as catalyst is of great interest, since, in addition to the action characteristic of esterase, it is capable of reproducing the asymmetric action of ketoaldomutase. Thus, for example, 2,4-dihydroxychalcone is converted by (+)-bromocamphorsulphonic acid to optically active 7-hydroxyflavonon (12):

The action of optically active β-bismethylamine- α-phenylethanol on benzyl- or α-naphthylglyoxal is apparently also similar to that of ketoaldomutase (13). The chemical model of hydroxynitrilase is to be found in the catalytic action of quinic alkaloids in the synthesis of optically active mandelonitrile from benzaldehyde and hydrocyanic acid. This reaction may be extended to other aldehydes (14). Prelog and Wilhelm (15) have studied in detail the effect of structure and configuration of catalyst molecules, such as quinine and quinidine derivatives, on the efficiency of the asymmetric catalytic synthesis of benzyllactic and mandelic nitriles.

The chemical models of enzymes are known not only among micro-heterogeneous catalysts but also in the field of heterogeneous catalysis. The basis of every heterogeneous catalytic process is the adsorption of reacting substances on to catalyst surfaces. Therefore, instances of asymmetric catalysis, where the catalyst itself exhibits an asymmetric structure, should be distinguished from those where the catalyst exhibits a symmetric structure, but has been deposited on to an asymmetric carrier. It may be expected that in both cases the asymmetric adsorption will cause asymmetric catalysis. Cotton cellulose, treated with ethylamine, is converted into a catalyst which, like the alkaloids, may act like carboxylase in the decomposition of camphoric acid or like hydroxynitrilase in the synthesis of (−)-mandelonitrile. Such a catalyst was obtained in 1932 by Bredig and Gerstner (16). Although the authors considered this example as the first instance of asymmetric heterogeneous catalysis caused by the optically selective action of the catalyst itself and not of the carrier, it appears that the mechanism of the asymmetric action of such a catalyst involves the asymmetric adsorption on the surface of the optically active cellulose followed by the ordinary non-specific catalysis.

The mechanism of the action of palladium, deposited on to silk, in the asymmetric hydrogenation of $C=N$ bonds, is similar (17).

Such a mechanism is supported by the asymmetric adsorption on cellulose which, recently, has found a wide application in the paper-chromatographic separation of amino acids (18, 19).

Actually, the attempt made by Ghosh (20) failed to bring about asymmetric catalysis on two-coloured thin metal films of high optical rotatory power. Consequently, until data are obtained on the asymmetric action of a catalyst not associated with an asymmetric carrier, there is no reason to assign the occurrence of an asymmetric effect to the special asymmetric structure of the catalyst.

In addition, this point of view is supported by positive results of experiments on the optically selective action of the catalysts prepared by the deposition of an optically non-specific catalyst on an asymmetric inorganic carrier. Schwab and co-workers (21), by using thin films of copper, platinum or nickel deposited on crystals of optically active quartz, have conducted at 400–500°C the optically selective decomposition of butanol-2 racemate. These experiments have been repeated and extended to include the dehydration of other alcohols (22).

Terent'ev and Klabunovskii (23) have thoroughly investigated the asymmetric dehydration and dehydrogenation of butanol-2 over various metal catalysts deposited on optically active quartz, and, in addition, have extended their application to the asymmetric synthesis of α- and β-diphenylpropionic acids by the hydrogenation of α-phenylcinnamic acid in a liquid phase and, also, to the synthesis of an optically active pinane from α-pinene. Ponomarev and Zelenkova (24) have used nickel deposited on quartz in the asymmetric synthesis under pressure of a number of furane derivatives.

By using a hydroxide catalyst deposited on quartz, Terent'ev, Klabunovskii and Budovskii have conducted the asymmetric cyanoethylation of 2-methylcyclohexanone in liquid phase. This reaction differs basically from the previous examples, since it does not take place at a high temperature, but at 20–30°C, under the so-called conditions of natural enzymatic syntheses (25).

As may be seen from the material presented, considerable data on the asymmetric action of enzymes has been obtained from chemical models, and, consequently, certain generalizations have been made. For example, chemical models of enzymes exhibit interesting properties: the extent of their action is incomparably wider than that of enzymes, although their action is not so strictly stereospecific.

If a given enzyme is able to act upon the reactions in question only with one index, the corresponding organic catalyst acts with a high enough specificity on reactions of diametrically different types. In Table 2 are compared enzymes, indices of their reactions and chemical models of enzymes.

It follows from the review of the material that, in the case of enzyme models of relatively simple structure, such as camphor derivatives, it is difficult to distinguish molecular fragments corresponding to a coenzyme or an apoenzyme. On the other hand, in the case of the quinic alkaloids, it may be stated that, for example, in the cyanhydrin synthesis, the configuration at carbon atom 9 in the alkaloid molecule is exclusively responsible for the configuration of the optically active hydroxynitrile formed.

In the case of asymmetric heterogeneous catalysts, the stage where the phenomenon of asymmetry appears may be still more easily separated from the catalytic process, since the first stage is reduced to asymmetric adsorption (26).

TABLE 2

Enzyme	Reaction index	Enzyme model
Hydroxynitrilase	$\begin{matrix} C & C & \equiv N \\ \| & \| \\ C & H \end{matrix}$	Alkaloids
Carboligase		Ethylamine on cellulose
Reductase	$\begin{matrix} C & H \\ \| & \| \\ O & H \end{matrix}$	Alkaloids
Esterase	$\begin{matrix} O & C \\ \| & \| \\ H & X \end{matrix}$ X=OH,Cl	Alkaloids
		Camphor derivatives
Ketoaldomutase	$\begin{matrix} C & H \\ \| & \| \\ C & O \end{matrix}$	Camphor derivatives
		Metal on quartz
Carboxylase	$\begin{matrix} C & H \\ \| & \| \\ C & -O \end{matrix}$	Alkaloids
		Ethylamine on cellulose
Unknown enzyme, action opposite to that of glutamino-dehydrase	$\begin{matrix} C & H \\ \| & \| \\ N & H \end{matrix}$	Palladium on silk
Unknown enzyme	$\begin{matrix} C & -C \\ \| & \| \\ H & O \end{matrix}$	Metals and oxides on quartz
Unknown enzyme	$\begin{matrix} C & H \\ \| & \| \\ C & H \end{matrix}$	Metal on quartz
Unknown enzyme	$\begin{matrix} C & C \\ \| & \| \\ C & H \end{matrix}$	Hydroxide on quartz

REFERENCES

1. Balandin A. A., *Zh. Ref. Fiz. Khim.* **61,** 900 (1929); *Izv. Akad. Nauk SSSR.* **4,** 624 (1955).
2. Klabunovskii E. I.: Sbornik Dokl. Mezh. Sov. Izd. Akad. Nauk SSSR, 1957, p. 107.
3. Wegler R., *Ann.,* **498,** 62 (1932).
4. Cohen H. L., Wright G. F., *J. Org. Chem.,* **18,** 432 (1953).
5. Bredig G., Fiske P. S., *Biochem. Z.,* **46,** 7 (1918); *ibid.* **249,** 241 (1932).
6. Pratesi P., La-Monna A., *Farmaco (Pavia), Ed. Sci.,* **11,** No. 1, 33 (1956); *Zh. Khim.,* 4218 (1957); *J. Am. Chem. Soc.,* **75,** 5476 (1953); *Gazz. Chim. Ital.,* **84,** 879 (1954).
7. Lipkin P. L., Stewart T. D., *J. Am. Chem. Soc.,* **61,** 3295, 3297 (1939).
8. Erlenmeyer H., *Helv. Chim. Acta,* **13,** 731 (1930).
9. Wegler R., *Ann.* **498,** 62 (1932); *ibid.,* **506,** 77 (1933); *ibid.,* **510,** 72 (1934).
10. Wuits H., *Bull. Soc. Chim. Belg.,* **30,** 30 (1921).
11. Maitland P., Mills M. N., *J. Chem. Soc.,* 987 (1936).
12. Fujise S., Sasaki H., *Ber.,* **71,** 341 (1936); *J. Chem. Soc. Japan,* **72,** 1073 (1951).
13. Ose S., Joshimura I., *Jakagaku Zasshi,* **77,** 730 (1957), *C. A.,* **17,** 856 (1957).
14. Bredig G., Minaeff M., *Biochem. Z.,* **249,** 241 (1932).
15. Prelog V., Wilhelm M., *Helv. Chim. Acta,* **37,** 1634 (1954).
16. Bredig G., Gerstner F., *Biochem. Z.,* **250,** 414 (1932); *ibid.,* **288,** 80 (1935).
17. Akobori S., *Nature,* **178,** 323 (1956); *Biokhimiya,* **22,** Nos. 1–2, 154 (1957).
18. Katake H., Sakan T., Nakamura N., Senoh S., *J. Am. Chem. Soc.,* **73,** 7973 (1951).
19. Weichert R., *Acta Chem. Scand.,* **8,** 1542 (1954).
20. Gosh J. G., *J. Indian Chem. Soc.,* **16,** 51 (1939).
21. Schwab G. M., Rost F., Rudolph Z., *Kolloid Z.,* **68,** 157 (1934); *Naturwiss.,* **12,** 237 (1932).
22. Stankiewicz A., *Qiss. Koenigsberg* (1938).
23. Terent'ev A. P., Klabunovskii E. I.: *Sb. Statei po Obshch. Khim.,* **2,** 1521, 1958 (1953); *Uch. Zap. Mosk. Gos. Univ.,* **151,** 145 (1951).
24. Ponomarev A. A., Zelenkova V. V., *Zh. Obshch. Khim.,* **23,** 1543 (1953); *Dokl. Akad. Nauk SSSR,* **87,** 423 (1952).
25. Terent'ev A. P., Klabunovskii E. I., Budovskii E. I., *Sb. Statei po Obshch. Khim.,* **2,** 1612 (1953).
26. Klabunovskii E. I., *Khim. Nauka i Promy.,* **2,** No. 2, 197 (1957).

VII. SOME APPLICATIONS OF ELECTRICAL CONDUCTIVITY MEASUREMENTS TO THE INVESTIGATION OF CATALYTIC PROCESSES ON SEMICONDUCTING OXIDE CATALYSTS

A. Bielański

1. INTRODUCTION

The electronic theory of chemisorption on semiconducting materials, the foundations of which are given by Vol'kenshtein (1), Hauffe (2), Dowden (3), Agrain and Dugas (4), Weisz (5) and others, postulates a close relationship between the electronic properties of the catalyst and its catalytic activity. Electrical conductivity measurements are readily made and may be used for characterizing the electronic state of a semiconductor. Consequently, a study of the relationship between the electrical conductivity of a catalyst and its catalytic activity is used as a verification of the electronic theory of catalysis. Such correlation may be discussed as

(i) a relationship between the catalytic activity and the initial conductivity shown by the catalyst before coming into contact with the substances taking part in the catalytic reaction;

or as

(ii) a relationship between the catalytic activity and the changes in the conductivity observed during the course of a catalytic reaction.

According to the electronic theory of chemisorption and catalysis, the relation between the initial electronic state of a catalyst and its catalytic activity results from the fact that the width of energy gap, position of bulk and surface impurity levels and also the position of the Fermi level, control not only the concentration of current carriers, free electrons and positive holes, present before catalytic reaction (and determining the initial conductivity of the catalyst), but also the number of molecules which may be chemisorbed in the course of catalytic reaction and the nature of

[93]

the chemical bond between the molecule and the surface. Both latter factors control at the same time the mechanism and velocity of the catalytic reaction.

Relationship (i) is usually investigated by the use of a series of samples prepared in exactly the same manner but differing in the concentration of impurities introduced into the crystal lattice. It is believed that the introduction of atoms of different valencies makes the Fermi level shift up or down, thus changing the electronic and catalytic properties of the catalyst.

In connection with relationship (ii), when the catalyst is exposed to an atmosphere containing the substrate and the products of the catalytic reaction, chemisorption of their molecules takes place, and this is equivalent to the formation of surface donor or acceptor centres. Subsequently, the concentration of free electrons and positive holes changes in the catalyst. At temperatures sufficiently low to avoid any appreciable diffusion of lattice defects from the surface to the bulk of the solid phase, only a thin surface layer of catalyst (about 10^{-4}–10^{-5} cm thick) takes part in this exchange of electrons. The concentration of current carriers in the boundary layer usually differs so much from their concentration in the bulk phase that, in the case of semiconductors with well-developed surface area, the surface conductivity becomes a factor controlling changes of the total conductivity (6). Chemisorption determines, however, not only the changes in the conductivity but also the velocity of the catalytic reaction. Although the relationship between conductivity and velocity is not necessarily a simple one, it can be shown that an investigation of both these magnitudes contributes to a better understanding of catalytic processes.

The aim of the present paper is to present a review of the work carried out at the School of Mining and Metallurgy, Cracow, on the changes in the electrical conductivity of some semiconducting oxide catalysts occurring during the catalytic dehydrogenation of aliphatic alcohols and the catalytic oxidation of carbon monoxide.

2. DEHYDROGENATION OF ALIPHATIC ALCOHOLS

a. Electrical conductivity measurements made during the catalytic reaction

The dehydrogenation of alcohols on oxide catalysts has been investigated by many authors. Balandin and his school have reported on the kinetics and thermodynamics of this reaction in numerous publications (7, 8). Recently, additional papers on the kinetics have been published by Garcia de la Banda and Kremenić Orlandini (9). These authors have also reviewed other publications in this field. Very little attention has, however, been given to the electronic processes accompanying the catalytic dehydrogenation of alcohols. Matveev and Boreskov (10) in 1955 stated that the electrical conductivity of ZnO catalyst changed appreciably in the course of methyl alcohol decomposition at its surface. The activity of the catalyst increased with increased conductivity. Similar results were obtained by Myasnikov and Pshezhetskii (11), who measured the electrical conductivity of the same catalyst in the course of isopropanol dehydrogenation. At the same time, our first results were published (12, 13), which concerned the electrical conductivity of other semiconducting catalysts during ethyl alcohol dehydrogenation. Similar investigations were also undertaken by Garcia de la Banda and his co-workers (14).

Our investigations concerned chiefly the dehydrogenation of ethyl and isopropyl alcohols. Both the n-type semiconducting oxides, ZnO, Fe_2O_3, CdO, and the p-type, Cr_2O_3, MgO, NiO, as well as mixtures of the two, were used as catalysts (12, 13, 15, 16, 17, 18, 19). Powdered substances were compressed under a pressure of 50 atm into cylindrical pellets weighing 1.5–2.0 g each. Several such pellets were introduced into the reaction chamber of a steady flow reactor (20), one of them being inserted between two platinum electrodes, which enabled the measurement of its electrical conductivity at any desired time. The electrical conductivity was measured with an alternating current (1 kc/s) Wheatstone bridge with a cathode ray oscillograph as zero point instrument.

Before each experiment the flow reactor was evacuated to a pressure of about 1 mm Hg and subsequently the vapours of a mixture of alcohol and water (mostly of the molar composition 1 : 10) were passed through with a velocity corresponding to 0.5 ml of liquid mixture per minute. By subsequent condensation of the vapours in a condenser cooled with liquid nitrogen and pumping off the hydrogen, the pressure in the flow reactor was maintained at a constant level of several mm Hg. Water was added in order to avoid pyrolysis and dehydration of the alcohols (21). Under these conditions, only aldehydes and ketones were detected in the condensation products, and their concentration was determined by means of hydroxylamine hydrochloride (22).

Exposing the catalyst to alcohol vapours is always accompanied by a distinct change in the electrical conductivity amounting to several orders of magnitude. After several minutes the conductivity reaches a constant value, but these changes in conductivity are reversible, i.e. after cutting

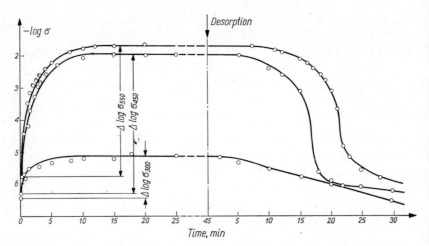

Fig. 1. Changes in $|\Delta \log \sigma|$ of the $ZnO-Fe_2O_3$ catalyst during dehydrogenation of ethyl alcohol (12).

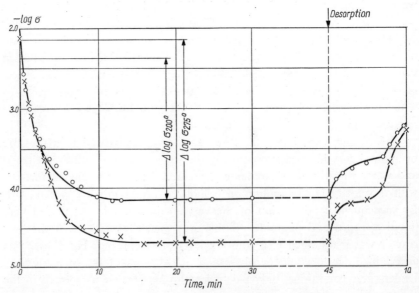

Fig. 2. Changes in $|\Delta \log \sigma|$ of the NiO catalyst during ethyl alcohol dehydrogenation (17).

off the flow of vapours and letting in air to a pressure of 1 mm Hg, the initial value is restored.

The direction of the changes in electrical conductivity depends on the type of semiconductivity of the catalyst. Conductivity of n-type catalysts, single or mixed, such as $ZnO-Fe_2O_3$ (Fig. 1), increases in the atmosphere of alcohols (12), while the conductivity of p-type catalysts such as NiO (Fig. 2) decreases (22). Mixtures of n- and p-type oxides show an increase or decrease in conductivity, depending on the predominant oxide present. The changes are always very marked, in some cases the conductivity changing by as much as a factor of 10^5. These changes are expressed as $|\Delta \log \sigma| = |\log \sigma_i - \log \sigma_f|$, σ_i being the initial conductivity of the catalyst and σ_f the constant value of conductivity assumed during the course of the catalytic reaction.

The direction of the changes in electrical conductivity shows that the chemisorption taking place on the surface of the catalyst is accompanied by the raising of the Fermi level, i.e. by an increase in the concentration of the free electrons and a decrease in the concentration of positive holes.

The behaviour of chromic oxide, Cr_2O_3, as well as mixtures containing an excess of Cr_2O_3 (15, 16), is very interesting. Up to temperatures of 450°C this behaviour does not differ from that of other p-semiconducting oxides, but above 450°C, the conductivity in ethyl alcohol vapours at first decreases and subsequently increases above the initial value, as shown in Fig. 3. The shape of the curve shows that as the concentration of chemisorbed molecules increases, an inversion of the conductivity from p- to n-type takes place. A similar effect was observed by Weisz, Prater and Rittenhouse (23) in the case of $Cr_2O_3-Al_2O_3$ catalyst during cyclohexane dehydrogenation and also by Garcia de la Banda and Hernáez Marín (14) in the case of isopropanol dehydrogenation on $ZnO-Cr_2O_3$ catalyst. It was also observed during chemisorption of oxygen on germanium (24) and on zinc oxide (25). Inversion of the conductivity type of a p-semiconductor occurs if the Fermi level of the surface layer of the solid is shifted so strongly upwards that it assumes a position in the upper half of the energy gap. In the case of Cr_2O_3, inversion may be caused by a marked increase in the number of chemisorbed molecules above 450–500°C. There also exists the possibility that the inversion is in some way related to the polymorphic transformation of Cr_2O_3 which was observed for various samples at 420–630°C by Wohlen and Wernung (26).

The changes in the electrical conductivity observed by us are believed to be almost entirely due to changes in surface conductivity. This view is also supported by the fact that the observed effects vanish if the surface of the sample becomes smaller. For example, as sintering of $ZnO-Fe_2O_3$ mixtures at temperatures of 700–1200°C takes place (which causes a decrease in surface area), the samples gradually lose their ability to change the

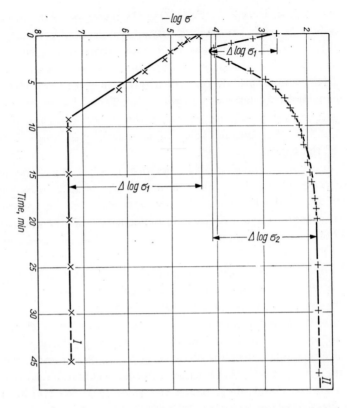

Fig. 3. Changes in $|\Delta \log \sigma|$ of the MgO–Cr$_2$O$_3$ catalyst during ethyl alcohol dehydrogenation (13).

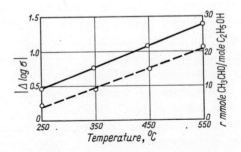

Fig. 4. Changes in $|\Delta \log \sigma|$ (full line) and r (dashed line) values as a function of temperature. Catalyst: 3MgO + Cr$_2$O$_3$ (13).

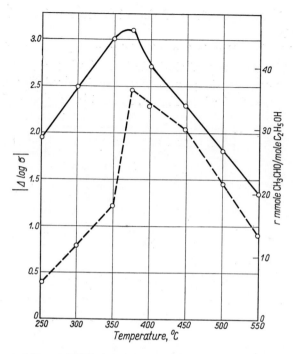

Fig. 5. Changes in $|\Delta \log \sigma|$ (full line) and r (dashed line) values as a function of temperature. Catalyst: $3ZnO+Cr_2O_3(15)$.

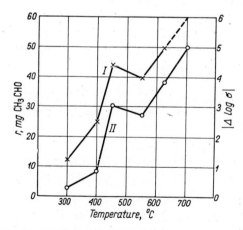

Fig. 6. Changes in $|\Delta \log \sigma|$ (curve I) and r (curve II) values as a function of temperature. Catalyst: $ZnO+Fe_2O_3(12)$.

7*

conductivity in the atmosphere of alcohol vapours and also become poor catalysts (12).

In addition to electrical conductivity measurements, the catalytic reaction yield r (amount of aldehyde formed when a given amount of alcohol–water vapours is passed with standard velocity through the apparatus) was determined. In Figs. 4, 5 and 6 $|\Delta \log \sigma|$ as well as r values

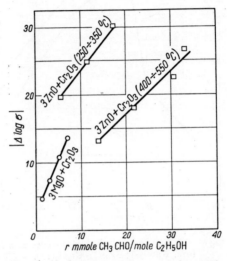

Fig. 7. $|\Delta \log \sigma|$ as a function of the catalytic reaction yield r.

are given as the function of temperature for several catalysts. The relationship of both values is well illustrated by plotting r as a function of $|\Delta \log \sigma|$. The plots are linear or consist of two linear sections (Fig. 7) and the relationship between both values may, therefore, be expressed within each linear section by the equation

$$r = A |\Delta \log \sigma| + B \tag{1}$$

where A and B are constants depending on the nature of the catalyst and the reagents (19).

Relationship (1) is to be considered as a first approximation only. Any attempt to derive this formula from theoretical considerations requires further investigation of the electrical and adsorptive properties of a complicated system: a porous polycrystalline pellet in contact with an atmosphere of reaction vapours. Nevertheless the linear relationship proves that the same factors control the velocity of the reaction as well as the changes in conductivity, and confirms the conclusion that, in this case, the molecular chemisorption which predominates determines the conductivity. Any attempt to elucidate which molecules play this role requires the conductivity measurements of the catalyst in an atmosphere of pure reagents, i.e. not only in an atmosphere of alcohol but also of aldehyde or ketone, hydrogen and water vapour. Such measurements were carried out for the NiO–isopropanol–acetone system and are described in the next section. Before relating these experiments it is necessary to present other observations collected in the course of the investigation on dehydrogenation of alcohols. The discussion here is confined to: (i) the results obtained with aliphatic alcohols other than ethyl alcohol, and (ii) some observations concerning the interrelation between the catalytic activity and initial conductivity.

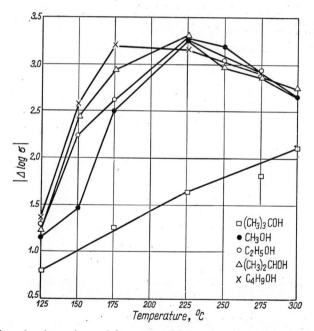

Fig. 8. $|\Delta \log \sigma|$ values observed in an atmosphere of various aliphatic alcohols as a function of temperature (27).

(i) The experiments were carried out using NiO catalyst and methyl, isopropyl, n-butyl and tertiary butyl alcohols (27), respectively. Alcohol-water mixtures of a molar composition 1 : 10 were applied. The curves of $|\Delta \log \sigma|$ values against $1/T$ for various alcohols are shown in Fig. 8.

The nature of the changes in the conductivity was analogous for all primary and secondary alcohols, i.e. for alcohols dehydrogenating to aldehyde or ketone. The $|\Delta \log \sigma|$ vs. $1/T$ graph for non-dehydrogenating tertiary butyl alcohol is quite different. These facts are in accordance with Balandin's view (28) that all alcohols show the same mechanism of dehydrogenation.

(ii) In the introductory chapter, the problem of the interrelation between the catalytic activity of a semiconducting catalyst and its initial electrical conductivity has been mentioned. Although this problem is in principle beyond the scope of the investigations discussed here, some interesting observations in this connection were made during the course of the work. In some cases, a correlation or an inverse correlation between the initial conductivity, σ_i, and $|\Delta \log \sigma|$ and r values could be observed. Such regularities were also observed by Treszczanowicz, Otwinowska and Ciborowski (29). Quite a striking relationship between σ_i, $|\Delta \log \sigma|$ and r was obtained in the case of ethyl alcohol dehydrogenation on mixed CdO–

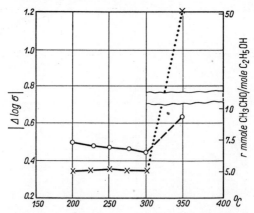

Fig. 9. Changes in $|\Delta \log \sigma|$ (full line) and r (dotted line) values as a function of temperature. Catalyst: MgO–CdO (18).

MgO catalyst, the initial conductivity of which (measured in air) was practically constant within the temperature range 100–500°C (18). When using this catalyst, constant reaction yield constant reaction yields and almost constant $|\Delta \log \sigma|$ values were observed in the range 200–300°C, while at more elevated temperatures CdO was reduced to Cd (Fig. 9).

The clear-cut correlation between σ_i and $|\Delta \log \sigma|$ and r values is, however, not a general rule.

b. The effect of individual reagents on the conductivity of NiO catalyst

PREPARATION AND PROPERTIES OF NiO CATALYST

For a detailed investigation on the effect of individual reagents on the electrical conductivity of a catalyst (30, 31, 32, 33), a preparation of nickel oxide was used. This was obtained by heating chemically pure nickel carbonate (F.O.Ch. Gliwice) in air at 600°C for 9 hours, which resulted in a green-grey powder. The molar ratio Ni:O calculated on the basis of an iodometric determination of excess oxygen according to Bunsen and Rupp (34) was 1 : 1.002. The excess oxygen determined in this way comprised not only the excess oxygen of the lattice but also oxygen which was chemisorbed on the surface. The BET surface area calculated from the adsorption of nitrogen was 2.9 m²/g. For the electrical conductivity measurements, NiO powder was compressed under a pressure of 50 atm into cylindrical pellets each weighing 1.5–2.0 g.

Curve *A*, Fig. 10, represents the temperature-dependence of the electrical conductivity of this NiO preparation as measured in air. The energy of activation E for electrical conductivity calculated from the equation $\sigma = \sigma_0 \exp\left(-\dfrac{E}{2kT}\right)$ is 0.63 ± 0.03 eV.

In the temperature region up to 350°C, the electrical conductivity of the NiO preparation, obtained by calcination of nickel carbonate in air, shows only slight dependence on the oxygen pressure p_{O_2}. At 300°C, for example, $\sigma = k\,p_{O_2}^{1/14}$. If, however, the sample is heated up to 450–600°C, evacuated to a pressure of 10^{-5} mm Hg and after prolonged evacuation cooled *in vacuo* to 300°C or a lower temperature, its electrical conductivity on introduction of oxygen changes proportionally to $p_{O_2}^{1/2.5}$.

On subsequently decreasing and increasing the pressure, the conductivity again changes proportionally to $p_{O_2}^{1/14}$. These results show that the surface of NiO exposed to air is covered with oxygen so strongly adsorbed that it cannot be desorbed even after prolonged evacuation at the temperature of the catalytic experiments. It is necessary to raise the temperature to about 400°C before slow desorption takes place.

Figure 10, curve *B*, shows the log σ vs. $1/T$ dependence for a sample of NiO deoxygenated *in vacuo*. Measurements of electrical conductivity were also carried out in a vacuum of 10^{-5} mm Hg. The desorption of oxygen is accompanied by a decrease in conductivity and an increase of energy of activation up to 1.13 ± 0.03 eV.

As the difference in electrical behaviour of oxygenated and deoxygenated samples is so pronounced, it was considered necessary to take additional measurements using both NiO preparations (30). All the experiments described in the following sections were carried out using a constant pressure equipment.

WATER VAPOUR

The exposure of the oxygenated as well as the deoxygenated catalyst to water vapour is not followed by any visible changes in the electrical conductivity. Similar results were obtained for all other catalysts. Thus, under the experimental conditions, water vapour is either not chemisorbed or—which is less probable—is chemisorbed but without exchange of electrons with the catalyst.

ISOPROPANOL

Isopropanol vapour, like the vapours of other alcohols, decreases the electrical conductivity of p-semiconducting catalysts. The chemisorbed isopropanol molecules create in some way donor centres at the surface.

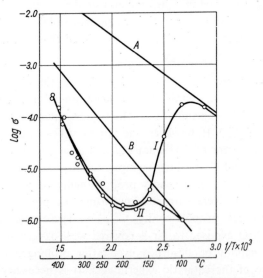

Fig. 10. The electric conductivity of NiO catalyst in isopropanol vapours (2 mm Hg). Curve *I*: oxygenated sample. Curve *II*: deoxygenated sample.
Curves *A* and *B*: conductivity as measured in air (oxygenated sample) and *in vacuo* (deoxygenated sample), respectively (33).

Figure 10 shows the log σ vs. $\dfrac{1}{T}$ dependence of oxygenated (curve *I*) and deoxygenated (curve *II*) samples of NiO in an atmosphere of isopropanol at a pressure of 2 mm Hg. Curves *A* and *B*, as stated, represent the log σ vs. $\dfrac{1}{T}$

dependence for the same samples, when the measurements are carried out in air or *in vacuo*, respectively. Figure 11 shows the $|\Delta \log \sigma|$ values corresponding to various temperatures for oxygenated and deoxygenated samples; $|\Delta \log \sigma|$ represents the difference between the log σ value measured

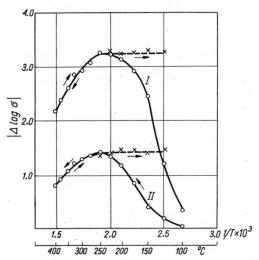

Fig. 11. $|\Delta \log \sigma|$ values of NiO catalyst in isopropanol vapours (2 mm Hg). Designations as in Fig. 10 (31, 33).

in air or *in vacuo* and the value of log σ measured on the same sample in an atmosphere of isopropanol. The heating and cooling curves are marked with arrows.

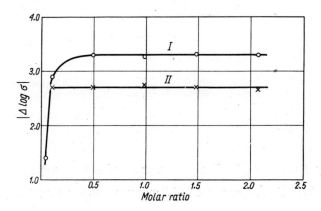

Fig. 12. $|\Delta \log \sigma|$ values as a function of the composition of isopropyl alcohol–water mixture (curve *II*) and acetone–water mixture (curve *I*). Temperature: 175°C (27).

The $|\Delta\log\sigma|$ values at a given temperature depend on the pressure of isopropanol. Figure 12, curve I, shows that $|\Delta\log\sigma|$ increases rapidly with rising isopropanol pressure and attains a constant, pressure-independent value. The state of saturation of the surface with chemisorbed molecules does not necessarily correspond to the true equilibrium state.

ACETONE

During chemisorption of acetone or acetaldehyde the conductivity of NiO decreases. Figure 13 shows the log σ vs. $\dfrac{1}{T}$ dependence of oxygenated

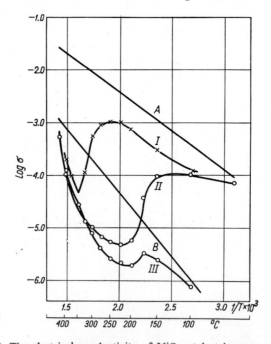

Fig. 13. The electrical conductivity of NiO catalyst in acetone vapours.
Curve I: oxygenated sample ($p_{acet.} = 10^{-1}$ mm Hg).
Curve II: oxygenated sample ($p_{acet.} = 2$ mm Hg).
Curve III: deoxygenated sample ($p_{acet.} = 2$ mm Hg).
Curves A and B: conductivity as measured in air (oxygenated sample) and *in vacuo* (deoxygenated sample), respectively (31, 33).

and deoxygenated samples in an atmosphere of acetone vapour at various pressures. As in Fig. 10, curves A and B represent the log σ vs. $\dfrac{1}{T}$ dependence as measured in air or *in vacuo*, respectively. At temperatures above 270°C the conductivity curves of oxygenated as well as of deoxygenated samples measured in acetone vapour are almost identical. This means that at these temperatures the surfaces of all samples are practically in the same state; namely, they are deoxygenated and covered with adsorbed acetone molecules. The desorption of oxygen from the surface must, therefore, occur after adsorption of a layer of acetone molecules. These facts may also be illustrated by $|\Delta \log \sigma|$ vs. $\dfrac{1}{T}$ curves. The $|\Delta \log \sigma|$ vs. $\dfrac{1}{T}$ values are dependent upon the acetone pressure in a way analogous to the acetone case, Fig. 12, curve

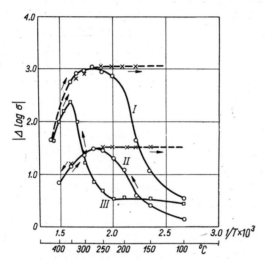

Fig. 14. $|\Delta \log \sigma|$ values of NiO in acetone vapours. Designations as in Fig. 13 (31, 33).

II. The values of $|\Delta \log \sigma|$ shown in Fig. 14, curves *I* and *II*, correspond to the pressure of acetone equal to 2 mm Hg. At this pressure full saturation of the surface with acetone molecules is reached. Curve *III*, in Fig. 14, shows the $|\Delta \log \sigma|$ values corresponding to an acetone pressure of 10^{-1} mm Hg at which no saturation is reached. Curve *I*, showing $|\Delta \log \sigma|$ values of the oxygenated sample, is situated much higher than curve *II*, giving the corresponding values of the deoxygenated sample. Curve *I* represents desorption of oxygen and adsorption of acetone, both processes contributing to a decrease in conductivity, while curve *II* represents adsorption of acetone only. The effects are, therefore, less pronounced.

The curves presented in Fig. 14 show a distinct analogy to chemisorption isobars and the following interpretation of their shape seems justified. The sections of the curves representing the behaviour of samples at temperatures below 250°C correspond to the non-equilibrium section of the isobar. In this region chemisorption velocity drops practically to zero before adsorption equilibrium is reached. As adsorption velocity increases with increasing temperature, the number of adsorbed molecules in the state of quasi-equilibrium, and the $|\Delta \log \sigma|$ values, also increase with temperature. At about 250°C adsorption velocity is sufficiently high to enable real equilibrium to be reached. According to the laws of thermodynamics, further increase in temperature results in diminishing adsorption and also in diminishing $|\Delta \log \sigma|$ values. In fact, above 250°C an increase in volume of acetone vapours due to their desorption was observed. The adsorption processes above 250°C are reversible and the cooling curve is nearly identical with the heating curve. On further cooling to temperatures below 250°C, adsorption and desorption velocities are again too small for the equilibrium to be reached; and for this reason the number of adsorbed molecules and, therefore, the $|\Delta \log \sigma|$ values do not change appreciably in this region (dotted line in Fig. 14).

It should be emphasized that the electrical behaviour of acetone on the surface of NiO is very similar to that of isopropanol. At temperatures above 250°C the $|\Delta \log \sigma|$ values for oxygenated samples are very similar, but these similarities are more striking in the case of deoxygenated samples, i.e. the effects of chemisorption can be observed without oxygen desorption interference. A comparison of curve *II* in Fig. 11 and curve *II* in Fig. 14 shows that both curves are nearly identical, corresponding to the adsorption of one and the same substance.

The surface deoxygenation of NiO catalysts in an atmosphere of alcohol as well as in an atmosphere of acetone can be proved directly (34) by the iodometric determination (35) of excess oxygen (concentration of Ni^{3+} ions) before and after the sample has been exposed to an atmosphere of isopropanol or acetone. The determination of excess oxygen after treatment of the catalyst with alcohol or isopropanol vapours was carried out without exposure to air. It was also noted that deoxygenation of NiO was accompanied by a colour change from grey to green.

HYDROGEN

Chemisorption of hydrogen, like that of acetone, is accompanied by the formation of donor centres at the surface of the NiO catalyst. Figure 15 shows several $\log \sigma$ vs. $\dfrac{1}{T}$ values for oxygenated and deoxygenated samples at various hydrogen pressures. The conductivity curve of oxygenated samples at lower temperatures does not differ very much from that obtained by heating NiO in air (curve *A*) and the $|\Delta \log \sigma|$ value only slowly increases with increasing temperature. After reaching a certain temperature (the higher this is, the lower the hydrogen pressure), deviations from the initial linearity of the curve are observed and the electrical conductivity

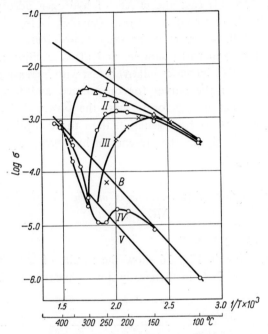

Fig. 15. The electrical conductivity of NiO catalyst in hydrogen (31, 33).
Curve *I*: oxygenated sample ($p_{H_2} = 10^{-1}$ mm Hg).
Curve *II*: oxygenated sample ($p_{H_2} = 2$ mm Hg).
Curve *III*: oxygenated sample ($p_{H_2} = 10$ mm Hg).
Curve *IV*: deoxygenated sample ($p_{H_2} = 2$ mm Hg).

falls to values below the conductivity of the deoxygenated samples. Samples treated with hydrogen at a pressure of 10 mm Hg reach minimum conductivity at 275°C (curve *III*). Heating to 300°C is accompanied by an increase in conductivity. In order to avoid reduction of the catalyst the sample was not heated to a higher temperature. On cooling (curve *V*) log σ changes linearly with $1/T$, the slope being similar to that of the sample deoxygenated *in vacuo* (curve *B*).

In an analogous experiment with an oxygenated sample in an atmosphere of hydrogen at a pressure of 2 mm Hg, observations were made up to a temperature of 350°C (curve *II*). At this temperature the sample underwent reduction accompanied by a sudden increase of conductivity. The surface

layer of the pellet became black and ferromagnetic. It was, however, possible
to heat without reduction another sample of NiO to the same temperature,
350°C in hydrogen at a pressure of 10^{-1} mm Hg (curve *I*). Curve *IV* shows
the behaviour of a deoxygenated sample when the pressure of hydrogen
was 2 mm Hg. In this case the effects of hydrogen adsorption are less
marked than with oxygenated samples (smaller $|\varDelta \log \sigma|$ values). The
curve begins to fall, however, at the same temperature as curve *II*, corresponding to the oxygenated sample, and after reaching a minimum at
250°C the conductivity increases relatively fast with increasing temperature.

A comparison of the curves for oxygenated and for deoxygenated
samples suggests that in the former case the observed decrease in conductivity is due more to deoxygenation than to adsorption of hydrogen.
There is a possibility that in the presence of hydrogen, oxygen is desorbed
as water vapour.

c. *Simultaneous effect of two reactants on the electrical conductivity of NiO catalyst*

ISOPROPANOL AND HYDROGEN

The curves given in Fig. 16 show the results of experiments carried
out with oxygenated NiO in the steady flow apparatus at 225°C. Initially

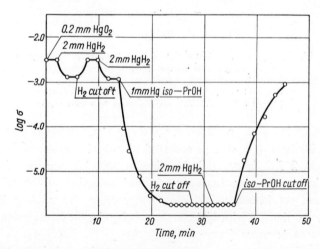

Fig. 16. Changes in log σ of NiO catalyst in hydrogen and in isopropanol vapours (33).

the apparatus was evacuated down to a pressure of 1 mm Hg, and after
the conductivity had reached a constant value, a current of hydrogen

was passed through ($p_{H_2} = 2$ mm Hg). The log σ value decreased from 2.42 to 2.85. After stopping the current of hydrogen and evacuating the apparatus, the initial conductivity value was restored, but the same effect was again produced by a subsequent flow of 2 mm Hg of hydrogen. If, in addition to hydrogen, isopropanol–water vapours corresponding to a pressure of 1 mm Hg of isopropanol were introduced, then a further decrease in conductivity was observed. If, after the conductivity reached a constant value, the hydrogen current was cut off, no further change in the conductivity was observed, and this condition was maintained if hydrogen was once more added to isopropanol vapours. If instead the current of alcohol–water vapours was cut off and only hydrogen passed through, the conductivity increased again. Similar results were obtained at 175°C. In another series of experiments similar results were obtained with ethyl alcohol.

All these experiments strongly suggest that hydrogen either does not adsorb at all, or adsorbs only very poorly, on a surface previously treated with alcohol, but alcohol may adsorb on a surface previously treated with hydrogen. It seems likely that chemisorbed atoms of hydrogen are removed from the surface either by atoms of alcohol or by the products of its dehydrogenation. This conclusion is also supported by kinetic experiments. The data given in Table 1 show that the presence of hydrogen in the

TABLE 1

Temperature, °C	Reaction yield r without addition of hydrogen, mmole C_3H_6O/mole C_3H_7OH	Reaction yield r in the presence of 10 mm of hydrogen, mmole C_3H_6O/mole C_3H_7OH
175	14.5	14.6
225	28.2	28.8

reaction chamber does not affect the rate of the catalytic reaction. This is possible only when a very small portion of the surface area is covered with adsorbed hydrogen.

ALCOHOLS AND ALDEHYDES OR KETONES

Experiments were carried out in the steady flow reactor. The apparatus was evacuated and a current of isopropanol–water or ethanol–water vapours introduced. After the conductivity had attained a constant value, vapours of acetone–water or acetaldehyde–water were introduced instead of the alcohol vapours. In another series of experiments the sequence was reversed.

The pressures of reagents were high enough to ensure full saturation of the surface (Fig. 12). Either no conductivity changes or only very slight ones were observed when the composition of gas phase was changed. Curves illustrating some of the experiments are given in Fig. 17. It must

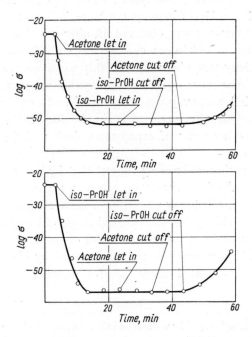

Fig. 17. Changes in log σ of NiO catalyst in acetone and in isopropanol vapours (33).

be remembered that exposing a surface previously treated with alcohol vapours to hydrogen causes a marked increase in conductivity, i.e. it causes total or partial desorption of alcohol and/or of the products of its decomposition. It is therefore evident that alcohol vapours are removed from the reaction chamber by a current of hydrogen. No similar effects were observed when acetone vapours were passed over the surface of NiO previously treated with isopropanol vapours. This behaviour suggests two possibilities: either the chemisorbed isopropanol molecules are desorbed and the number of adsorbed acetone molecules happens to acquire just the value corresponding to the same conductivity change as in an atmosphere of isopropanol, which is not likely, or the isopropanol immediately after adsorption is decomposed into quickly desorbing hydrogen and slowly desorbing acetone which saturates the surface to the same extent as when in contact with acetone vapours. In such a case the desorption of ace-tone is the rate-determining factor of the over-all process.

Acetone further differs from hydrogen in its effect on the kinetics of dehydrogenation. As has been stated, hydrogen has no effect, but the addition of acetone to isopropanol slows down the reaction to a marked degree. At a temperature of 200°C, for example, the addition of 1% acetone to the isopropanol–water mixture decreases the reaction yield by as much as 40%.

ISOPROPANOL AND OXYGEN

The results given in Section 2 (b) show that the introduction of isopropanol or acetone vapours to the oxygenated surface of NiO causes the desorption of oxygen, which cannot be attained in the same tem-perature region (below 350–400°C) by applying a vacuum of the order of 10^{-5} mm Hg. Oxygen must therefore be removed by the adsorbed molecules of isopropanol or acetone. The reverse process has also been observed: *in vacuo* the electrical conductivity of a sample treated with isopropanol or acetone increases slowly, indicating slow desorption. Introduction of air into the apparatus immediately increases the electrical conductivity until the value is reached which was observed in air before adsorption of organic reagents. In the presence of excess oxygen, adsorption takes place with simultaneous displacement of adsorbed acetone or alcohol molecules from the surface. Mutual displacement of adsorbed oxygen and isopropanol or acetone molecules takes place whenever there is an excess of one of these components. By proper selection of oxygen and alcohol vapour pressures, one may reach the state when the fractions of the surface area covered with oxygen and isopropanol or acetone are of the same order. In this case, oxygen should affect the rate of catalytic reaction. Dereń, Haber and Wilkowa (32) determined the reaction yield and changes in electrical conductivity brought about by addition of oxygen or air to the isopropanol–water vapours. Similar experiments were conducted with ethyl alcohol.

The experiments were carried out in a steady flow reactor. Figures 18 and 19 show the curves obtained for ethyl alcohol, and similar results were obtained for isopropyl alcohol. The ethanol–water mixture contained 10 molar per cent of alcohol; the vapour pressure in the apparatus was main-tained at 10 mm Hg, the oxygen pressure being 6 mm Hg. If air was deli-berately not admitted into the apparatus, some oxygen could be introduced as dissolved in the alcohol–water mixture evaporated in the reactor, but its pressure could not be higher than 10^{-3}–10^{-4} mm Hg.

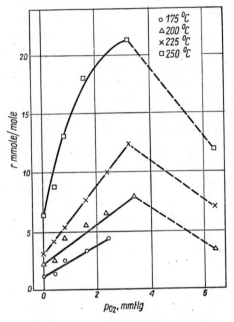

Fig. 18. The effect of oxygen pressure on the catalytic reaction yield (dehydrogenation of ethyl alcohol) (32).

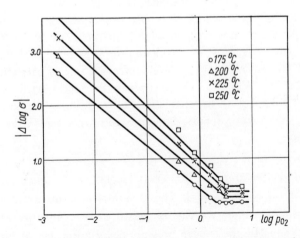

Fig. 19. The effect of oxygen pressure on the $|\Delta \log \sigma|$ values observed during ethyl alcohol dehydrogenation (32).

Introduction of air into the apparatus definitely increased the reaction yield, and at an oxygen pressure of 3.2 mm Hg this reached a maximum (Fig. 18). In contrast the $|\Delta \log \sigma|$ values at first decreased with increasing oxygen pressure (Fig. 19). The value of $|\Delta \log \sigma|$ is constant at pressures corresponding to the maximum on the yield curve. These results are discussed in the next section.

d. The mechanism of isopropanol dehydrogenation on NiO catalyst

The results given in the introduction to this paper show that there is a close relationship between the electrical conductivity changes $|\Delta \log \sigma|$ of a semiconducting oxide catalyst and the catalytic reaction yield r observed during aliphatic alcohol dehydrogenation. This relationship proves that the same factor directly or indirectly controls both the $|\Delta \log \sigma|$ and r values. Evidently, the factor responsible is the chemisorption of one or more molecular species taking part in the reaction. A discussion of the surface processes accompanying catalytic dehydrogenation must also take into account the desorption of oxygen occurring under the influence of reactants.

All-over processes are fairly complicated and this probably accounts for the failure to derive the empirical formula (1) based on the electronic theory of chemisorption and catalysis, the theory which deals with much simpler systems. Nevertheless, in this discussion based on experimental results, some definite conclusions pertaining to the mechanism of catalytic alcohol dehydrogenation (32) will be presented. Although the dehydrogenation of isopropanol has been chiefly considered, it is believed that the results may be applied to the dehydrogenation of other aliphatic alcohols on NiO.

Catalytic dehydrogenation of isopropyl alcohol must consist of the following stages:

$$C_3H_7OH_{(gas)} \underset{k_1'}{\overset{k_1}{\rightleftarrows}} C_3H_7OH_{(ads)} \tag{a}$$

$$C_3H_7OH_{(ads)} \underset{k_2'}{\overset{k_2}{\rightleftarrows}} C_3H_6O_{(ads)} + 2H_{(ads)} \tag{b}$$

$$2H_{(ads)} \underset{k_3'}{\overset{k_3}{\rightleftarrows}} H_{2\,(gas)} \tag{c}$$

$$C_3H_6O_{(ads)} \underset{k_4'}{\overset{k_4}{\rightleftarrows}} C_3H_6O_{(gas)} \tag{d}$$

The arrows indicate the direction and the symbols above and below the rate constants for the reactions. Any one particular stage may comprise more than one process. Garcia de la Banda and Kremenić Orlandini (9), for example, assume that adsorption of isopropanol on Cr_2O_3 takes place in stages on two neighbouring active centres. Also, some of the reactions given above may occur simultaneously. According to the stationary state theory, the reaction rates in all the stages are the same, but, depending on the rate constants, the surface concentration of all or some reagents may be of the same order or the surface may be almost entirely covered with one molecular species only.

As has been stated in the case of the NiO catalyst, the introduction of hydrogen into the reaction chamber (to a pressure of 10 mm Hg) does not affect the velocity of isopropanol dehydrogenation. This implies that under the conditions of alcohol dehydrogenation the rate constant k_3 for the desorption of hydrogen is much greater than the rate constant k_3' for its adsorption. Hydrogen forming during the reaction desorbs, therefore, very fast even when only a small fraction of the surface area is covered with its adsorbed atoms, and, consequently, the desorption of hydrogen does not represent the rate-controlling factor. Similar kinetic results were obtained by Bogdanova et al. (28) during the investigation of an oxide catalyst, the composition of which was not stated. This behaviour of hydrogen is not, however, a general rule. Garcia de la Banda and Kremenić Orlandini (loc. cit.) stated that in the case of isopropanol dehydrogenation on Cr_2O_3 the addition of hydrogen caused a decrease in reaction rate.

In contrast to the behaviour of hydrogen, the addition of acetone to isopropanol considerably retards the dehydrogenation on NiO. The rate constant k_4 for desorption of acetone must, therefore, be much lower than the rate constant k_4' for adsorption of acetone and the surface concentration of acetone cannot be very small. The relationship between the rate constant k_2 of surface reaction and the rate constant k_4 of acetone desorption determines the proportion of the surface covered with alcohol and with acetone molecules, and these are of the same order if k_2 and k_4 are of the same order, but if the surface is covered mainly with acetone in the course of reaction, then $k_2 \gg k_4$. As pointed out by Balandin and Kiperman (37), there is no possibility of determining by means of kinetic investigations only which of the two rate constants is greater. Nor did the investigations on electrical conductivity changes during the course of the reaction solve the problem, as the introduction of alcohol, acetone and hydrogen changes the catalyst conductivity in the same direction.

Nevertheless it seems that some experimental facts strongly suggest the second possibility, i.e. that during the course of the reaction, the surface of the catalyst is covered mainly with acetone and that the rate-determining factor is desorption of acetone. According to this hypothesis, molecules of alcohol immediately after their adsorption change into molecules of slowly desorbing acetone and rapidly desorbing hydrogen. Exposure of NiO to an atmosphere of isopropanol would, therefore, cover the surface with acetone molecules. The presence of acetone would also directly or indirectly determine the changes of electrical conductivity.

These suppositions are based chiefly on the following facts:

(1) As Fig. 10, curve *II*, and Fig. 13, curve *III*, indicate, the isobars showing the log σ values of the deoxygenated NiO samples in an atmosphere of isopropanol and of acetone are nearly identical. Both isobars at pressures of 2 mm Hg correspond to the region of pressures in which $|\Delta \log \sigma|$ at a given temperature is independent of the pressure, i.e. the surface is saturated (and not necessarily in a state of equilibrium) with sorbate molecules.

(2) As Fig. 8 indicates, there is a marked difference between the electrical behaviour of dehydrogenating alcohols (primary and secondary aliphatic alcohols) and non-dehydrogenating tertiary butyl alcohol. Although in both cases the electrical conductivity of NiO is reduced, the effect caused by dehydrogenating alcohols is much stronger and the $|\Delta \log \sigma|$ value reaches a common maximum at approximately 250°C, for all such alcohols as well as for acetone or acetaldehyde. The chemisorption of non-dehydrogenating alcohol has a less marked effect and there is no maximum on the $|\Delta \log \sigma|$ vs. $1/T$ graph. As the hydroxyl group is most probably in some way responsible for this effect, this same group must also be active in chemisorption of primary and secondary alcohols. In the former case (non-dehydrogenating alcohols), however, there are no further transformations; in the latter case (dehydrogenating alcohols) fast dehydrogenation and transformation in chemisorbed aldehyde or ketone takes place. This explains why the observed effect under the influence of dehydrogenating alcohol vapours is analogous to that observed in vapours of aldehyde or ketone.

(3) The results described in Section 2 (*a*) and (*b*) show that isopropanol or the products of its dehydrogenation are desorbed in hydrogen but do not desorb in acetone vapours. These facts may be more readily understood when one assumes that the surface of the catalyst in contact with isopropanol is covered mainly with acetone molecules.

We can therefore summarize our argument by stating that the experiments with additions of hydrogen and acetone to alcohol show that during the catalytic reaction the surface of the NiO catalyst was covered mainly with either acetone molecules or molecules of isopropanol and acetone. Analysis of the electrical data is in favour of the former assumption. According to our hypothesis, the changes in the electrical conductivity of NiO catalyst during isopropyl alcohol dehydrogenation are due to the predominant covering of the surface with acetone molecules. This is consistent with the views expressed by Wicke (38) and Eucken (39).

The experiments related to the adsorption of acetone and alcohol on oxygenated and deoxygenated NiO samples clearly indicate that, under the conditions of the experiments, the observed conductivity change is due not only to the chemisorption of acetone but also to the simultaneous desorption of oxygen. The strongly adsorbed oxygen molecules are expelled from the surface by the excess of acetone molecules. The desorption of oxygen molecules from the surface by simultaneous adsorption of acetone is, therefore, more effective at temperatures up to 300°C than removal of oxygen by evacuation. This removal of oxygen from the surface by acetone or, generally speaking, by reactants may be reversed. The electrical conductivity measurements of NiO catalyst show that—depending on experimental conditions—in some cases evacuation of acetone or isopropanol vapours from the reaction chamber causes only slight increase of the conductivity, indicating that desorption of organic reagents is only slight. Letting a little air into the apparatus causes a rapid increase of the conductivity to the initial value before the experiment and therefore causes adsorption of oxygen and desorption of acetone.

3. OXIDATION OF CARBON MONOXIDE

The second catalytic reaction investigated by means of electrical conductivity measurements was the oxidation of carbon monoxide on NiO (46). This is a standard reaction in catalytic research. The electronic processes associated with it were investigated by Wagner and Hauffe (40), by authors of the Bristol school: Garner, Gray, Stone and their co-workers (41), Roginskii and Keer (42), Schwab and Block (43), Parravano (44) and Rienäcker (45). The aim of our research was to study more systematically the changes of the electrical conductivity during CO oxidation within a wide range of concentration of reactants.

The catalyst used for this investigation was the same as that described in Section 2 (b). The experimental equipment differed in that instead of the steady flow reactor used in the study of dehydrogenation a constant volume quasi-static reactor, similar to the one used by Schwab and Block (43), was employed.

The behaviour of the NiO catalyst in an atmosphere of oxygen has been described in Section 2 (*b*). In air at room temperature its surface becomes covered with strongly chemisorbed oxygen which cannot be desorbed even *in vacuo* at a temperature below 400°C. Chemisorption of oxygen always increases the conductivity, i.e. it is accompanied by the formation of surface acceptor centres.

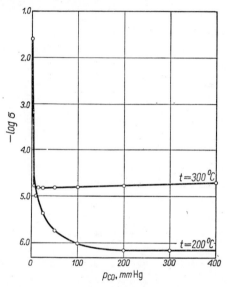

Fig. 20. The electrical conductivity of NiO catalyst as a function of carbon monoxide pressure (46).

In an atmosphere of carbon monoxide at 200–300°C the electrical conductivity of the samples decreased to a value lower by a factor of $10–10^2$ than the value shown at the same temperature by a deoxygenated sample *in vacuo*. These results are interpreted as chemisorption of CO-forming donor centres which probably is accompanied by desorption of oxygen in the form of CO_2. Figure 20 shows the value of electrical conductivity of NiO as a function of CO pressure at 200 and 300°C.

Carbon dioxide under these conditions does not affect the conductivity of NiO at temperatures of 200–300°C.

In the study of electrical conductivity changes during a catalytic reaction, it is necessary to standardize previously the samples in order to obtain

a reproducible initial conductivity. In the case of isopropanol dehydrogenation, the catalyst was only standardized in low vacuum. In the study
of CO oxidation, two standardizations, namely, in oxygen and in carbon
monoxide, were applied. Fresh NiO pellets were kept in the reaction chamber
in an atmosphere of either of the two gases at the temperature selected
for the reaction until no further conductivity changes were registered.
Subsequently an appropriate volume of another reagent was added and
the measurements recorded.

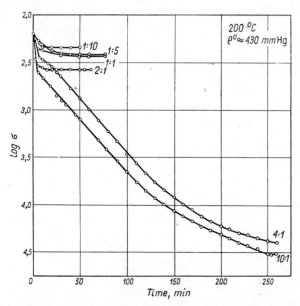

Fig. 21. The changes in log σ value during CO oxidation in CO–O_2 mixtures of
varying composition. Temperature of the reaction: 200°C. NiO catalyst standardized
in oxygen (46).

Figure 21 shows the electrical conductivity changes observed when to
the sample of NiO catalyst, standardized in oxygen at 200°C, CO was
subsequently added in varying amounts. The corresponding changes in
the partial pressure of carbon monoxide are shown in Fig. 22. There are
two distinct groups of conductivity curves: the curves corresponding to
CO–O_2 mixtures of stoichiometric composition or containing an excess
of oxygen and the curves corresponding to the mixtures with an excess
of CO over the stoichiometric ratio 2:1. In the former case there is only
a small initial change (a decrease) in the conductivity, which soon reaches
a constant level, and the reaction therefore occurs on a catalyst showing

a constant conductivity. In the latter case quite appreciable conductivity changes are observed, and these changes persist even after the end of the catalytic reaction.

These results show that when stoichiometric or less than stoichiometric amounts of CO are added, the area of the surface covered during standardization does not change to any extent. On the other hand, significant changes

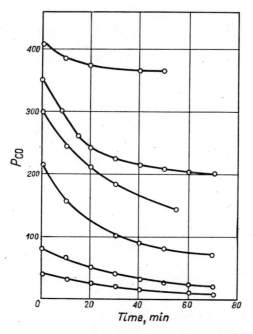

Fig. 22. The changes in partial pressure of carbon monoxide during its oxidation when CO–O_2 reacting mixtures of varying composition are used. Temperature of the reaction: 200°C. Catalyst standardized in oxygen.

occur when excess of CO is introduced, and the direction of these changes indicates that the concentration of surface donor centres in the p-semiconducting NiO catalyst have increased and/or the concentration of acceptor centres has decreased. This corresponds to the chemisorption of CO and/or desorption of oxygen.

Figure 23 shows the conductivity curves (log σ against time) corresponding to the measurements taken at 300°C. Only very slight changes of log σ value are observed in the case of mixtures of gases containing an excess of oxygen. The total change of log σ in CO-rich mixtures is—on the other hand—much larger than at 200°C, and almost equal to the value attained by NiO samples kept in pure CO at 300°C.

Just above 300°C, in oxygen-rich mixtures, no changes of σ are observed, showing that under these conditions the electronic state of the catalyst surface is the same during the catalytic reaction as it was after standardization. This means that the concentration of chemisorbed oxygen attained

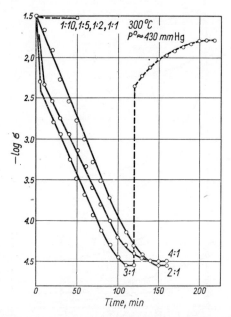

Fig. 23. The changes in log σ value during CO oxidation in CO–O$_2$ mixtures of varying composition. Temperature of the reaction: 300°C. NiO catalyst standardized in oxygen. The dashed line is a desorption curve observed during evacuation of gases after the reaction (46).

during standardization above 300°C is preserved in the course of a catalytic reaction in an oxygen-rich gaseous medium. This maintenance of coverage of the NiO surface is only possible if the rate-determining step of carbon monoxide oxidation is as follows:

$$O_{(ads)} + CO_{(gas)} = CO_{2(gas)} \tag{2}$$

It must be followed by rapid chemisorption of oxygen. Depending on the form in which oxygen is chemisorbed, Eq. (2) may be written:

$$O^-_{(ads)} + CO_{(gas)} + \oplus = CO_{2(gas)} * \tag{2a}$$

---

* $\oplus$ is a symbol for a positive hole.

or

$$O_{2(ads)}^- + CO_{(gas)} = CO_{2(gas)} + O_{(ads)}^- \tag{2b}$$

In principle, reacting oxygen may also be taken from the surface layer of the crystal lattice (45):

$$O_{(surface)}^{-2} + CO_{(gas)} + 2 \oplus = CO_{2(gas)} \tag{2c}$$

The corresponding equations of the rapid chemisorption of oxygen evidently are:

$$O_{2(gas)} = 2O_{(ads)}^- + 2 \oplus \tag{3a}$$

$$O_{2(gas)} = O_{2(ads)}^- + \oplus \tag{3b}$$

$$O_{2(gas)} = 2O_{(surface)}^{2-} + 4 \oplus \tag{3c}$$

The oxidation of CO expressed by the equation may either obey the Rideal mechanism or it may comprise two stages: slow chemisorption of CO:

$$CO_{(gas)} + \oplus = CO_{(ads)}^+ \tag{4a}$$

and fast surface reaction:

$$CO_{(gas)}^+ + O_{(ads)}^- = CO_{2(gas)} \tag{4b}$$

resulting in the surface concentration of chemisorbed CO^+ molecules being practically negligible.

A sample standardized in an atmosphere of CO gave the following results. The upper curve in Fig. 24 shows the changes in CO pressure and the lower one the changes in log σ value when, after standardization at 275°C and $p = 381$ mm Hg, oxygen was added to CO in the reaction chamber. Addition of oxygen up to a partial pressure of 100 mm Hg practically did not change the conductivity or the CO pressure, thus indicating that oxidation did not take place. In order to initiate the reaction it was necessary to raise the oxygen partial pressure to 27 mm Hg. This second addition of oxygen was accompanied by a sudden increase in conductivity which decreased in the course of reaction in accordance with the amount of oxygen used up. This same phenomenon was observed on each subsequent addition of oxygen.

The fact that no reaction occurs on the NiO surface previously saturated with chemisorbed carbon monoxide if the oxygen pressure is only 10 mm Hg proves that the reaction of the Rideal type between chemisorbed CO and gaseous oxygen:

$$CO_{(ads)}^+ + O_{2(gas)} = CO_{2(gas)} + O_{(ads)} + \oplus \tag{5a}$$

or

$$2CO^+_{(ads)} + O_{2(gas)} = 2CO_{2(gas)} \qquad (5b)$$

is not possible. At higher pressures of oxygen, as conductivity measurements show, adsorption of O_2 takes place and promotes the catalytic oxidation of CO.

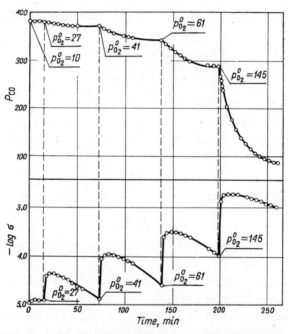

Fig. 24. The changes in the electrical conductivity of the catalyst and in CO partial pressure observed when oxygen was introduced at different time intervals at 275°C. The NiO catalyst standardized in CO atmosphere (46).

4. CONCLUSIONS

As mentioned in the introductory section, the electronic theory has made possible this coherent and logical account of the electronic processes accompanying chemisorption and catalysis. The direct verification of these results presents, however, quite appreciable difficulties in that the actual systems are more complicated than the idealized models on which the theory is based. The experimental results described show that in the case of a semiconducting oxide catalyst it is not only the interaction between the surface of the catalyst and the reagents which must be taken into account, but also complicated processes of adsorption and desorption of oxygen. The reacting system cannot, therefore, be discussed as a catalyst–reactant system but as a catalyst–oxygen–reactant system.

These results confirm the opinion expressed by Boreskov in one of his recent papers (47), namely, that for the full understanding of a catalytic process, it is necessary not only to take into account the influence exerted by the catalyst on reacting molecules, but also the changes of the catalyst itself as a result of interaction with the reactants. These changes may greatly affect the catalytic activity of the catalyst and were in fact o bserved in both reactions investigated.

In the dehydrogenation of alcohols, two extremes are possible: the catalyst with its surface previously covered with adsorbed oxygen may become deoxygenated during the reaction with oxygen-free reagents; or the catalyst with the surface covered with adsorbed acetone molecules loses these and its surface is covered with oxygen when air is let in instead of alcohol or acetone vapours. Evidently, between these two extreme surface states, many intermediate states may exist when the surface is covered with molecules of adsorbed reactants as well as with molecules or atoms of adsorbed oxygen. Such states will occur when air is added to the reacting alcohol vapours. In this case one may expect the removal of oxygen from the surface of NiO by adsorbing acetone molecules to be much weaker; correspondingly one may expect smaller $|\Delta \log \sigma|$ values than those actually observed. Letting in air up to a p_{O_2} of 3.2 mm Hg also increases the catalytic reaction yield, which may result from the change in catalyst activity caused by an increased number of oxygen molecules at the surface. More investigations are, however, necessary to explain in detail the mechanism of this increased activity.

In the catalytic oxidation of CO on NiO, conductivity measurements reveal two possible extreme cases: when the surface of the catalyst is saturated with chemisorbed oxygen and when it is saturated with chemisorbed carbon monoxide. These conditions are attained by standardization of the samples in either an atmosphere of oxygen or an atmosphere of carbon monoxide. Both these surface states may be retained after standardization—for some time at least—in an oxygen–carbon monoxide mixture. The obvious difference, however, is that an oxygenated surface promotes CO oxidation, while a surface of NiO covered with CO precludes oxidation. All intermediate states of coverage are possible, but increasing CO coverage contributes to the increased activation energy of the catalytic reaction (46).

Oxygenation and deoxygenation of the catalyst observed at temperatures of 200–300°C is evidently a process taking place only at the surface or in the uppermost layer of the catalyst. At higher temperatures during which diffusion of defects into the bulk phase is possible, the interior of catalyst crystallites will also suffer similar changes.

Although the electrical conductivity measurements are not interpreted quantitatively in these investigations, they are discussed qualitatively in terms of the electronic theory of chemisorption and catalysis. The results described confirm the value of electrical conductivity measurements for catalytic research, especially if they are applied together with kinetic investigations. The changes in electrical conductivity are sensitive indicators of the surface changes of a catalyst covered with chemisorbed molecules.

REFERENCES

1. Vol'kenshtein F. F.: Elektronnaya teoriya kataliza na poluprovodnikakh. Fizmatgiz. Moscow, 1960.
2. Hauffe K., *Advances in Catalysis*, **7**, 213 (1955); *ibid.*, **9**, 187 (1957).
3. Dowden D. A., *J. Chem. Soc.*, 242 (1950).
4. Agrain P., Dugas C., *Z. Elektrochem. Angew. Physik. Chem.*, **156**, 363 (1952).
5. Weisz P. B., *J. Chem. Phys.*, **20**, 1483 (1952); *ibid.*, **21**, 1531 (1953).
6. Hudson A. R.: Semiconductors (N. B. Hannay, Ed.). New York, 1959, p. 543.
7. Balandin A. A., *Advances in Catalysis*, **10**, 96 (1958).
8. Balandin A. A.: Voprosy khim. kinetiki, kataliza i reaktsionnoi sposobnosti. Akad. Nauk SSSR, Otd. Khim. Nauk. 1955, p. 461.
9. Garcia de la Banda J. F., Kremenić Orlandini G., *Instituto de Quimica Fisica, C.S.I.C. Technical Note*, No. 1, Madrid, 1958.
10. Matveev K. N., Boreskov G. K., *Probl. Kinetiki i Kataliza, Akad. Nauk SSSR,* **8**, 165 (1955).
11. Myasnikov N. A., Pshezhetskii S. I., *Probl. Kinetiki i Kataliza, Akad. Nauk SSSR,* **8**, 175 (1955).
12. Bielański A., Dereń J., Haber J., *Bull. Acad. Polon. Sci., Classe III,* **3**, 223 (1955).
13. Bielański A., Dereń J., Haber J., *Bull. Acad. Polon. Sci., Classe III,* **3**, 497 (1955).
14. Garcia de la Banda J. F., Hernáez Marin J., *Ann. Real. Soc. Espan. Fis. y Quim.,* Ser. **53 B**, 499 (1957).
15. Dereń J., Haber J., Mrowec S., *Bull. Acad. Polon. Sci., Classe III,* **4**, 107 (1956).
16. Bielański A., Dereń J., Haber J., Mrowec S., *Bull. Acad. Polon. Sci., Classe III,* **4**, 533 (1956).
17. Bielański A., Dereń J., Haber J., Wilkowa T., *Bull. Acad. Polon. Sci., Classe III,* **5**, 197 (1957).
18. Bielański A., Dereń J., Haber J., Wilkowa T., *Bull. Acad. Polon. Sci., Classe III,* **5**, 673 (1957).
19. Bielański A., Dereń J., Haber J., *Nature,* **179**, 668 (1957).
20. Bielański A., Dereń J., Haber J., Nedoma J., *Przemysł Chem.,* **12**, 642 (1956).

21. Miyata O., *Report No. BIOS (JAP)* 922.
22. Bauer K. M., Moll H.: Die organische Analyse. Leipzig, 1954.
23. Weisz P. B., Prater C. D., Rittenhouse K. P., *J. Chem. Phys.*, **21**, 2236 (1953).
24. Schultz W., Harten H., *Z. Elektrochem. Angew. Physik. Chem.*, **60**, 20 (1956).
25. Fojt L., Weidenhaler P.: Abstracts of XVIII Celostatni Chemicky Sjezd, Ostrava ČSR, June 1961, p. 41.
26. Abegg R.: Handbuch der anorganischen Chemie, Vol. 1. Leipzig, 1927, p. 119.
27. Bielański A., Dereń J., Haber J., Wilkowa T., *Bull. Acad. Polon. Sci., Ser. Sci. Chim. Geol. Geogr.*, **7**, 339 (1959).
28. Bogdanova O. K., Balandin A. A., Shchetova A. P., *Izv. Akad. Nauk SSSR, Otd. Khim. Nauk*, **7**, 787, 795; *ibid.*, **8**, 909 (1957).
29. Treszczanowicz E., Otwinowska H., Ciborowski S.: 2nd International Congress of Catalysis. Paris, 1960, paper No. 85.
30. Bielański A., Dereń J., Haber J., Słoczyński J., *Bull. Acad. Polon. Sci., Ser. Sci. Chim. Geol. Geogr.*, **7**, 333 (1959).
31. Dereń J., Haber J., Słoczyński J., *Bull. Acad. Polon. Sci., Ser. Sci. Chim.*, **8**, 391 (1960).
32. Dereń J., Haber J., Wilkowa T., *Bull. Acad. Polon. Sci., Ser. Sci. Chim.*, **8**, 399 (1960).
33. Bielański A., Dereń J., Haber J., Słoczyński J.: 2nd International Congress of Catalysis. Paris, 1960, paper No. 81.
34. Unpublished results.
35. Jander G., Jahr K. F.: Massanalyse. Vol. 1, p. 89, Berlin, 1940.
36. Bielański A., Dereń J., Haber J., *Bull. Acad. Polon. Sci., Ser. Sci. Chim. Geol. Geogr.*, **7**, 345 (1959).
37. Balandin A. A., Kiperman S. L., *J. Chim. Phys.*, **55**, 363 (1958).
38. Wicke E., *Z. Elektrochem.*, **53**, 279 (1949).
39. Eucken A., *Naturwiss.*, **36**, 48 (1949).
40. Wagner C, Hauffe K., *Z. Elektrochem. Angew. Physik. Chem.*, **44**, 172 (1938).
41. Stone F. S.: Chemisorption. London, 1957, p. 205; Gray T. J., Darby P. W., *J. Phys. Chem.* **60**, 201, 209 (1959).
42. Roginskii S. Z., Keer N. L., *Izv. Akad. Nauk SSSR, Otd. Khim. Nauk*, **21** 183 (1957).
43. Schwab G. M., Block J., *Z. Physik. Chem.*, **1**, 42 (1954); *J. Chim. Phys.*, **51**, 664 (1954); Block J., Chon H., *Z. Elektrochem.*, **60**, 912 (1956).
44. Parravano G., *J. Am. Chem. Soc.*, **75**, 1448, 1452 (1953).
45. Rienäcker G., Buchholtz E., *Z. Anorg. Chem.*, **290**, 325 (1957).
46. Bielański A., Dereń J., Haber J., Słoczyński J., *Z. Physik. Chem.*, **24**, 345 (1960).
47. Boreskov G., *Zh. Fiz. Khim.*, **32**, 2733 (1958).

VIII. PROBLEMS OF CHEMICAL CATALYSIS IN CONNECTION WITH THE FISCHER-TROPSCH SYNTHESIS OF HYDROCARBONS

Z. SOKALSKI

1. SURFACE CONCENTRATION OF ACTIVE CENTRES ON FERROUS CONTACTS USED FOR THE FISCHER-TROPSCH HYDROCARBON SYNTHESIS

Fundamental investigations concerning chemical catalysis aim at a quantitative expression of activity. As the catalyst surface is energetically heterogeneous, one might expect that there is some relationship between the contact activity and the heterogeneous surface distribution of energy. The quantitative expression of the surface heterogeneity is the function of the distribution of active centres according to the activation energy of adsorption. The quantitative expression of activity in defined reaction conditions is the reaction rate. Generally we may assume that the reaction rate, when a catalyst is acting, can be expressed by means of the following equation:

$$\frac{dx}{dt} = A \cdot \varphi(k_x) \cdot \psi(C_x) \tag{1}$$

where: A — a constant, characteristic of the given system;
k_x — the adsorption rate constant of the reactant x;
C_x — the concentration of the reactant x in the gaseous phase.
The value k_x can be taken from Arrhenius's equation:

$$k_x = B \cdot e^{-\frac{E}{Rt}} \tag{2}$$

where E denotes the activation energy of adsorption.
The value of E in equation (2) is determined from the equation expressing the distribution function of the activation energy of adsorption:*

---

* This type of function is the most common one in catalysis.

$$E = \frac{1}{\alpha_x} \cdot \ln \frac{\rho(E)}{H_x} \tag{3}$$

where α_x, H_x are constants, while $\rho(E)$ is the distribution function. Substituting (2) and (3) into equation (1) we obtain:

$$\frac{dx}{dt} = B' \cdot e^{-\varphi\left(\frac{1}{\alpha_x RT} \cdot \ln \frac{\rho(E)}{H_x}\right)} \cdot \psi(C_x) \tag{4}$$

In equation (4) the values α_x and H_x are characteristic for a given distribution function $\rho(E)$ and for a given reagent.

The rate $\frac{dx}{dt}$ of the catalytic reaction is a measure of the efficiency of a process, if the process is carried out under the same conditions of temperature, pressure, and rate of flow of reactants for every unit of the contact mass. Therefore

$$W = b \cdot \frac{dx}{dt}$$

where b is the proportionality coefficient.

Using the two values α_x and H_x it is possible to solve for W:

$$W = \varphi(\alpha_x, H_x) \tag{5}$$

The following two conditions for selection of the proper catalyst series, composed of n contacts, are applied:

1. The function $\rho(E)$ for a contact series of different activity must be a function of the same type. Only the values H_x and α_x may vary, as the contacts are changed.

2. Selection due to the modification of contacts.

Taking into consideration the two types of contact modification (2), i.e. the structural modification denoted by $\varepsilon_{(str.)}$ as well as the gaseous modification $\varepsilon_{(gas)}$, where

$$W = f(\varepsilon_{(str.)}, \varepsilon_{(gas)}) \tag{6}$$

it must be assumed that for a series of contacts the following condition should be fulfilled, namely, that the efficiency is for practical purposes the function of only one type of modification, viz.:

$$W = f(\varepsilon_{(str.)}) \quad \text{or} \quad W = \varphi(\varepsilon_{(gas)})$$

If a contact series being investigated is chosen in such a way that the efficiency W according to equation (6) depends on both the structural and the gaseous modification, the value W in equation (5) would be a more complicated function. Therefore the contact series should be selected in such a way that the influence of only one type of modification is dominating. It would prove to be very convenient if the modification could be carried out by the reactants of the given catalytic reaction which would definitely influence the contact activity. Those conditions are fulfilled by iron and cobalt catalysts as employed in the Fischer-Tropsch synthesis of hydrocarbons (3). In the case of iron contacts, it has been shown empirically that the influence of the gaseous modification is more pronounced.

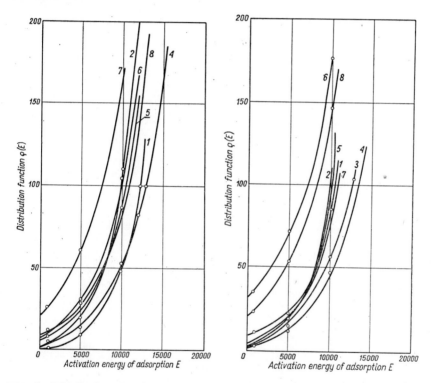

Fig. 1. Distribution function $\rho(E)$ for hydrogen adsorption on an iron catalyst modified in various ways (cf. Table 1).

Fig. 2. Distribution function $\rho(E)$ for carbon oxide adsorption on an iron catalyst modified in various ways (cf. Table 1).

In our investigations a series of eight iron catalysts, modified by gaseous reactants, such as CO, H_2 and N_2, were used. Nitrogen, being inert, was used as a diluent for the CO and H_2 mixtures. By determining separately the adsorption of three reactants at temperatures of 60°C, 140°C and

193°C, it was proved that all the eight contacts fulfilled the first condition. The adsorption isotherms, drawn as $p = $ const., are in agreement with the equation

$$q = a \cdot t^{\frac{1}{n}},$$

and, therefore, the distribution function

$$\rho(E) = H \cdot e^{\alpha \cdot E}$$

is valid.

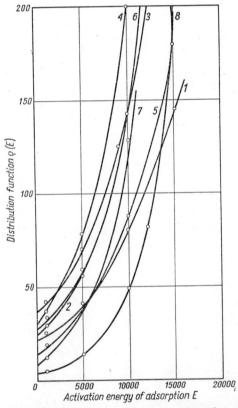

Fig. 3. Distribution function $\rho(E)$ for carbon dioxide adsorption on an iron catalyst modified in various ways (cf. Table 1).

These functions are represented in Fig. 1 as curves *2* and *3* for a temperature of 193°C.

In order to solve equation (5) at a temperature of 193°C, the relationship between the numerical values α_x and H_x for the reactants H_2, CO and CO_2 on the one hand and W, α, on the other must be found (cf. Table 1).

TABLE 1

	Consecutive number of catalysts							
For CO_2	1	2	3	4	5	6	7	8
$\alpha \times 10^4$	1.29	1.78	1.22	1.87	1.73	1.66	2.52	3.59
$H \times 10^7$	21.44	24.51	37.10	30.58	15.65	28.50	10.13	3.65
For CO	1	2	3	4	5	6	7	8
$\alpha \times 10^4$	3.45	3.02	3.16	2.73	2.44	1.75	2.52	2.95
$H \times 10^7$	3.43	4.50	2.44	3.27	8.04	31.10	6.92	20.0
For H_2	1	2	3	4	5	6	7	8
$\alpha \times 10^4$	3.60	3.30	2.30	2.80	2.60	2.52	2.00	2.200
$H \times 10^7$	1.35	2.17	5.20	2.86	6.25	8.25	16.7	10.2

At first the Roginskii equation (4) was applied in order to establish any relationship existing between the so-called contact activities A_x and the reaction efficiency W. This last was determined experimentally. The values H_x and α_x appear in the following equation:

$$A_x = \frac{H_x RT \cdot e^{\alpha E}}{\alpha_x RT - 1} \cdot k_0$$

The calculated values of A_x are represented graphically in Figs. 4 and 5, where

$$A_x = \varphi(W)$$

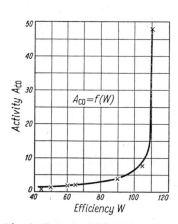

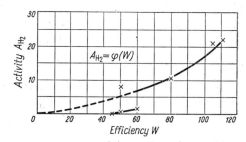

Fig. 4. Contact activity (according to Roginskii's equation) versus process efficiency, computed for carbon oxide.

Fig. 5. Contact activity (according to Roginskii's equation) versus process efficiency, computed for hydrogen.

The values of A_x have been calculated for both reactants H_2 and CO. It has also been proved that the values for A_{H_2} definitely deviate from a continuous function in a certain range.

Hence, it may be concluded that the discontinuity of the function is caused by the fact that in the formula $A = \varphi(W)$ the values of α_x and H_x result from the individual adsorption of various reagents, whereas the reaction efficiency is influenced by the collective adsorption of all the reagents together. And thus the problem investigated is one of adsorption, in which all the reagents of the synthesis take part according to the chemical equation with the number of reaction advance $\lambda = 1$:

$$2CO + H_2 = [-CH_2-] + CO_2 \qquad (7)$$

Generally, however, for $\lambda = n$

$$2nCO + (n+1) H_2 = C_nH_{(2n+2)} + nCO_2 \qquad (8)$$

It, may be assumed that on the contact surface during a catalytic reaction under stabilized conditions, defined quantities of reagents are adsorbed. Not all the adsorbed molecules or atoms, however, take part in the reaction, as a proportion of the adsorbed molecules are either too strongly or too weakly adsorbed. The number of the adsorbed molecules, involved in the reaction on the catalyst surface, in relation to the surface area, is the active surface concentration. The elementary reaction, defined by equation (7), takes place at the surface and involves this active surface concentration. Under controlled conditions of synthesis, a stationary state between the adsorption and desorption of active concentrations of reagents is developed. Therefore it may be assumed that under stationary conditions in a given catalytic reaction, the ratio of the active concentrations of the reagents C_x is constant. The surface concentrations may be expressed as activities of the reagents:

$$\frac{a_{CO_2} \cdot a_{CH_2}}{a_{CO}^2 \cdot a_{H_2}} = \zeta$$

where a is the activity of the given reagent.

If we assume the activity $a_{[-CH_2-]} = 1$, then we obtain

$$\frac{a_{CO_2}}{a_{CO}^2 \cdot a_{H_2}} = \zeta \qquad (9)$$

Expressing the activity by means of the activity coefficient, the above may be reduced in the following way:

$$\frac{C'_{CO_2}}{(C'_{CO})^2 \cdot C'_{H_2}} \cdot \frac{\gamma'_{CO_2}}{(\gamma'_{CO})^2 \cdot \gamma'_{H_2}} \qquad (10)$$

where C'_x denotes the total concentration of the adsorbed reagent x. Comparing equation (9) with equation (10), we derive

$$\frac{C'_{CO_2}}{(C'_{CO})^2 \cdot C'_{H_2}} \cdot \frac{\gamma'_{CO_2}}{(\gamma'_{CO})^2 \cdot \gamma'_{H_2}} = \frac{a_{CO_2}}{a^2_{CO} \cdot a_{H_2}} \tag{11}$$

The right-hand part of this equation can be expressed in terms of the concentrations of active surface reagents, for which the activity coefficients equal 1. Then

$$\frac{C'_{CO_2}}{(C'_{CO})^2 \cdot C'_{H_2}} \cdot \frac{\gamma'_{CO_2}}{(\gamma'_{CO})^2 \cdot \gamma'_{H_2}} = \frac{C_{CO_2}}{(C_{CO})^2 \cdot C_{H_2}} \tag{12}$$

The active concentrations concern the number of molecules reacting on the catalyst surface, which are adsorbed on each surface unit within a narrow range of the activation energy of adsorption

$$\Delta E_a = E_{max.} - E_{min.}$$

The active coefficients γ_x are values correcting the total surface concentration of the adsorbed reagents according to the mean activation energy of adsorption $\overline{E}_a$ within the range ΔE_a. The ratio of active concentrations in the stationary state of the synthesis is fixed in such a way that the condition stated in equation (12) should be fulfilled. The right-hand part of equation (12) simultaneously defines the contact activities. The contact activity can be expressed, therefore, by means of active surface concentrations of the reagents. The activity increases to the same extent as the products, concentration, as a result of the active surface concentrations of the reactants, assumed as units. Into equation (10), instead of general surface concentrations of the reactants, it is possible to introduce the values for α_x, using the well-known equation of Bangham-Bart and that of Roginskii, $\frac{1}{n} = \alpha RT$. So, then, in place of the general surface concentration of adsorbed reactants one might use α_x coefficients. In this way new equations are derived:

$$C'_{CO_2} = \frac{1}{\delta_{CO_2} \cdot \alpha_{CO_2}} \tag{13}$$

$$(C'_{CO})^2 = \frac{1}{\delta^2_{CO_2} \cdot \alpha^2_{CO}} \tag{14}$$

$$C' = \frac{1}{\delta_{H_2} \cdot \alpha_{H_2}} \tag{15}$$

where δ_x are the coefficients for a given catalyst at stable reaction conditions.

If (13), (14) and (15) are substituted into equation (12), we obtain

$$\frac{\alpha_{CO}^2 \cdot \alpha_{H_2}}{\alpha_{CO_2}} \cdot \frac{\dfrac{\delta_{CO}^2}{(\gamma'_{CO})^2} \cdot \dfrac{\delta_{H_2}}{\gamma'_{H_2}}}{\dfrac{\delta_{CO_2}}{\gamma'_{CO_2}}} = \frac{C_{CO_2}}{(C_{CO})^2 \cdot C_{H_2}} \quad *$$

If

$$\frac{\dfrac{\delta_{CO}^2}{(\gamma'_{CO})^2} \cdot \dfrac{\delta_{H_2}}{\gamma'_{H_2}}}{\dfrac{\delta_{CO_2}}{\gamma'_{CO_2}}} = \beta_a$$

and

$$\frac{\alpha_{CO}^2 \cdot \alpha_{H_2}}{\alpha_{CO_2}} = \alpha_a \qquad\qquad (15a)$$

then we get

$$\alpha_a \cdot \beta_a = a_a$$

According to the above-stated definition of activity,

$$W = \lambda \cdot a_a$$

in which λ is the proportionality coefficient; and so we get

$$\lambda = \frac{W}{a_a}$$

In this way for a given series, composed of eight catalysts, based on theoretical considerations, the values of α_a may be calculated according to equation (15a) from the measurements of α_x. On the other hand, for the same series of catalysts, based on the experimental data, the process efficiency W can be determined. Using these data in a co-ordinate system of α_a versus W, an experimental curve may be drawn, expressing the change of the coefficient β_a and representing the value on which the heterogeneity of the catalyst surface is dependent.

These curves are shown in Fig. 6. In the graph the values for $\dfrac{\alpha_{CO}^2 \cdot \alpha_{H_2}}{\alpha_{CO_2}}$ were plotted as the abscissae, while the values for W served as ordinates. The process efficiencies are expressed in grams of the synthesis products per 1 N m³ of the gas used. The function of α_a versus W is a discontinuous curve.

---

* Based on this value, in the gas phase eventually a thermodynamic equilibrium is reached.

From the graph represented in Fig. 6 it can be deduced that two groups of catalysts exist. One might suppose that these catalysts have a different chain-breaking activity towards the methylene radical [—CH₂—]. Thus it would be possible to deal with two series of polymerization radicals, denoted as R and S. The polymerization coefficient in accordance with theoretical data should be expressed as follows:

$$Sp = \frac{\text{total rate of polymerization}}{\text{rate of chain-breaking}}$$

where Sp denotes the polymerization coefficient. The chain-breaking rate is a characteristic property of a catalyst. To prove these assumptions, a graph representing the function

$$\frac{\alpha_{CO}^2 \cdot \alpha_{H_2}}{\alpha_{CO_2}} = f(W')$$

was plotted. Here W' is the efficiency of the heaviest hydrocarbon synthesis produced in the reaction (Fig. 7). In this case the sum of the paraffin wax and heavy petrol contents is expressed in percentage form.

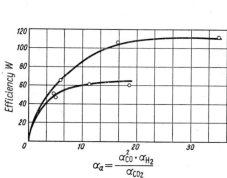
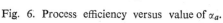
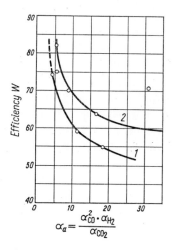

Fig. 6. Process efficiency versus value of α_a.   Fig. 7. Efficiency of heavy paraffins versus value of α_a.

In this way again two curves are given, corresponding to the curves plotted in the co-ordinate system of α_a and W.

The second curve is displaced in relation to the first towards higher hydrocarbons for the same numerical values of α_a, i.e. it is displaced by a definite polymerization coefficient. Consequently, in order to determine the functional interdependence between activity and efficiency of the process, it is necessary to select the correct catalyst series for investigation.

In a system of co-ordinates α_a versus W the curves converge to a point, viz. the intersection of the co-ordinates. There α_a equals 0, and according to the equation concerning the heterogeneity coefficient (5):

$$\varepsilon_a = \frac{2}{\alpha_a + 2H \cdot e^{\alpha_a \cdot E}}$$

in the case where

$$\alpha_a \gg 2H \cdot e^{\alpha_a \cdot E}$$

we get

$$\varepsilon_a = \frac{2}{H}$$

If α_a tends to 0, then $\varepsilon = \dfrac{1}{H}$; this means that when the heterogeneity coefficient tends towards 0, then $\alpha_a \to 0$.

Both curves may result from an apparently heterogeneous surface. Thus the function characteristic for a given series of contacts can be composed of many curves of the same functional character.

The differences between the whole series of curves is due only to the coefficients, which are constant for each respective curve, while the same character of the function is maintained. In our further considerations it would be interesting to show to what an extent the two values $H_{H_2} = \varphi(W)$ are interdependent. In the graphs the values for H_{H_2} and for W are based on experimental data with suitably chosen scalar coefficients. Practically, both functions are identical, i.e.

$$\alpha_a = \varphi(W) \frac{1}{H_{H_2}} = \psi(W)$$

$$\frac{d\alpha_a}{d\varphi(W)} = \frac{d \dfrac{1}{H_{H_2}}}{d\psi(W)}$$

A special case is when $\alpha_a = \dfrac{1}{H_{H_2}}$. In the equation of the distribution function, according to the activation energy of adsorption, we have

$$\rho(E) = H_{H_2} \cdot e^{\alpha_a \cdot E}$$

and, dividing the equation by H_{H_2},

$$\frac{1}{H_{H_2}} \cdot \rho(E) = e^{\alpha_a : E}$$

Therefore, for a given series of contacts the relation between H_{H_2} and α_a has been determined. It seems possible that the value H_{H_2} is of particular importance and responsible for the breaking of polymerization chains, i.e. active spots of atomization of molecules (Fig. 8).

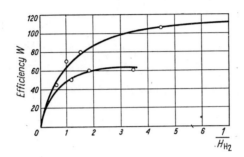

Fig. 8. Efficiency W versus $\dfrac{1}{H_{(H_2)}}$.

If H_{H_2}, for instance, tends towards infinity ($H_{H_2} \to \infty$), which may be interpreted as a nearly homogeneous surface as far as the hydrogenation factor is concerned, and therefore the chain-breaking factor in the process, then

$$\frac{1}{H_{H_2}} = 0 \qquad \text{and} \qquad W = 0$$

which is in accordance with the graph represented in Fig. 8.

2. THE DISTRIBUTION FUNCTION OF ACTIVE CENTRES ACCORDING TO THE ACTIVATION ENERGY OF ADSORPTION OF IRON CATALYSTS FOR A HYDROCARBON SYNTHESIS BY THE FISCHER-TROPSCH METHOD

The distribution function $\rho(E)$ is important for heterogeneous catalysis, and two methods of determining its dependence on the activation energy of adsorption have been suggested.

The first may be regarded as a development of the approximation method proposed by Roginskii; the second is based on symbolic operational calculus. Both methods result in the same final expression, in accordance with the following equation:*

$$\rho(E) = H^* \cdot e^{\alpha \cdot E} \tag{16}$$

---

* The notation is taken from Roginskii's papers.

where

$$H^* = \frac{a\beta}{k_0 \cdot RT \cdot T(1-\beta)} \cdot \beta = \frac{1}{n} \tag{17}$$

in which $T(1-\beta)$ is Euler's function.

Formulae (1) and (17) represent the solution of the equation

$$\gamma(t) = \int_0^{k_0} e^{-kt} \cdot \rho(k) \cdot dk$$

The numerical value of H^* is, however, different from that expected from Roginskii's equation (6)

$$\rho(E) = H \cdot e^{\alpha \cdot E}$$

where

$$H = \frac{a \cdot \beta}{k_0^\beta \cdot RT}$$

Considering the experimental data, it has been proved that the difference between the numerical values of H and H^* amounts to about 30%. The method based on operational calculus proves the definition of H^* to be correct.

The value H^* was used to evaluate the distribution function according to equation (16).

Experimentally it has been proved that for the eight samples of catalysts investigated the distribution function, as has been stated above, may be expressed by means of equation (16).

For a distribution function of this type, which is general in chemical adsorption, Roginskii's activity coefficient is defined by the formula

$$A = \frac{H \cdot RT \cdot e^{\alpha \cdot E}}{\alpha RT - 1} \cdot k_0 \tag{18}$$

The basic problem is to give a formula for the activity coefficient A, which should be expressed in data easily measurable.

Equation (18) was mathematically transformed into a more simple formula:

$$A = \frac{a^n}{n-1}$$

3. HETEROGENEITY OF CATALYST SUPPORT SURFACES IN KINETIC MEASUREMENTS

Among the natural polydisperse substances, used as catalyst supports, silica with a polydisperse structure is of particular importance. A number of valuable papers, e.g. by Stöber (8), Zhdanov (9), Weyl (10) and Kiselov (11), describe investigations on various polymorphic forms of these substances. Natural silica as an industrial catalyst support should be examined in such a way that its required characteristics should be determined under conditions approximating the technological conditions of catalyst processing.

The mounting of a catalyst on a support is generally achieved in aqueous solutions of electrolytes. Therefore, the latter are suitable media in which to determine the characteristics of supports. Although the scientific literature concerning catalyst supports, and particularly naturally occurring substances, is extensive, only few physico-chemical investigations have been carried out.

Recently, in papers published by Anderson (12), Pernoux (13), Gartenmann (14), Błaszkowska (15), Tomassi and Palczewska (15a), this problem has been dealt with more accurately. Taking into account the adsorption ability of a catalyst support in aqueous solutions of electrolytes, the adsorption process may be regarded as a kind of loading current, while the loading potential is an electrokinetic potential of the support particles. In accordance with this approach the characteristic properties should be expressed in terms of ionic adsorption from aqueous solutions of electrolytes.

We assume that the mass decrease of a coagulated suspension of a support having a given distribution function can be represented by the formula

$$-\mathrm{d}m = \varepsilon[m] \cdot \mathrm{d}t \tag{19}$$

or, in case of definite values, by means of the equation

$$-\Delta m = \varepsilon[m] \cdot \Delta t$$

where $[m]$ is the suspension concentration in the examined medium, and t is the time.

To represent the solution of equation (19) as an integral with defined limits is difficult, owing to the very complicated character of adsorption and coagulation phenomena.

If the experiments are carried out in unit volume, then for quick and complete coagulation the concentration $[m]$, as well as the whole mass of the coagulated substance, is changed from $[m]$ to zero in time Δt.

In this case the decrease $-\Delta m$ equals $[m]$. Maintaining the same volume of suspension in the examined medium, its concentration $[m]$ can be altered by weighing out larger and larger portions of the mass m_i. As the masses m_i are coagulated separately during a set of experiments, each process can be expressed by means of a separate equation:

$$\Delta m_1 = \varepsilon_1 \cdot [m_1] \cdot \Delta t_1$$
$$\Delta m_2 = \varepsilon_2 \cdot [m_2] \cdot \Delta t_2 \qquad (20)$$
$$\Delta m_n = \varepsilon_n \cdot [m_n] \cdot \Delta t_n$$

The coagulation of the masses $m_1, m_2 \dots m_n$ can be performed by using the same portions of an electrolyte. Among the electrolytes used for this purpose, the most suitable is a $1/10$ N aqueous solution of $Th(NO_3)_4$. The

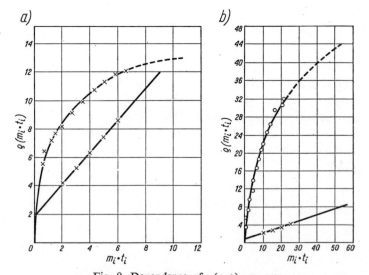

Fig. 9. Dependence of $\rho(m_i t_i)$ on $m_i t_i$:
a) for colloidal quartz glass, b) for a support from Piotrowice.

equations from m_1 to m_n represent implicit functions. These functions can be replaced by another mathematical function, based on effective electrical charges adsorbed from an aqueous solution of ions, causing the coagulation. This is represented by the following equation:

$$-\Delta m = \varepsilon Q \cdot \Delta t \qquad (21)$$

where Q is the effective electric charge of the ions causing the coagulation and ε is the coefficient, dependent on the quality of the electrolyte and the surface nature of the polydispersoid system. For a given catalyst support with a given distribution function

$$Q = k \cdot S$$

where S is the surface of the coagulated suspension with a mass m. So, then, equation (21) can be put in another form, viz.

$$-\Delta m = \varepsilon \cdot k \cdot S \cdot \Delta t \tag{22}$$

or

$$-\Delta m = \varepsilon' \cdot k \cdot S \cdot \Delta t$$

Owing to a much greater accuracy in weighing the mass m than in measuring S, it is more convenient to use equation (20), even though it is expressed as an implicit function. Since the successive values of m_i are known from experimental data, based on the co-ordinates system of m_i versus $(m_i \cdot t_i)$ we can draw a curve (Fig. 9). The curves represented in the graph become straight lines if they are traced in the co-ordinates system of

$$\ln \frac{m_{max.}}{m_{max.} - m_i} - m_i \cdot t_i$$

The experimental data, from which the graphs in Figs. 9a and 9b are drawn, are given in Tables 2 and 3.

In this way the equation of a given experimental straight line is of the following type:

$$\ln \frac{m_{max.}}{m_{max.} - m_i} = k \cdot m_i t_i + b$$

where $m_{max.}$ is the largest mass of the coagulated substance when the time of coagulation tends towards infinity; k is a constant, t_i is the coagulation time of the mass m_i, and b is another constant. The equation representing the function m_i can be written as follows:

$$m_i = \left\{ m_{max.} \left[1 - e^{-(km_i t_i + b)} \right] \right\} v \tag{23}$$

or, if we replace m_i by S_i, we get the following form:

$$m_i = \left\{ m_{max.} \left[1 - e^{-(k \cdot S_i t_i + b)} \right] \right\} v \tag{24}$$

where S_i denotes the surface of successive portions of the support m_i;

TABLE 2

No. of experiment	Mass m'_1, grams	Time t, seconds	Dry mass of the coagulated substance m_i, grams	$m_i t_i$
1	0.400	8	0.0495	0.3960
2	0.450	10	0.0560	0.5600
3	0.500	12	0.0645	0.7440
4	0.550	15	0.0680	1.020
5	0.600	17	0.0720	1.2240
6	0.650	20	0.0760	1.5200
7	0.700	25	0.0815	2.0375
8	0.750	30	0.0910	2.7300
9	0.800	35	0.0990	3.4650
10	0.850	40	0.0750	4.3000
11	0.900	45	0.1120	5.0400
12	0.950	50	0.1180	5.9000
13	1.000	54	0.1214	6.5556

$$m_1 = 84.5 \qquad m_2 = 96.0 \qquad m_3 = 105$$

$$m_{max.} = \frac{84.5 \times 105 - (96)^2}{84.5 + 105 - 96 \times 2} = 137$$

m_i	$m_{max.} - m_i$	$\dfrac{m_{max.}}{m_{max.} - m_i}$	$\log \dfrac{m_{max,}}{m_{max.} - m_i}$
84.5	52.5	2.6	0.41
96	41	2.33	0.52
105	32	4.28	0.63
112	25	5.47	0.74
118	19	7.2	0.85

v — the constant volume, in which the ionic adsorption is taking place, thus causing the coagulation;

k, b — the characteristic constants for the given polydispersoid system;

k — the slope of the straight line;

b — the intersection of the straight line with the Y-axis.

The value of k may be determined by rearranging equation (23) and differentiating it with respect to $m_i t_i$:

$$\frac{d \ln \dfrac{m_{max.}}{m_{max.} - m_i}}{d(m_i t_i)} = k \qquad (25)$$

TABLE 3

No. of experiment	Mass m'_1, grams	1/10N Th(NO₃)₄, millilitres	Time t, seconds	Dry mass of the coagulated substance m_i, grams	$m_i t_i$
1	0.200	0.05	25	0.0740	1.850
2	0.250	0.05	28	0.0960	2.528
3	0.300	0.05	33	0.1150	3.795
4	0.350	0.05	35	0.1375	4.812
5	0.400	0.05	37	0.1655	6.123
6	0.450	0.05	40	0.1855	7.420
7	0.500	0.05	42	0.2045	8.589
8	0.550	0.05	45	0.2200	9.900
9	0.600	0.05	47	0.2430	11.421
10	0.650	0.05	50	0.2605	13.025
11	0.700	0.05	55	0.2920	16.060
12	0.750	0.05	65	0.3200	20.800

$$m_1 = 278 \qquad m_2 = 311 \qquad m_3 = 340$$

$$m_{\text{max.}} = \frac{278 \times 340 - (311)^2}{278 + 340 - 2 \times 311} = 550$$

m_i	$m_{\text{max.}} - m_i$	$\dfrac{m_{\text{max.}}}{m_{\text{max.}} - m_i}$	$\log \dfrac{m_{\text{max.}}}{m_{\text{max.}} - m_i}$
231	319	1.73	0.24
278	272	1.98	0.295
311	239	2.31	0.363
340	210	2.62	0.42

Next we can assume that

$$m_i = \alpha N_i, \qquad m_{\text{max.}} = \alpha N_{\text{max.}} \tag{26}$$

where α is the proportionality coefficient, N_i the number of spots on the adsorption surface of a support occupied by ions in an interval of time t_i, and $N_{\text{max.}}$ the maximum number of spots occupied on the support surface after a long time, theoretically after an infinite time. When inserting equation (26) into equation (23) we obtain

$$N_i = \{N_{\text{max.}} \cdot [1 - e^{-(km_i t_i + b)}]\} v \tag{27}$$

where $N_{\text{max.}}$ denotes the maximum number of spots occupied on the support surface, for which the coagulation lasts for an infinitely long time at a given electrolyte concentration.

This equation expresses the number of occupied active spots on the support as a function of time. In other words, when the suspension mass in consecutive support samples gets larger and larger, while the same initial concentration of the electrolyte is maintained, then we approximate

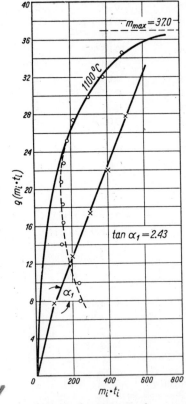

Fig. 10. Change of the constant value k versus $m_i t_i$ for a support with a kinetic range defined as $k = \tan \alpha_1$.

the mass, for which the time necessary for occupying the active spots on a unit surface to coagulate the support theoretically will become infinitely large.

If the same number of free active spots on the support surface can be expressed by means of the following equation:

$$(N_{max.} - N_i) = N_i^0$$

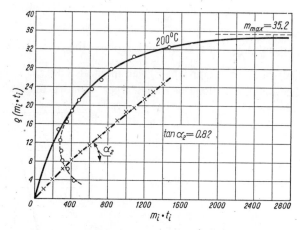

Fig. 11. Change of the constant value k versus $m_i t_i$ for a support with a kinetic range defined as $k = \tan \alpha_2$.

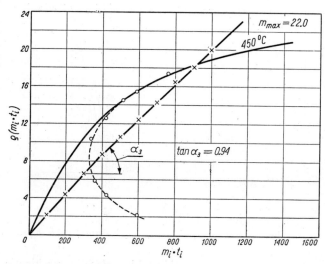

Fig. 12. Change of the constant value k versus $m_i t_i$ for a support with a kinetic range defined as $k = \tan \alpha_3$.

where N_i is the number of the unoccupied spots still free to be occupied within the time t_i, then equation (23) will take the form

$$k = \frac{1}{m_i t_i} \cdot \frac{N_{(i-1)}^0}{N_i^0}$$

Thus the quotient $\dfrac{N_{(i-1)}^0}{N_i^0}$ is a coefficient representing the rate of decrease of unoccupied spots on a support in given intervals ($\Delta m_i t_i$). This treatment possesses the advantage that by using larger support masses m_i we can

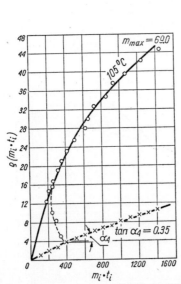

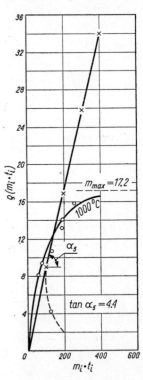

Fig. 13. Change of the constant value k versus $m_i t_i$ for a support with a kinetic range defined as $k = \tan \alpha_4$.

Fig. 14. Example of the unchangeability of the constant k defined as $k = \tan \alpha_5$.

easily control the course of coagulation taking place in the kinetic range, i.e. within such a range of $m_i t_i$ that the condition of k being constant ($k = $ const.) is fulfilled.

The kinetic range is defined by lower as well as upper limits. Repeated experiments have proved that the lower limit of the kinetic range begins with a defined numerical value m_i for a given support, which might be called the kinetic threshold. Above the kinetic threshold the numerical value of k is practically constant. The kinetic threshold of the supports can be easily determined if one uses support samples possessing relatively increased surfaces in comparison with the initial surface. The kinetic threshold of various support samples is shown in Figs. 10, 11, 12, 13 and 14, in which it is denoted by the apex of the respective angles α. As may be seen from the graphs, the kinetic threshold depends on the variation of the numerical value of k. Above the threshold, which is determined by $\tan \alpha$, the value of k remains constant up to the upper limit of the kinetic range. The upper limit is determined by the support mass, for which $m_i = m_{crit.}$. Within the limits of the kinetic range the coagulation is very quick, taking place in the whole of the mass. When the numerical value of $m_{crit.}$ is outside the kinetic range, the coagulation becomes fractional.

EXPERIMENTAL PART

The examined support is weighed out in samples of from 0.10 to 1 g, each sample being 0.05 g heavier than the preceding one. The samples are put into test-tubes of 20 ml volume, and 15 ml of water is added. The contents are thoroughly shaken, and then the samples are set aside for four minutes for sedimentation of the coarser suspensions, and finally 10 ml of the aqueous suspensions is pipetted out into a separate test-tube.

Next 0.05 ml of 1/10N aqueous solution of $Th(NO_3)_4$ is added, and after short but vigorous mixing the time of coagulation is measured. Finally, the dry mass of the coagulated substance, after evaporation of the water, is weighed.

The experimental data obtained in this way are represented in a graph (Fig. 9a). The experimental data, here presented, were obtained for a support prepared from siliceous earth mined in the district of Sandomierz (16). In order to prove that the constant k does not depend on the degree of surface covered by Th^{4+} ions, the measurements were carried out on supports subjected to an introductory adsorption of Th^{4+} ions. This introductory adsorption was performed as follows.

To 1000 ml of H_2O suitable portions of 1/10N $Th(NO_3)_4$ were introduced, and then 20 g of the support was added. After one hour at room temperature, the mixture was filtered through a Büchner funnel, and the coagulation measurements were made on the dried and weighed samples. The curves based on these experiments are shown in Fig. 16.

In order to determine to what extent the curves conform with equation (23), the value of $m_{max.}$ for each curve has been determined using the formula

$$m_{max.} = \frac{m_1 \cdot m_3 - m_2^2}{m_1 + m_3 - 2m_2}$$

Given the value for $m_{max.}$, the invariability of

$$\ln \frac{m_{max.} - m_i}{m_{max.} - m_{i+1}} = a$$

for the same ranges of $\Delta m_i t_i$ was proved.

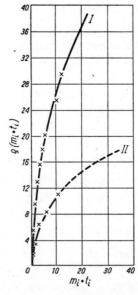

Fig. 15. Dependence of $\rho(m_i t_i)$ on $m_i t_i$ showing the slope change of curves caused by roasting siliceous earth from Gaj Ravine (Wąwóz Gaja):
I—raw siliceous earth roasted at 700°C;
II—raw siliceous earth without roasting.

From the value of a, based on several experiments, the average value of $\bar{a}$ could be determined, from which again k was calculated.

It has been established that the differences between $\bar{a}$ and the corresponding values of a are permissible and do not exceed experimental errors. In Table 4 the data for the first series of experiments are shown.

For practical purposes the value of $\bar{a}$ is constant for the whole range of $1/10$ N $Th(NO_3)_4$ concentrations. Therefore, for the series of examined

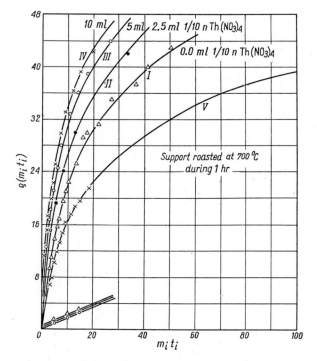

Fig. 16. Dependence of $\rho(m_it_i)$ on m_it_i for supports I, II, III, IV and V:
I—for a support without introductory adsorption; II, III, IV—for a support with intro-
ductory adsorption using $1/10$ N $Th(NO_3)_4$ in amounts given at each respective curve;
V—for a support without introductory adsorption, roasted at 700°C for 1 hour.

supports, the support surface is homogeneous, as $\bar{a}$ is not affected by the
ratio of surface screening by Th^{4+} ions.

The change to heterogeneity is very marked when supports I, II, III
and IV are compared with a support roasted for an hour at a temperature
of 700°C. The mean value of $\bar{a}$ for unroasted supports is 1.08, while for
a roasted support it is 1.11. The value of $\bar{a}$ is fundamental for the determination of the constant k. Table 5 gives values for constant k, obtained
from the first series of experiments, as well as the values of $\dfrac{k}{S}$, calculated
from the same experiments, where S represents the specific surface of
the support. From the data in this table the numerical value of $\dfrac{k}{S}$ for
a roasted support clearly indicates the heterogeneity changes of the surface
as the support passes from an unroasted to a roasted state. As the

TABLE 4

No. of curve (Fig. 16)	$m_{max.} = \dfrac{m_1 \cdot m_3 - m_2^2}{m_1 + m_3 - 2m_2}$	a_1	a_2	a_3	a_4	a_5	a_{mean}
I	846	846	846	846	846	846	
		196	246	300	338	370	
		649	598	546	508	476	
		1.08	1.09	1.08	1.07		1.08
II	744	744	744	744	744	744	
		220	257	297	330	361	
		524	487	447	414	383	
		1.075	1.09	1.08	1.08		1.08
III	677	677	677	677	677	677	
		192	235	270	298	320	
		485	442	407	379	357	
		1.09	1.09	1.08	1.08		1.08
IV	579	579	579	579	579	579	
		186	220	245	270	288	
		393	359	334	309	291	
		1.10	1.08	1.08	1.06		1.08
V	372	372	372	372	372	372	
		112	142	166	188	197	
		260	230	206	184	175	
		1.13	1.12	1.10	1.087		1.11

numerical value of k for an unroasted support is constant and independent of surface adsorption of thorium ions, the covering of active spots for the same support mass will take place in accordance with the same equation, namely,

$$N_i = \left\{ N_{max.}\left[1 - e^{-(km_i\,t_i + b)}\right]\right\} v$$

It should, however, be noted that the influence of the factor b will diminish as the numerical values expressed by $e^{-km_i\,t_i}$ increase in comparison with the factor e^{-b}.

The shape of the curves drawn according to equation (27) is determined by the values of k_i and $N_{max.}$. The value k depends on the surface character and is changed by thermal variations, which depend on the temperature.

TABLE 5

Support from Piotrowice (Fig. 16) Mode of preparation	Surface S, m²/g	Mass in scales	$\dfrac{m_{max.} - m_{i+1}}{m_{max.} - m_{i+2}}$ a_{mean}	$\dfrac{1}{\Delta(m_i t_i)} \cdot \log \dfrac{m_{max.}^k - m_{i+1}}{m_{max.} - m_{i+2}}$	$\dfrac{k}{S}$
I Without introductory adsorption	34	579	1.08	1.56×10^{-2}	4.6×10^{-4}
II Without 2.5 ml 1/10 N Th(NO₃)₄	34	677	1.08	1.56×10^{-2}	4.6×10^{-4}
III 5 ml 1/10 N Th(NO₃)₄	34	747	1.08	1.56×10^{-2}	4.6×10^{-4}
IV With introductory adsorption of 10 ml 1/10 N Th(NO₃)₄	34	846	1.08	1.56×10^{-2}	4.6×10^{-4}
V Roasted for 1 hour at a temperature of 700°C	24	372	1.11	2.02×10^{-2}	9.1×10^{-4}

The factor k, being independent of the degree of surface screening, influences the energetic properties of active spots. In Fig. 17 a number of curves are shown. They delineate the different ways of surface modification.

As the roasting temperature increases, the following chemical transfor mations may be taking place:

$$\underset{\overset{|}{-}\text{Si}\overset{|}{-}\text{O}\overset{|}{-}\text{Si}\overset{|}{-}}{\overset{\text{OH} \quad \text{OH}}{}} \longrightarrow -\text{Si}\overset{\text{O}}{\underset{\text{O}}{}}\text{Si} \; + H_2O$$

$$\underset{\text{H}}{\overset{\text{H}}{}}\text{Si}\underset{\text{OH}}{\overset{\text{OH}}{}} \longrightarrow \text{Si}{=}\text{O} \; + H_2O$$

These transformations represent the dehydration process taking place on the support surface at the expense of the neighbouring hydroxyl groups. At sufficiently high temperatures the dehydration occurs at the expense of those hydroxyl groups distributed at different parts of the surface. The heating process, followed by roasting and sintering, results in a decrease of the specific surface of the support.

The roasting of siliceous and diatomaceous earths, which are the raw materials for making supports, is essential in order to remove organic impurities and to retard the peptization process, which takes place in

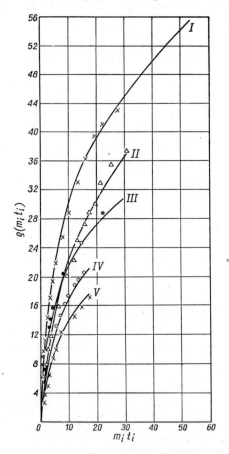

Fig. 17. Dependence of $\rho(m_i t_i)$ on $m_i t_i$ for differently modified supports: I—support modified by means of Th^{4+} ions, II—unmodified and unroasted support used as starting material, III—support modified by means of an aqueous solution of $NaNO_3$, IV—support modified by roasting at 700°C for 1 hour, V—support modified by $NaNO_3$ and by roasting for 1 hour at 700°C.

the aqueous alkaline medium, required for the mounting of the contact mass on the support.

An essential property of the supports is their adaptability for the preparation of cobalt catalysts, used in the Fischer-Tropsch synthesis, and this depends on the choice of the optimum roasting temperature for each given raw material. The change in character of the support surface, resulting from the roasting operation, is represented in the graph by a slope increase of the curve $m_i = \rho(m_i \cdot t_i)$ versus the ordinates axis X (Fig. 17). For another series of supports the same change, due to roasting, leads to different results. The curve slope decreases after roasting (Figs. 15 and 18). It has been experimentally proved that four basic groups of supports (Fig. 19) may be prepared from siliceous earth.

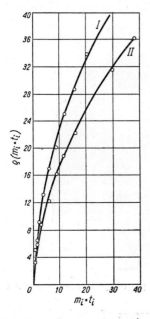

Fig. 18. Dependence of $\rho(m_i t_i)$ on $m_i t_i$ for curves expressing a slope change due to roasting of the support at 700°C: *I*—support from the Gaj Ravine (Wąwóz Gaja) roasted at 700°C, *II*—the same support not roasted.

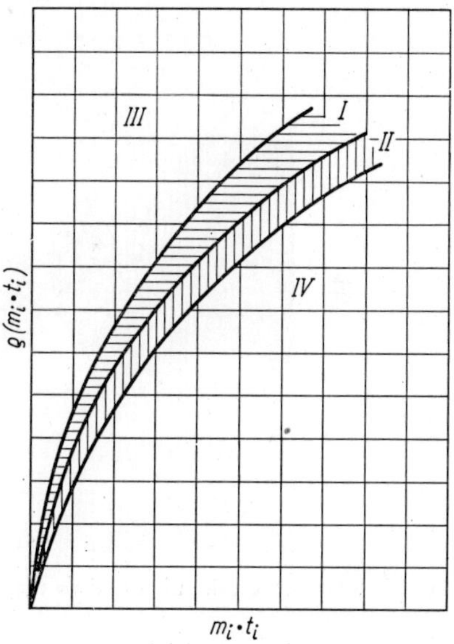

Fig. 19. Graph expressing property ranges of supports applied to catalysts: *I*—supports with slight roasting, *II*—slightly hydrophobic supports, *III*—area of roasted supports, *IV*—area of hydrophobic supports.

As a result of roasting, the areas *III* and *IV* produce products unsuitable for catalyst supports.

The peptization process of supports in aqueous media has been observed through an electron microscope.

The particles of supports, made from unroasted siliceous earths, become, after some time in aqueous solutions, partially diffused in shape. This is the main disadvantage of unroasted supports. Many physico-chemical changes take place during the technological processing of a support as a result of peptization in an alkaline aqueous solution, required for mounting the catalyst on a support.

The fact that the production of cobalt supports cannot be repeated is due to the peptization occurring to different degrees and depending on the distribution function according to r (which is the radius of the support's particles) of the polydispersoid system (Figs. 20 and 21). The roasted supports, as may be seen under an electron microscope, have quite different features (Figs. 22 and 23). The contours of siliceous earth

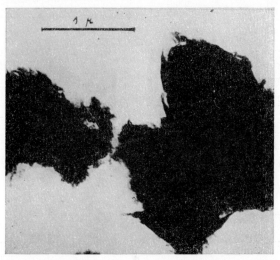

Fig. 20. Siliceous earth submitted to the action of petrol (gasolene) for 10 minutes.

particles are sharp, which proves that the process of peptization has been stopped. And this is also shown by microscopic examination of supports made from roasted siliceous earth (Figs. 24 and 25). Roasted supports do not undergo such undesirable changes in alkaline media as shown by unroasted supports.

As a result of roasting, some stabilization of the peptization of supports is achieved, and thus a greater reproducibility of the contact activity is possible, in so far as the properties of the supports as a result of roasting correspond to areas I and II (Fig. 19).

Although prolonged roasting provides stabilization against peptization, at the same time the support surface is considerably decreased, e.g. from 40 m^2 to 1 m^2. This earth is, therefore, unfit for the production of contacts because of the very small specific surface. In fact such contacts very soon become aged.

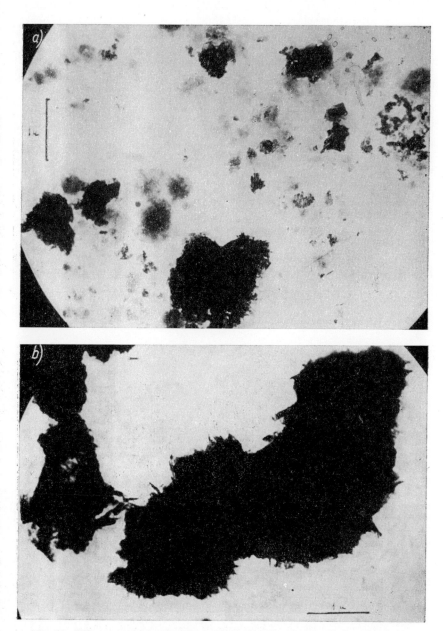

Fig. 21. Siliceous earth soaked in water *a*) for 60 minutes, *b*) for 10 minutes.

Fig. 22. Electron micrograph of kieselguhr and its fragments, magnified 20,000 times.

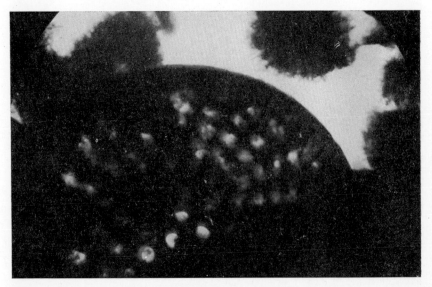

Fig. 23. Electron micrograph of kieselguhr in comparison with diffused particles of siliceous earth.

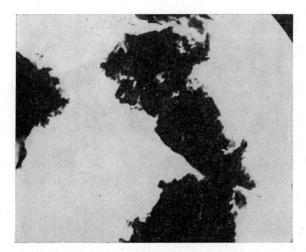

Fig. 24. Roasted kieselguhr after 60 minutes' soaking in water.

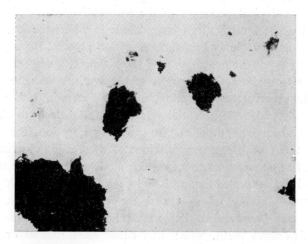

Fig. 25. Roasted kieselguhr after 10 minutes' soaking in water.

Within the temperature range of strong dehydration, a partial stabilization against peptization is achieved, and in addition the supports become very hydrophobic, and this makes the mounting of hydrophilic contacts on their surface difficult.

4. STATIC INVESTIGATIONS INTO THE HETEROGENEITY OF SUPPORT SURFACES

From the experimental data and the numerical values of k, calculated by means of the kinetic equation of ionic adsorption on support surfaces, the characteristics of a support surface for different roasting temperatures can be given.

Kinetic investigations according to these methods can be successfully applied to catalyst supports made of such substances as siliceous earth. Microscopic investigation of this earth reveals (under magnification $\times 500$) that it consists of particles of various sizes and approximately spherical in shape. In contrast to siliceous earths, kieselguhrs, i.e. "diatomea", are very different in size and geometrical shape. The heterogeneity of the geometrical shape of the kieselguhrs makes it comparatively difficult to define the kinetic range for the measurement of coagulation based on ionic adsorption. Therefore, in the case of typical diatomea systems, frequently used in technological processes of the Fischer-Tropsch synthesis, it was necessary to base investigations on methods in which the diatomea are used as an immovable bed in the adsorption process. It was, therefore, decided to prevent the coagulation of the kieselguhrs and for the sake of comparison to make a similar series of observations on siliceous earths. In order to observe the adsorption, a set of dyes with either a negative or positive electrokinetic potential was used; this helped to characterize the support surfaces as to their active spots of adsorption. The adsorption was carried out with aqueous solutions of dyes, using chromatographic columns. The first measurements, in which static methods were used, gave no results. It was expected that an interdependence or relationship between the adsorption ability of dyes and the roasting temperature of the support would be revealed. Experimental data were obtained for 10 samples of siliceous earth, which had either been roasted or dried for one hour. Over a temperature range of 100–1000°C the difference of successive roasting temperatures was 100°C.

In order to obtain curves illustrating precisely the changes in the surface properties of the adsorbent with changes of temperature, it was decided to adopt a new conception of increasing the electrostatic forces acting between the support surface and the dye particles, penetrating in the form of an aqueous solution through the static bed. For this purpose several sample supports, each with differing energetic properties, were submitted to an introductory adsorption of Th^{4+} ions, using $Th(NO_3)_4$ solutions of suitable concentrations. It was assumed that the several surfaces would be modified in accordance with their different energy properties and that a distinct differentiation in the adsorption of the $Th(NO_3)_4$ ions would appear. If, according to Gouy's theory, the double electrical layer, as far as ions are concerned, is diffused, then the partner of an adsorbed ion should "easily" stick to a hypothetical surface with an opposite electrical charge to that of the support surface. Therefore the electrostatic forces acting between the support surface and the dye particle may be increased or decreased. The main problem, in this case, is the choice of a suitable dye with the proper electrokinetic potential as well as the optimum concentration of the $Th(NO_3)_4$ solution, so that the dye will act as the second surface. For this reason a series of observations, based on a variety of dyes, was made, together with adsorption from a range of twelve different concentrations of aqueous $Th(NO_3)_4$ solutions. The normality of the concentrations used in these investigations is marked in the graphs. The graphs also show the results of the first series of observations, using methyl blue, which has a positive electrokinetic potential in aqueous solution, i.e. a potential opposite to that of the support, which is negative.

The graphs of the functions show that the extrema of the function (Figs. 26, 27, 28) in the case of unmodified support surfaces are less distinct and tend to be greatly increased in modified surfaces. This effect is enhanced as the ionic concentration of Th^{4+} as the modifying medium increases. The Piotrowice I support reveals one very sharp extremum, while Piotrowice II has one sharp and one less distinct extremum, the support from Kissatibi having two sharp and one less distinct extremum. Quite different results are obtained in the experiments using fuchsine with a negative electrokinetic potential (Figs. 29 and 30). In this case the adsorbing ability of the dye increases proportionately, as the Th^{4+} ion concentration decreases; and it attains a maximum value in the absence of Th^{4+} treatment. The Piotrowice II support in experiments with fuchsine has two extrema, while the Kissatibi support shows one sharp and one less distinct extremum. In order to represent the problem of heterogeneity of support surfaces quantitatively in the form of a function of the roasting temperature, the amount of the adsorbed dye was plotted against the concentration of $Th(NO_3)_4$. Figures 31 and 32 represent this function using methyl blue as the dye. This curve of the function may be adjusted to agree with the general equation:

$$A = A_{max}.(1-e^{-k \cdot c - b})$$

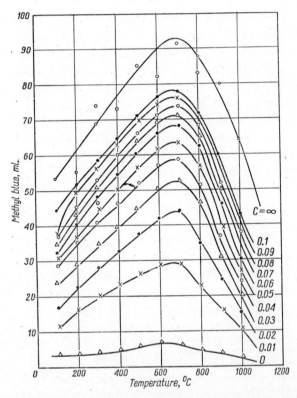

Fig. 26. Dependence of the amount of methyl blue (in ml), adsorbed by 1 gram of siliceous support from Piotrowice, on the roasting temperature when suitable concentrations of $Th(NO_3)_4$ are used. Attention should be drawn to the discrete extremum of a curve for which the ionic concentration of Th^{4+} equals zero.

where A is the amount of the adsorbed dye, depending on the concentration c of the aqueous solution of $Th(NO_3)_4$; k is a constant, characteristic for a given support surface, roasted at a given temperature; b is a constant.

The best adjustment is achieved for the Kissatibi support curves. In a logarithmic system the curves have different slopes, which proves that

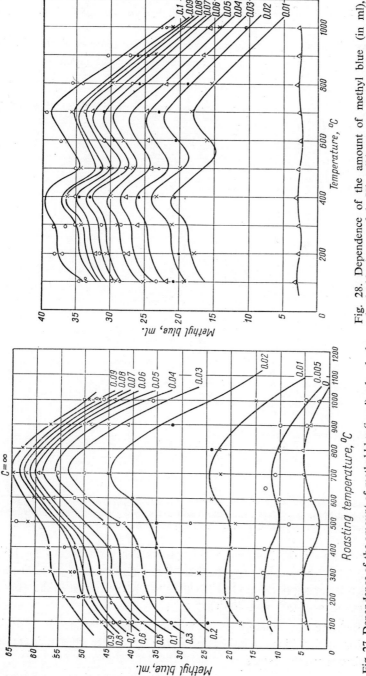

Fig. 28. Dependence of the amount of methyl blue (in ml), adsorbed by 1 gram of the Kissatibi support, on the roasting temperature when suitable concentrations of Th(NO₃)₄ are used. Attention should be drawn to the discrete extrema in the case of the unmodified support of Th(NO₃)₄.

Fig. 27. Dependence of the amount of methyl blue (in ml), adsorbed by 1 gram of support II from Piotrowice, roasted for 1 hour, on the roasting temperature when suitable concentrations of Th(NO₃)₄ are used.

the heterogeneity of supports is affected by the roasting temperature (Fig. 33).

In experiments using fuchsine dyes with a negative electrokinetic potential, the curves of $A = \varphi(C)$ are expressed by the equation

$$A = A_{max.} \cdot e^{-k \cdot c - b}$$

and the curves of $A = \psi(t)$ are expressed graphically in Figs. 34 and 35.

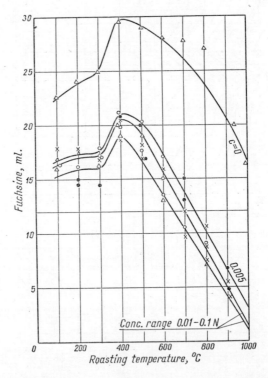

Fig. 29. Dependence of the amount of fuchsine, expressed in ml, adsorbed by 1 g of the support (Kissatibi earth), roasted for 1 hour, on the roasting temperature. The support has been previously treated with a Th(NO₃)₄ solution as denoted in the graph.

In the case of the Piotrowice II supports for surfaces not modified by Th(NO₃)₄, there are two maxima for temperatures of 200 and 500°C, while for supports modified by Th(NO₃)₄ the two maxima appear at temperatures of 200 and 400°C.

For fuchsine the sequence of increasing maximum values is opposite to that for methyl blue. In this case, as the dye concentration increases the maximum value decreases.

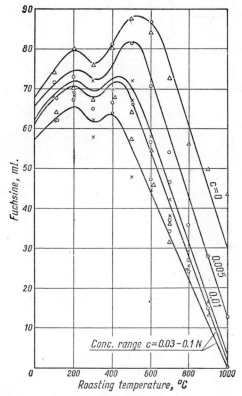

Fig. 30. Dependence of the amount of fuchsine, expressed in ml, adsorbed by the Piotrowice II support, on the roasting temperature. Support previously treated with a Th(NO₃)₄ solution of a concentration as denoted in the graph.

For the Piotrowice I support	Balance of extrema Temperature in °C	Number of maximum values
Methyl blue	700	1
	200	1
	400	1
	500	1
For the Kissatibi support		4
Methyl blue	200	1
	400	1
	700	1
	400	1
		4
Fuchsine		

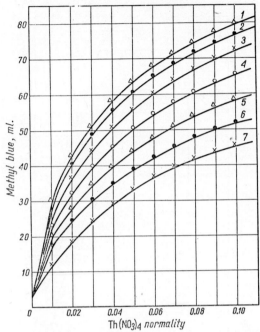

Fig. 31. Dependence of the amount of methyl blue, expressed in ml, adsorbed by 1 g of siliceous earth from Piotrowice (corroded with 18% HNO₃), roasted for 1 hour, on the concentration of the Th(NO₃)₄ solution, used for support activation. Roasting temperatures:

$1-700°C, 2-600°C, 3-500°C, 4-400°C, 5-300°C, 6-200°C, 7-110°C.$

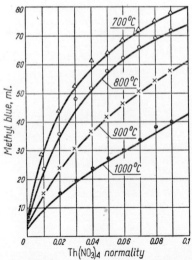

Fig. 32. Dependence of the amount of methyl blue, expressed in ml, adsorbed by 1 g of siliceous earth from Piotrowice (corroded with 18% HNO₃), roasted for 1 hour, on the concentration of the Th(NO₃)₄ solution, used for support activation.

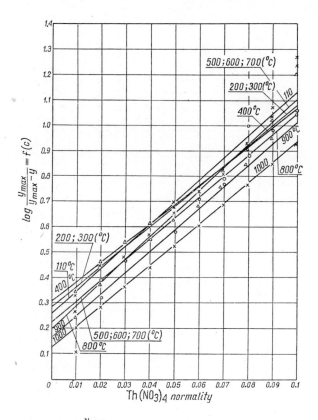

Fig. 33. Dependence of $\dfrac{y_{\text{max.}}}{y_{\text{max.}} - y}$ on the Th(NO$_3$)$_4$ concentration at different roasting temperatures.

As a result of using two dyes, one with a positive, the other with a negative, electrokinetic potential, the surface characteristics may be defined as the maximum of the function

$$A = \varphi(t)$$

By using different Th(NO$_3$)$_4$ concentrations for separate samples, the characteristics of the support may be expressed according to the graph represented in Fig. 36, which shows the functions

$$b = f(t) \quad \text{and} \quad k = f(t)$$

for a Piotrowice I support.

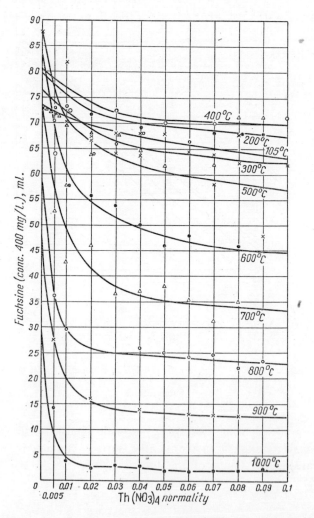

Fig. 34. Dependence of adsorbed fuchsine, expressed in ml per 1 g of the Piotrowice II support, on the concentration of the Th(NO₃)₄ solution, used for support activation, at different roasting temperatures.

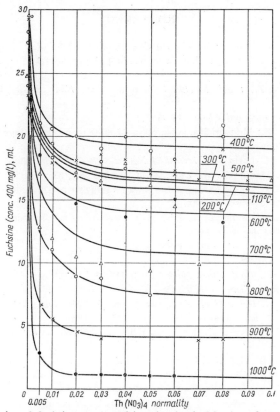

Fig. 35. Quantity of fuchsine, expressed in ml, adsorbed by 1 g of support (Kissatibi earth), versus concentration of the $Th(NO_3)_4$ solution, used for support activation, at different roasting temperatures (roasting for 1 hour).

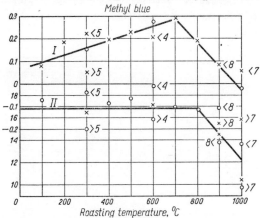

Fig. 36. Dependence of the coefficient b (curve I, points marked by x, mean values by o) and the coefficient k (curve II, points marked by o, mean values by x) on the roasting temperature t.

REFERENCES

1. Roginskii S. Z., *Probl. Kinetiki i Kataliza, Akad. Nauk SSSR*, **4**; Roginskii S. Z.: Monografiya. Adsorptsya i kataliz na neodnorodnykh poverkhnostyakh. Moscow, 1948.

2. Roginskii S. Z., *Probl. Kinetiki i Kataliza, Akad. Nauk SSSR*, **4**, 34 (Mody-fikatory).

3. Mitoraj K., *Przemysł Chem.*, **11** (1955).

4. Roginskii S. Z.: Monografiya. Adsorptsya i kataliz na neodnorodnykh poverkhnostyakh. Moscow, 1948.

5. Man'ko N. M., Levin V. I., *Izv. Akad. Nauk SSSR, Otd. Khim. Nauk*, **3**, 409 (1953); Keer N. P., Man'ko N. M., *Dokl. Akad. Nauk SSSR*, **83**, 713 (1952).

6. Roginskii S. Z.: Monografiya. Adsorptsya i kataliz na neodnorodnykh poverkhnostyakh. p. 131. Moscow, 1948.

7. Roginskii S. Z.: Monografiya. Adsorptsya i kataliz na neodnorodnykh poverkhnostyakh; p. 408. Moscow, 1948.

8. Stöber W., *Kolloid Z.*, **149**, 1 (1956).
   Stöber W., *Kolloid Z.*, **145**, 17 (1956).

9. Zhdanov S. P., *Dokl. Akad. Nauk SSSR*, **115**, 5 (1957).

10. Weill J., *Chem. Zentr.*, **126**, 22 (1955).

11. Kiselov A. V., *Dokl. Akad. Nauk SSSR*, **106**, 6 (1956); *ibid.*, **115**, 2 (1957); *ibid.*, **114**, 3 (1957); *ibid.*, **116**, 6 (1957); *ibid.*, **117**, 6 (1957).

12. Anderson R. B., Krieg K., Selingmann B. O., Neill W. E., *Ind. Eng. Chem.*, **39**, 1548 (1947).
    Anderson R. B., Hall K., Selingmann B., *J. Am. Chem. Soc.*, **69**, 3114 (1947);
    Anderson R. B., *Ind. Eng. Chem.*, **39**, 1618 (1947); *ibid.*, **40**, 2347 (1948).

13. Pernoux M., *J. Chim. Phys.*, **47**, 229 (1950).

14. Gartenmann E.: Mikrostruktur und Aktivitäts-Untersuchungen an Kobalt-Katalysatoren. Zürich, 1953.

15. Błaszkowska R., Szperl A., *Przemysł Chem.*, **13** (1957).

15a. Tomassi W., Palczewska W., *Roczniki Chemii*, **28**, 263 (1954).

16. Kamieński M., Sokalski Z., *Roczniki Polskiego Towarzystwa Geologicznego*, XIX, No. 2 (1949).

IX. STUDIES ON KINETICS AND SELECTIVITY IN DEHYDROGENATION PROCESSES OF ALCOHOLS

E. Treszczanowicz

During studies on kinetics of the catalytic dehydrogenation of isopropyl alcohol, S. Ciborowski (1,2) found that, in the temperature range of 130–160°C, the known kinetic equations derived by A. A. Balandin and A. W. Frost cannot be applied to the course of the reaction for all alcohols.

The equations have been derived from and based on studies of dehydrogenation of lower alcohols at temperatures above 250°C, when the equilibrium is markedly shifted in the direction of the carbonyl compounds and the reaction is irreversible. Assuming the irreversibility of the course of the reaction, the kinetics do not satisfy the equation of the same reaction at lower temperatures, when the rate of the reverse reaction, i.e. that of hydrogenation, is still important (3).

The investigations conducted by S. Ciborowski (1,2) on the statics of the reaction at 230°C indicate that the maximum thermodynamically possible degree of dehydrogenation of isopropyl alcohol to acetone under atmospheric pressure is 0.786 instead of 1.0.

The kinetic equations derived by O. M. Hougen and K. M. Watson (4,5) for reversible catalytic reactions are of such a complex form that they are of little practical value. Consequently, S. Ciborowski has derived a new, general, integrated equation (1,2) which may be applied to reversible reactions: $A \rightleftarrows B + C$.

In the derivation of the dependence of the rate of reaction on the composition of reactants in the gaseous phase, the reasoning applied by S. Ciborowski was similar to that applied by the authors of the equations mentioned above. But the presentation of the equation in a clear form, which permits integration of the relation obtained, and the introduction of the maximum thermodynamically possible degree of dehydrogenation into the equation, are original.

S. Ciborowski has applied the known assumptions concerning the mechanism of dehydrogenation of alcohols on copper catalysts at higher temperatures to the lower temperature regions. Therefore, it was assumed that the reaction occurs in the kinetic region on the solid catalyst with a homogeneous surface and strong adsorptive properties (large adsorption coefficients of reactants on this catalyst).

The rate of the reaction is directly proportional to the surface concentration of the reactant adsorbed on the surface of the catalyst and the rate of the reverse reaction is proportional to the product of surface concentrations of the reactants adsorbed.

The equation derived by S. Ciborowski is the following:

$$\frac{K_1}{V_0} = A_1 y + B_1 \ln\left(1 - W\frac{y}{m}\right) + C_1 \ln\left(1 - \frac{y}{m}\right)$$

where: coefficients

$$A_1 = \frac{(m-W-1)^2}{W}; \quad B_1 = \frac{m(m-1)^2}{W^2(1-W)}$$

$$C_1 = \frac{(m-W)^2 m}{1-W}; \quad W = 2m - mz - 1$$

K_1 — the reaction rate constant,

V_0 — the rate of introduction of the reactant into the reaction space per unit time,

y — the conversion of the reactant after passage through the catalyst,

m — the maximum conversion (degree of dehydrogenation) of the reactant thermodynamically possible under the given conditions,

z — the sum of relative adsorption coefficients of reaction products $(z = z_2 + z_3)$.

The equation derived is in agreement with the results of investigations conducted by S. Ciborowski on the dehydrogenation of isopropyl alcohol and, apparently, is valid for other reversible catalytic reactions of the type

$$A \rightleftarrows B + C$$

A discussion of this equation has shown that for an irreversible reaction, i.e. when the maximum thermodynamically possible degree of dehydrogenation $m = 1$ and $W = 1-z$, the equation derived by S. Ciborowski will take the form

$$\frac{K_1}{V_0} = (1-z)y + z \ln\frac{1}{1-y}$$

which is identical with the equation derived by A. W. Frost for cases of strong adsorption of reactants (6):

$$V_0 \ln \frac{1}{1-y} = \beta V_0 y + \alpha$$

where β and α are coefficients independent of V_0 but dependent on the quality of the catalyst and the temperature.

At higher temperatures, when the value of z—the sum of adsorption coefficients of products—is 1 and the reaction is irreversible, i.e. $m = 1$, the equation derived has the form

$$\frac{K_1}{V_0} = -\ln(1-y) = \ln \frac{1}{1-y}$$

which is also identical with the equation for a particular case derived by A. V. Frost when the coefficient of this equation $\beta = 0$:

$$V_0 \ln \frac{1}{1-y} = \alpha = \text{const.}$$

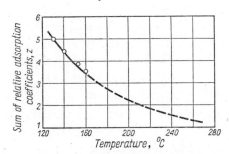

Fig. 1. Dependence of z, the sum of relative adsorption coefficients of reaction products, on temperature.

In calculating the values of K_1 and z from his own equation, S. Ciborowski found that the value of z is dependent on temperature and independent of the activity of the catalyst (Fig. 1).

Using copper catalysts S. Ciborowski observed the same phenomena noticed earlier by A. E. Agronomov (7) during investigations of the dehydrogenation reaction of isopropyl alcohol with zinc oxide as catalyst. The values of z, calculated by S. Ciborowski, show a regular drop with rise of temperature. Extrapolated to temperatures of about 250°C, they approach unity in agreement with the results of the investigations on the dehydrogenation of alcohols at these temperatures conducted by

A. A. Balandin and A. Bork (3,8,9). During the investigation of the kinetics of dehydrogenation reactions of isopropyl alcohol in the presence of various copper catalysts, attention has been given to Raney catalysts, which are particularly active but insufficiently selective.

The selectivity of these catalysts has been studied by J. Sznajder in connection with the dehydrogenation of cyclohexanol to cyclohexanone (10, 11). It was found that, in the presence of some of these catalysts at temperatures ranging from 220 to 340°C, the main reaction is, to a great extent, accompanied by the secondary dehydration reaction of cyclohexanol to cyclohexene.

In the case of other reactions, the distillation curves of the crude product indicate that they either do not take place at all or only to a small extent.

Kinetic measurements made in the presence of several different copper catalysts led J. Sznajder to conclude that the secondary reaction of dehydration of cyclohexanol to cyclohexene is always characterized by an activation energy which is in every case larger than that for dehydrogenation. Thus, for example, in the presence of the catalyst, the activation energy for the dehydration of cyclohexanol has been estimated as 5860 kcal/mole, whereas the activation energy of dehydrogenation amounted to 4420 kcal/mole. This is further supported by the fact that the dehydration of cyclohexanol to cyclohexene occurs only at temperatures higher than those required for dehydrogenation.

It has been observed for the first time that the oxidation–reduction regeneration process of Raney dehydrogenation copper catalysts, containing above 2% of unreacted aluminium, may cause a catalyst mutation, i.e. a change in action towards dehydration (Table 1, No. 3 catalyst), as, for example, in the case under consideration.

The process of formation of a catalyst may thus terminate only during its regeneration. The catalytic inertness of metallic aluminium towards cyclohexanol in the range of temperatures investigated would indicate that, under dehydrogenation conditions, the formation of aluminium oxide through aluminium alcoholate should not be anticipated.

It has been found by X-ray examination that, during the oxidation–reduction regeneration of Raney copper catalysts, the size of crystallites decreases from 10^{-3} to 10^{-6} cm, thus leading to the assumption that the occurrence of the secondary reaction of cyclohexanol dehydration is due to the surfaces being covered with aluminium oxide which becomes acces-

TABLE 1

STUDIES ON THE SELECTIVITY OF DEHYDROGENATION BY RANEY COPPER CATALYSTS. THE
EFFECT OF OXIDATION-REDUCTION ON THE CATALYST SELECTIVITY

| Composition and method of preparation of Cu–Al alloy | Catalyst prepared by treating Cu–Al alloy | | | Coefficient of selectivity $S = \dfrac{a}{b}$ [a] | |
	No.	Method of preparation	Al content in weight %	Before regeneration	After regeneration
58.8% Cu 41.2% Al Slowly chilled	3	Surface treatment of the alloy (grains)	Internal parts of grains remain untreated—Al content is the same as in the alloy	27.6	4.6
56.5% Cu 43.5% Al Slowly chilled	19	Full treatment of the alloy (pellets)	14.1	4.0	3.2
	21	,, ,,	9.3	6.1	3.9
32.0% Cu 68.0% Al Fast chilled [b]	16	,, ,,	1.4	84.5	81.3

[a] Average value calculated from several experiments conducted at 260°C and at a space velocity of 4.51 litres/litre of catalyst · hr.

[b] Composition of the alloy similar to that of a eutectic mixture of the Cu–Al system (33.0% Cu, 67.0% Al).

sible only during regeneration or after formation of the aluminium oxide under conditions of the regeneration process.

In contrast to data in the literature, it has been proved that aluminium oxide even at 240°C catalyses the dehydration reaction of cyclohexanol, there being about 45% conversion.

It should be pointed out that the oxidation–reduction regeneration of Raney catalysts containing less than 2% metallic aluminium does not bring about any marked change in the selectivity of the catalyst.

J. Sznajder has shown that the selectivity of a Raney copper catalyst approximately corresponds to that of electrolytic copper under comparative conditions ($S = 84$ in comparison with $S = 134$) only after the aluminium content has been lowered to 2%.

Here, the selectivity, S, has been expressed in the manner frequently used in the literature, i.e. by giving the ratio of the amount, a, of the primary product to the amount, *b*, of the secondary product which is formed at the same time:

$$S = \frac{a}{b}$$

The selectivity of Raney copper catalysts has been improved after passing from the region of external diffusion to one near the kinetic region

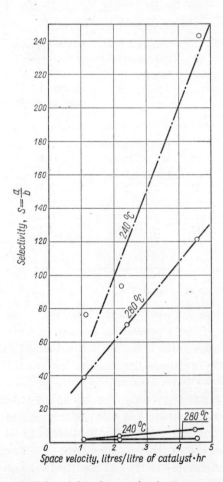

Fig. 2. Studies on the selectivity of dehydrogenation by Raney copper catalysts. Dependence of the selectivity on the space velocity at various temperatures for two different catalysts (of low and high Al percentage):

　　　　———·———·—— Catalyst 20 (about 2% Al)
　　　　——————————— Catalyst 21 (about 10% Al)

(Fig. 2). An improvement in the selectivity has also been observed (Fig. 3) on passing from fine grains (diam. about 2 mm) to coarser grains (diam. about 5 mm).

Therefore, in both cases the ratio of the rate of the primary reaction to that of the secondary reaction undergoes changes.

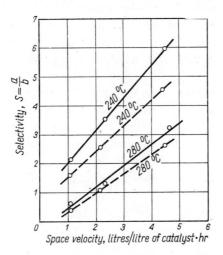

Fig. 3. Studies on the selectivity of dehydrogenation by Raney copper catalysts. Dependence of the selectivity on the space velocity at various temperatures for the same catalyst of two different grain sizes:

—————— Catalyst 21 (about 10% Al) coarse grains (about 5 mm)

— — — — Catalyst 21 (about 10% Al) fine grains (about 2 mm)

It follows from these experiments that the rate of the secondary reaction of dehydration of cyclohexanol to cyclohexene has been retarded by internal diffusion and that the rate of the primary reaction of dehydrogenation of cyclohexanol practically does not undergo changes.

Such behaviour of a catalyst can only be understood by assuming that the two simultaneously occurring reactions are of different kinetic orders.

A decrease in cyclohexanol concentration within the coarse grains of the catalyst will cause, first of all, a decrease in the rate of a reaction of a higher order: in this case, dehydration. Therefore, as has actually been observed, a catalyst of finer grains will favour a dehydration reaction at the expense of dehydrogenation.

The selectivity of a catalyst has also been enhanced and the secondary reaction of dehydration retarded by strong adsorption of water vapour supplied together with the cyclohexanol. Furthermore, deterioration in selectivity during stability tests on catalytic action is proof that active dehydrogenating centres are being predominantly blocked.

For instance, the coefficient of selectivity dropped from $S = 272$ to $S = 202$ after 68 hours of dehydrogenating at 240°C.

Studies conducted by J. Sznajder also on the selectivity of Langenbeck copper catalysts, prepared by decomposing copper–aluminium mixed salts, have shown, at a somewhat lower activity, a higher selectivity, $S = 800$–1030, than that of electrolytic copper and Raney copper of a low Al content.

It appeared, however, that Langenbeck copper catalysts, subjected to oxidation–reduction regeneration under the same conditions as used for other copper catalysts, lose their initial high selectivity after regeneration ($S = 50.5$). The original selectivity may be restored only by considerably prolonging the time of regeneration.

This phenomenon is considered due to the presence of calcium oxide in these catalysts.

When hydrogen is passed during the dehydrogenation of the catalyst, calcium oxide makes the reduction of copper oxide to metallic copper more difficult.

As explained before, copper oxide exhibits a dehydrating action under the conditions of cyclohexanol dehydrogenation, thus impairing selectivity. Also, it has been explained that the activity of electrolytic copper is diminished by the recrystallization of the copper.

The high catalytic stability of Raney copper may be accounted for by a rise of the recrystallization temperature of copper due to the presence of aluminium in catalysts of this type.

The diminished activity of copper catalysts with time is due to a decrease in the number of micropores as a result of recrystallization, and this is supported by stability tests performed on Raney copper catalysts.

Although, in catalysts of this type, recrystallization occurs only to a relatively small extent, it has been found in determinations performed by the mercury method that after 180 hours of action the number of micropores ($< 1 \mu$) decreased from 62 to 42% by volume and the number of macropores ($> 1\mu$) increased from 10 to 18% by volume, the specific area of the catalyst being decreased from 4.1 to 3.0 m²/g.

Account should be taken, however, of the slight decrease in the number of micropores due to plugging with decomposition products of cyclohexanol (after 180 hours of action 1.47% C is present in the catalyst).

The change in selectivity of the catalyst depends on the methods of preparation and has been studied by the author, taking as an example the dehydrogenation of cyclohexanol on zinc–iron catalysts.

Two catalysts—alloys of very similar compositions (12.5 and 12.8% Fe)—were prepared differing only in the cooling method used during their preparation (12). In addition, we have been concerned with the effect of the methods of preparation of these alloys on the selectivity of their action.

Metallographic studies have shown that the alloy catalyst 1 (curve *1* in Fig. 6), containing 12.5% Fe and prepared by slow chilling, exhibited the coarse crystalline structure of the eutectoid $\Gamma + \delta$ (gamma+delta) of the hexagonal crystals of δ-phase, constituting mixed crystals and estimated previously to be an intermetallic compound $FeZr_7$ (Fig. 4).

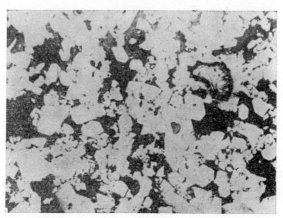

Fig. 4. Macrostructure of a slowly chilled zinc–iron alloy catalyst (12.5% Fe). Magnification 100× (white spots in the pattern represent magnified well-developed alloy crystals; black spots are voids between alloy grains).

The structure of this alloy corresponds to equilibria at lower temperatures.

The activity of catalyst 1 was a little lower than the initial activity of fast chilled catalyst 2 of the same composition.

Catalyst 1, in contrast to fast chilled catalyst 2, acted selectively and did not bring about the occurrence of the secondary reaction of the decomposition of cyclohexanol.

The stability of activity of this catalyst 1 was high in contrast to the low stability of activity of catalyst 2.

The activation energy for dehydrogenation in the presence of catalyst 1 was constant and amounted to 41.3 kcal/mole.

Alloy catalyst 2, containing almost the same amount of iron (12.8%), has shown no selective action in contrast to the former catalyst.

As shown by metallographic analysis, fast chilled catalyst 2 (curve *2* in Fig. 6) has exhibited a fine crystalline structure (Fig. 5) corresponding to equilibrium established at high temperatures; among others, η-phase rich in zinc.

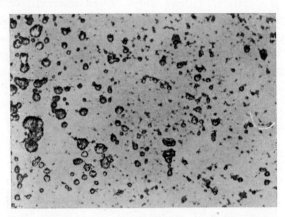

Fig. 5. Macrostructure of fast chilled zinc–iron alloy catalyst (12.8% Fe). Magnification 100 ×.

This alloy catalyst showed no selectivity, since in addition to the primary reaction it caused a secondary reaction of decomposition of cyclohexanol to gaseous products. In experiments with catalyst 2 this was evidenced by the amount of hydrogen larger by several per cent than would correspond to the amount of cyclohexanol formed, and by CO_2 and CO contents in gaseous products formed in the process (12).

In addition, under the conditions of dehydrogenation at 390°C free zinc distilled off together with vapours and gases and condensed in the form of a zinc mirror on the cooler walls of the glass reactor.

The activation energy (calculated from curve *2*, Fig. 6) decreased rapidly and in experiments 1–2 amounted to $E_{H_2} = 52.9$ kcal/mole; in experiments 2–3 to $E_{H_2} = 30.5$ kcal/mole; and, finally, in experiments 3–5 it dropped to $E_{H_2} = 15.5$ kcal/mole.

An analogous drop in activation energy has also been observed in the second series of experiments conducted at temperatures ranging from 325 to 405°C and in the third series at 350–450°C (Fig. 6, curve *2'* and curve *2"*).

The initial high activity of catalyst 2 (expressed in terms of reaction rate constant, K) decreased very rapidly, due to continuous changes in the catalyst surface. The reaction rate constant, K, decreased from the value of 1.46 (experiment 3) at 368°C almost tenfold to the value of 0.13 (experiment 19).

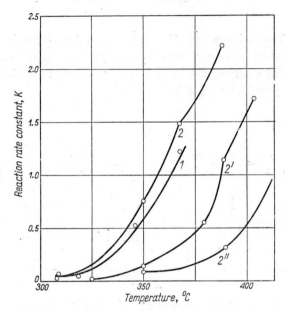

Fig. 6. Relation for rate constant of cyclohexanol dehydrogenation in the presence of: *1*—slowly chilled zinc–iron catalyst (12.5% Fe) after the first series of 19 experiments, *2*—fast chilled zinc–iron catalyst (12.8% Fe) during first three experiments, *2'*—fast chilled zinc–iron catalyst (12.8% Fe) during next three experiments, *2''*—fast chilled zinc–iron catalyst (12.8% Fe) during next three experiments.

In order to elucidate the cause underlying the different activities and stabilities of catalytic action of the two zinc–iron alloy catalysts of identical composition but chilled at different speeds, E. Treszczanowicz, B. Lipka and A. Jurewicz using the method of W. Tomassi, studied the behaviour of these catalysts used as powder electrodes in the standard cell (13).

It was anticipated that the application of this method would permit characterization of the surfaces in question by measuring the potential of the powder electrodes prepared from the alloys in question and investigation of the relation between this potential and the catalyst activity.

The measurements of the powder electrode potential were conducted in a standard cell by the following scheme:

		Aqueous	
(Pt) Zn, Fe	Ethanolic solution of KCl	saturated solution of KCl	Hg_2Cl_2, Hg

In the Tomassi method (14, 15), a powder electrode is used in potential measurements and consists of a platinum wire surrounded by a finely divided catalyst placed in a small test-tube (2 cm high and 5 mm in diameter) provided with a hole (Fig. 7).

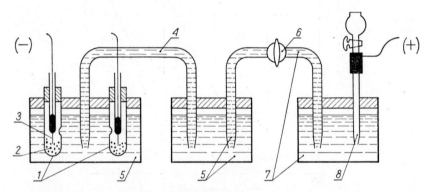

Fig. 7. Scheme of the apparatus for potentiometric measurements: *1*—electrodes, *2*—divided alloy, *3*—platinum outlet electrode, *4*—salt bridge filled with alcoholic solution of potassium chloride, *5*—alcoholic solution of potassium chloride, *6*—salt bridge with a closed cock, *7*—saturated solution of potassium chloride, *8*—calomel electrode.

The test-tube was inserted into a larger vessel containing an alcoholic concentrated solution of potassium chloride. This solution entered the test-tube through the hole and covered both the powder and the wire.

The divided catalyst strongly affected the small amount of the solution which filled the space between grains, thus altering the activity of ions.

The potential at the wire–electrolyte solution interface was considerably altered, due to interaction in the presence of the divided catalyst.

The measurements of powder electrode potentials have been made using a saturated calomel electrode as the reference electrode. The apparatus used is illustrated in Fig. 7.

Under these conditions the powder electrode potential equals numerically the electromotive force of the standard cell. The results of the measurements of the values of powder electrode potentials, rate constants, K, of cyclohexanol dehydrogenation at 350°C (given comparatively), activation energies, and the macrostructure of the two investigated catalysts of identical composition have been given in Table 2.

TABLE 2

PROPERTIES OF SOME CATALYSTS INVESTIGATED

No. of catalyst	Powder electrode potential, mV	Reaction rate constant at 350°C	Activation energy, kcal/mole	Metallographic structure	Remarks
Catalyst 1	− 790	0.6	41.3	Coarse-grained alloy. Eutectoid $\Gamma + \delta$	Permanent catalytic activity Constant powder electrode potential
Catalyst 2	−1018 − 830	0.74−0.07	52.9−15.5 (at the initial stage of action)	Fine-grained alloy. η- and γ-phases	Rapid drops of activity and powder electrode potential
Catalyst 3	− 981	Not determined	Not determined		Rapid drops of activity and powder electrode potential

E. Treszczanowicz, B. Lipka and A. Jurewicz have found a parallel relation between the value of the potential and the activity expressed in terms of reaction rate constant, K. Fast chilled alloy catalyst 2 exhibited a larger value of the powder electrode potential (−1018 mV) in comparison with slowly chilled alloy catalyst 1 (−790 mV).

The value of the potential decreased from −1018 to −860 mV after the reaction of dehydrogenation had continued for several hours.

Similarly, the activity of catalyst 2—reaction rate constant—decreased steadily (Fig. 6).

Thus, the existence of free zinc crystals or crystals rich in zinc in alloy catalyst 2, which exhibited non-selective action, manifested itself by a high powder electrode potential similar to that of pure zinc, −1070 mV

(Fig. 8). However, a considerably lower powder electrode potential and a stabilized activity at a somewhat lower level (0.6) than the initial activity of catalyst 2 (0.74) corresponded to mixed crystals appearing in slowly chilled alloy catalyst 1 of selective dehydrogenating action.

The potentiometric characteristics of each alloy gave a better insight into the structures and made it possible to establish differences between the two alloys of identical composition but different structures.

The value of powder electrode potential measurements has been checked on zinc–iron alloy catalyst 3 taken from industrial works (Table 2). These measurements resulted in the detection of crystals of free zinc, and the prediction of its non-selective behaviour in the dehydrogenation of cyclohexanol.

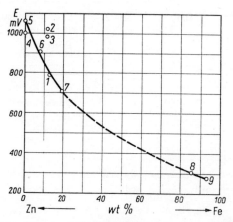

Fig. 8. Dependence of powder electrode potential on the iron content for slowly chilled zinc–iron alloys:

1—for a slowly chilled alloy, 2—for a fast chilled alloy, 3—for an alloy prepared at an industrial works in 1954, 4—for zinc, technical grade, 5—for zinc, reagent grade, 6, 7, 8, 9—for slowly chilled alloys of iron contents 8.4, 18.6, 83 and 93%, respectively.

Figure 8 shows the dependence of the powder electrode potential on iron content for zinc–iron alloys with the iron content ranging from 0 to 100%.

It should be noted that the alloy catalysts with the highest powder electrode potential exhibited activity even at lower temperatures. Catalysts 8 and 9 with the lowest powder electrode potential (−300 and −280 mV), on the other hand, exhibited a noticeable activity only at temperatures above 500°C. This was accompanied by such a high affinity of cyclohexanol to the alloy that the former was not only dehydrogenated but also decomposed into unsaturated hydrocarbons, carbon monoxide and carbon black, while the catalyst was converted into dust.

REFERENCES

1. Ciborowski S.: Badania nad kinetyką odwracalnej kontaktowej reakcji odwodor niania alkoholu izopropylowego. Doctoral thesis, Instytut Chemii Ogólnej, Warszawa, 1955.
2. Ciborowski S.: Étude de l'hydrogenation de l'acetone en alcool sopropylique et de deshydrogenation de l'alcool isopropylique en acetone, *Chemie Industrie*, 3, 240 (1958).
3. Bork A., *Z. Phys. Chem.*, **B33**, 443 (1958).
4. Hougen O. A., Watson K. M., *Ind. Eng. Chem.*, **35**, 529 (1943).
5. Hougen O. A., Watson K. M.: Chemical Process Principles, Part III. New York—London, 1947.
6. Frost A. V., *Vestn. Mosk. Univ.*, **2**, 55 (1958).
7. Agronomov A. E., *Vestn. Mosk. Univ.*, **6**, 109–123 (1951).
8. Bork A., Balandin A. A., *Z. Phys. Chem.*, **B33**, 54–72 (1936).
9. Bork A., Balandin A. A., *Z. Phys. Chem.*, **B33**, 435–442 (1936).
10. Sznajder J., Czerwińska B.: Badania nad kontaktami miedzianymi w reakcji od wodorniania cykloheksanolu. Part I. Kontakty szkieletowe typu Raneya. Wpływ sposobu przygotowania na działanie kontaktu, *Chemia Stosowana*, **3**, 399 (1959).
11. Sznajder J.: Untersuchung von Kupfer-Kontakten. Einfluss der Herstellungsmethode auf die katalytische Selektivität u. Aktivität. Sammelwerk—*Katalyse. Sonderheft*, 1959; *Bericht von der Hauptjahrestagung 1958. Chemische Gesellschaft*. Berlin.
12. Treszczanowicz E., *Przemysł Chem.*, 445 (1957).
13. Treszczanowicz E., Lipka B., Jurewicz A., *Chemia Stosowana*, **3**, 319 (1958).
14. Tomassi W., *Przemysł Chem.* 603 (1953).
15. Tomassi W., Libuś Z., *Przemysł Chem.*, 382 (1956).

X. THE MAGNETIC PROPERTIES AND STRUCTURE
OF SOME METALLIC CONTACTS

W. Trzebiatowski

The theory of heterogeneous catalysis may be considered from two aspects: (1) A. A. Balandin's theory of geometrical factor, and (2) the theory of electronic factor, the importance of which was realised and first applied to catalysis by Pisarzhevskii, Roginskii, Shul'ts (1928), and independently, and almost simultaneously, by Nyrop.

As a result of the development of the electronic structure of matter, it became possible to apply the basic principles to metals and semiconductors in their function as catalysts and to determine the electronic factors involved in chemical catalysis. Semiconductors are particularly suitable for investigation, since their electronic structure may change within wide and yet controlled limits. Using electrical conductivity measurements, thermoelectrical properties and the Hall effect, it is possible to determine the type and at the same time the electronic structure of a semiconductor, during its period of action as a catalyst. Many scientists have been engaged on this problem, and in particular the following should be mentioned: Roginskii, Vol'kenshtein, Dowden, Garner, Gray, Hauffe, Rienäcker, Schwab, and others. The investigations concerned the relationship between the electronic structure of the catalyst and its catalytic function. Most frequently used in these investigations are contacts of metals, bulk semiconductors, or thin layers of these substances evaporated *in vacuo*.

Metallic contacts supported on carriers, usually compounds such as SiO_2, Al_2O_3 and other oxides, are less suitable for investigation, as it is difficult to differentiate between the physical properties of a thin metallic layer and those of the support, i.e. the carrier. Besides, it cannot be assumed that a thin layer of metal supported on the carrier has the same electronic structure as the bulk metal.

Magnetic methods are suitable for investigations on similar contacts as they differentiate between the properties and electronic structure of the metal and the carrier, provided the metal and carrier differ sufficiently in their magnetic properties. Thus the most convenient objects for investigation are paramagnetic or ferromagnetic metals on diamagnetic carriers.

The magnetic methods applied for the examination of contact catalysts were introduced by P. W. Selwood (1) and consist in a proper use and interpretation of the basic Curie-Weiss law, valid for paramagnetic substances:

$$\chi = \frac{C}{T-\Theta}$$

The first investigations were carried out on paramagnetic ions of transition metals like Cr^{3+}, Mn^{4+} and others, supported on carriers like Al_2O_3. On the basis of magnetic measurements it was possible to determine the degree of oxidation of the metals for which an interesting effect of degree of oxidation induced by the carrier had been proved. By the application of the Weiss constant, it was also possible to infer the number of ions making up the island-like fragments adsorbed on the surface of the carrier. G. F. Hüttig (2), on the basis of measurements of magnetic properties, also proved interesting intermediate stages in the synthesis of ferrites from their components.

Particularly suitable for magnetic investigations are contacts with ferromagnetic metals possessing marked magnetic properties which may be observed even in very low concentrations. Thermomagnetic analysis is applied to the quantitative determination of the metals. As ferromagnetic properties are to a certain extent connected with the size of metal grain, the degree of dispersion of metal grains supported on the carrier may also be determined.

In the Soviet Union, the magnetic investigations of contacts, carried out by N. I. Kobozev et al. (3), were applied to very thin metallic layers on carriers. The results obtained were interpreted by the author as a confirmation of his own theory of catalysis, namely, the "assembly" theory.

The investigations, initiated at the Institute of Structural Researches of the Polish Academy of Sciences and at the 1st Department of Inorganic Chemistry at the Wrocław Technical University, aimed at the structure elucidation of the metallic layers supported on the carriers, as very little was known concerning their physical state, beyond the electron-microscopic and X-ray determinations of the geometrical grain size. The electronic structure of a thin metallic layer on the carrier as compared with the bulk metal may change under the influence of various factors which should be mentioned: (1) the action of the support, i.e. carrier, in close contact with the metal, (2) the effect of adsorbed gases, (3) the degree of disintegration. It was anticipated that the application of magneto-chemical methods, together with X-ray examinations, and determination of activity and specific surface, would reveal new data concerning the crystalline nature and electronic structure of metallic contacts on carriers.

The investigations were applied to paramagnetic palladium and platinum, ferromagnetic nickel, and more recently cobalt contacts on diamagnetic carriers like γ-Al_2O_3, and finally activated carbon. In the case of metals such as nickel and cobalt, their ferromagnetic properties also permit the determination of the degree of dispersion of the metal. These metals were chosen because their electronic structure in the atomic as well as in the bulk state is better known than it is for other metals.

Preparation of these contacts consisted in obtaining the γ-Al_2O_3 carrier free from ferromagnetic impurities and adsorbing onto it from a salt solution the required amount of metal also of the highest spectrographic purity, followed by reduction with hydrogen and degasification of the contacts in high vacuum.

In addition, the surface of the carrier was determined by the BET method with nitrogen, and the crystalline structure of the contacts was X-ray controlled by the use of powder cameras of normal size.

Palladium and platinum contacts (4, 5, 6). The results of magnetic measurements made on palladium contacts are in part presented in Table 1.

The results of X-ray examinations established that in the case of palladium in concentrations of 9.1—4.8% all the lines of palladium are visible, while with concentrations of 2.4 and 2.0% they are only partly visible, although in all these cases they corresponded to the lattice constants of the bulk metal of $a = 3.88$ Å. The remaining contacts show only weak lines of palladium. In platinum contacts of series I, with concentrations of 0.35—0.04%, it was not possible to find the lines of platinum. Also, in the case of series II, contacts with concentrations of 1.2 and 0.2% Pt show only the lines of the carrier.

The magnetic properties of palladium contacts show that the palladium contained in them is of lower magnetic susceptibility than bulk palladium. The magnetic susceptibility of palladium diminishes as the concentration of the metal in the contact decreases, so that at 2% Pd it is only $+0.03 \times 10^{-6}$ instead of $+5.17 \times 10^{-6}$ for the bulk metal. An explanation

TABLE 1

PALLADIUM CONTACTS

No.	Composition of sample	Coefficients of magnetic susceptibility			Sur-face area, m^2/g	Relative filling of surface with monoatomic layer of palladium
		$\chi \times 10^6$ measured	$\chi \times 10^6$ calculated additively	$\chi Pd \times 10^6$		
1	Pure carrier γ-Al$_2$O$_3$	−0.385	—	—	266	—
2	Powdered palladium	+5.17	—	+5.17	—	—
3	Mechanical mixture 5.6% Pd on γ-Al$_2$O$_3$	−0.07	−0.074	+5.2	—	—
4	9.1% Pd on γ-Al$_2$O$_3$	−0.06	+0.120	+3.2	120	0.1385
5	8.0% Pd on γ-Al$_2$O$_3$	−0.06	+0.059	+3.7	—	0.1203
6	7.0% Pd on γ-Al$_2$O$_3$	−0.22	+0.004	+2.0	—	0.1041
7	6.2% Pd on γ-Al$_2$O$_3$	−0.28	−0.041	+1.3	—	0.0914
8	4.8% Pd on γ-Al$_2$O$_3$	−0.36	−0.118	+0.1	164	0.0697
9	2.4% Pd on γ-Al$_2$O$_3$	−0.33	−0.252	+1.9	216	0.0340
10	2.0% Pd on γ-Al$_2$O$_3$	−0.37	−0.274	+0.03	195	0.0282

of this phenomenon cannot be found in the oxidation of palladium to PdO, nor in the hydrogen content, which—as known—causes considerable diminution of paramagnetism of palladium, as is shown by X-ray diagrams of contacts after careful degasification in high vacuum at 200°C for 20 hr. The concentration of hydrogen in palladium, which may cause the decrease of the susceptibility coefficient down to the observed value, would correspond to a high percentage of atomic hydrogen H, which in turn would induce the formation of a β-phase in the Pd–H system; this, however, is not supported by X-ray analysis.

The fact that palladium, especially in low concentrations, appears in the contact in the form of separate atoms, or some atomic complexes (assemblies according to Kobozev), may be accepted as a contributing factor. Although the decrease of susceptibility coefficient of palladium, which in the metallic state has the structure $d^{9.4} \cdot s^{0.6}$, and in the atomic state $d^{10} \cdot s^0$, being diamagnetic, could partly account for the phenomenon; this does not seem likely, as measurements of the nitrogen adsorption. proved that an increase in palladium concentration is accompanied by a considerable diminution of the proper surface of contact.

The dispersion of palladium in atomic or "assembly" form could cause only a small change of surface. Even in a concentration of 2% Pd, which in the case of a monoatomic layer occupies only 0.0282 of the total carrier surface, the presence of crystalline palladium can still be proved by X-ray analysis, showing that a greater part of the metal is in the form of crystalline complexes. These complexes partly block the capillary channels of γ-Al$_2$O$_3$, thus contributing to a diminution in the specific surface of contacts.

Palladium has a large thermionic work function of the order of 5 eV. Adsorption of hydrogen on thin layers of metals of this kind brings about a diminution of their electrical resistance (7), as a result of the transfer of electrons from hydrogen to the metal. Hydrogen at a temperature of 90°K, on a thin layer of nickel, for example, is so strongly adsorbed that at this temperature it cannot be pumped off. As palladium can be completely degasified at increased temperatures, this explanation is not only improbable, but may be definitely excluded, as the surface of metal contacts may be completely purified by bombardment with helium or argon ions.

Another possible explanation for the decrease of paramagnetism of palladium could be an increase in the ratio of surface atoms to the total number of atoms in the crystal. The surface atoms have specific attributes (Tamm), although at present there is no information on the magnetic properties of atoms of this kind.

Further, the interaction of metal with the carrier at the surface of contact, as well as the effect of the carrier on the electronic structure of metal, should be taken into account. It is known that metal, when contacted with a semiconductor of the n-type, can become an acceptor of electrons. However, as the electronic properties of γ-Al$_2$O$_3$ are not well known, it is difficult at present to state whether this interaction is significant or not. Experiments with semiconductors of the n-type, using zinc oxide as the carrier, are in progress and indicate that the activity practically disappears. This seems to confirm the belief that the carrier exerts a pronounced influence upon the properties of the metal.

Changes of the activity of contacts are also interesting. Palladium contacts with concentrations of 2% Pd exhibit an activity as high as 90.5% for benzene conversion. On the other hand, a contact with a concentration of 0.46% Pd shows only 13.0% activity. This is in keeping with the catalytic properties of nickel. P. Selwood found that the activity of a nickel contact rapidly decreases as the concentration of nickel is diminished.

The results of magnetic measurements on platinum contacts (5, 6) are different (Table 2).

TABLE 2

PLATINUM CONTACTS

No.	Composition of contact	Coefficients of magnetic susceptibility				Relative filling of carrier surface with monoatomic layer of Pt
		$\chi \times 10^6$ measured		$\chi \times 10^6$ calculated additively		
		Temperature, °C				
		18	−193	18	−193	
	Series I					
1	Pure carrier γ-Al$_2$O$_3$	−0.36	−0.35	—	—	(280 m²/g)
2	Pure platinum	+0.973	+1.083	—	—	—
3	9.7% Pt on γ-Al$_2$O$_3$	−0.26	−0.22	−0.23	−0.19	0.078
4	3.4% Pt on γ-Al$_2$O$_3$	−0.31	−0.29	−0.31	−0.28	0.026
5	1.4% Pt on γ-Al$_2$O$_3$	−0.34	−0.31	−0.34	−0.31	0.01
6	0.35% Pt on γ-Al$_2$O$_3$	−0.32	−0.30	−0.35	−0.32	0.0025
7	0.07% Pt on γ-Al$_2$O$_3$	−0.33	−0.30	−0.36	−0.33	0.0005
8	0.04% Pt on γ-Al$_2$O$_3$	−0.36	−0.33	−0.36	−0.33	0.0003
	Series II					
9	4.1% Pt on γ-Al$_2$O$_3$	−0.31	−0.28	−0.31	−0.27	0.031
10	2.5% Pt on γ-Al$_2$O$_3$	−0.33	−0.32	−0.33	−0.30	0.019
11	1.2% Pt on γ-Al$_2$O$_3$	−0.33	−0.30	−0.34	−0.31	0.0088
12	0.2% Pt on γ-Al$_2$O$_3$	−0.37	−0.34	−0.36	−0.33	0.0015

The investigations have established that even at high dilution of platinum in the surface layer no real difference in the magnetic properties of platinum is observed. In platinum contacts of both series I and II, the magnetic susceptibility of the platinum is practically unchanged in comparison with that of the bulk metal. Even if the platinum concentration is as low as 0.2—0.04%, resulting in only a small part of the carrier surface being covered, equal to 0.0015 in series II and 0.0005 and 0.0003 in series I, the susceptibility coefficient of the contact is within limits of experimental accuracy $\pm 0.03 \times 10^{-6}$, and this is in keeping with the susceptibility calculated additively on the basis of percentage platinum in the contact. The atomization of platinum, unlike that of palladium, is associated with greatly increased magnetic susceptibility, as platinum atoms possess the electronic structure $d^9 \cdot s^1$. By assuming only the spin moment, atomic platinum should at room temperature show a gram susceptibility of $+17.5 \times 10^{-6}$, while the gram susceptibility of metallic platinum is equal to $+0.97 \times 10^{-6}$.

On the basis of magnetic examinations, it may be concluded that crystalline platinum predominates in contacts even if the X-ray diagrams do not reveal a distinct crystalline structure. Platinum contacts belonging to series II and prepared by Kobozev's method are more fine-grained than the contacts of series I.

The results of these investigations do not, however, permit the term *superparamagnetism* to be applied to the phenomenon described by Kobozev (3) for examples of diluted platinum, silver and other contacts.

According to the data obtained by this author, a metal covering the carrier surface to only a small extent shows paramagnetic susceptibility increased by hundreds, and even thousands, of times. If the Kobozev effect were observed, then the susceptibility of platinum, e.g. in a sample with a degree of coverage of 0.0015 (series II), could have values from about 300×10^{-6} to about 3000×10^{-6}. The susceptibility of the sample would then increase from about $+0.2 \times 10^{-6}$ to about $+5.6 \times 10^{-6}$. The accuracy of the measurements ($\pm 0.03 \times 10^{-6}$) is quite sufficient to distinguish the susceptibilities from the additive value -0.36×10^{-6}. A comparison of these results with those on contacts with different degrees of coverage justifies the same conclusions.

Nickel and cobalt contacts (8). In the case of nickel and cobalt contacts the measurements of magnetic properties were used to determine their composition and texture, namely, (a) the contents of free metal, and (b) the degree of dispersion.

It is known that contacts after reducing with hydrogen sometimes contain, in addition to metal, considerable quantities of oxides. The reduction of the metal oxide in the contact is difficult, as at increased temperature oxides of nickel or cobalt can react with the carrier, forming compounds such as silicates or aluminates.

In order to determine the concentration of metal in a contact by the magnetic method, it is necessary to determine the saturation magnetization of the sample, and this is difficult in a ferromagnet, owing to the state of great dispersion. In this case a state of magnetic saturation is not reached even in a strong field, and extrapolation becomes necessary. Here the application of the empirical Heukelom (9) formula is necessary:

$$\frac{1}{\sigma} = \frac{1}{\sigma_\infty} + \frac{1}{(\alpha H)^{0.9}}$$

Plotting the dependence of $\dfrac{1}{\sigma}$ on $\dfrac{1}{H^{0.9}}$ and extrapolating the straight line to $\dfrac{1}{H^{0.9}} = 0$, the value $\dfrac{1}{\sigma_\infty}$ may be obtained for the contact.

At a temperature of 20°C for pure nickel $\sigma_\infty = 54.5$. Then the weight content of nickel in the contact is $\dfrac{\sigma_\infty \text{ of contact}}{\sigma_\infty \text{ of pure nickel}} \, 100.$

This method requires careful degasifying of the nickel contact, as the magnetization curve of a non-degasified contact shows lower values of the magnetization than a degasified contact of the same quantitative composition (Fig. 1).

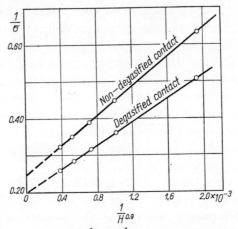

Fig. 1. Extrapolation in the system $\dfrac{1}{\sigma} - \dfrac{1}{H^{0.9}}$ in order to obtain the σ values (for the same sample).

Results of the determinations of nickel are presented in Table 3.

The results obtained by the magnetic method were verified by chemical analysis. Thus, with proper experimental arrangement, the volume of hydrogen evolved during solution of the contact sample in dilute sulphuric acid was measured, and the agreement of the results shows that both these methods are entirely satisfactory.

However, magnetic measurements of ferromagnetic contacts enable not only the determination of the concentration of the metal, but also the determination of the average dispersion of the metal. Heukelom and co-workers (9) had already noticed that the magnetization curve of a nickel contact can be, with good approximation, replaced by a straight line calculated according to the simplified Langevin formula for paramagnetic contacts

$$\frac{\sigma}{\sigma_\infty} = \frac{1}{3}\frac{\mu H}{RT}$$

TABLE 3
NICKEL CONTACTS

No. of sample	Total content of Ni, %	Time and temperature of reduction		Magnetization			Diameter of crystallite mean, Å	Content of Ni calculated from σ_∞, %	Content of metallic Ni (chemically determined), %	Degree of transition of C_6H_6 into C_6H_{12}, %
		hr	°C	Degasified contact, σ_∞	Non-degasified contact, σ_∞	μd				
1	20	6	400	8.00	—	4.70×10^{-17}	55.5	14.7	14.3	94
2	20	2	400	9.62	9.10	6.62×10^{-17}	62.0	17.6	15.6	85.5
3	20	6	350	6.67	5.55	3.90×10^{-17}	52.0	12.3	12.1	83.5
4	20	2	350	7.15	—	5.90×10^{-17}	60.0	13.1	12.9	87.0
5	20	6	300	5.00	4.80	8.77×10^{-17}	69.0	9.18	9.40	77.0
6	20	2	300	4.70	4.47	1.01×10^{-17}	72.0	8.60	8.26	70.5
7	10	6	400	4.72	—	3.61×10^{-17}	50.5	8.66	7.13	93
8	10	2	400	2.32	—	2.72×10^{-17}	46.0	4.27	3.7	85
9	10	6	350	3.23	2.70	2.51×10^{-17}	45	5.93	4.8	98
10	10	2	350	2.90	2.20	2.48×10^{-17}	45	5.3	5.0	83
11	10	6	300	1.59	1.45	3.97×10^{-17}	52.1	2.92	2.92	91
12	5	6	400	1.67	1.67	3.15×10^{-17}	48.5	3.07	3.00	—
13	2	6	400	0.50	0.48	2.97×10^{-17}	48	0.92	0.7	34
14	2	6	400	0.43	0.41	3.94×10^{-17}	52	0.80	—	38

This possibility results from the fact that the influence of a magnetic field upon small particles of a ferromagnetic contact resembles its interaction with molecules or paramagnetic ions. The thermal excitation of very small particles of a ferromagnetic contact, of the order of 10^{-7}cm, counteracts the directing action of the field. Therefore, complete orientation is only attainable in very strong fields, and hence the necessity of extrapolation to $H = \infty$. However, under the experimental conditions used, the above approximation is not sufficiently accurate. Thus, the calculation of the μ value, i.e. the magnetic moment of a single nickel crystal, significant for obtaining the data necessary for calculation of its diameter, has been based on a new principle.

The Langevin function

$$\frac{\sigma}{\sigma_\infty} = \coth \frac{\mu H}{kT} - \frac{kT}{\mu H}$$

for $\frac{\mu H}{kT} < \pi$ can be expanded in an exponential series:

$$\frac{\sigma}{\sigma_\infty} = \frac{\mu H}{3kT} - \frac{1}{45} \left(\frac{\mu H}{kT} \right)^3 + \frac{2}{945} \left(\frac{\mu H}{kT} \right)^5 - \frac{1}{4125} \left(\frac{\mu H}{kT} \right)^7 + \dots$$

For $\frac{\mu H}{kT} < 1$ only an insignificant error is made by omitting exponential terms beyond the first one, which leads to the above relation. These terms cannot be omitted—without making a significant error—when $\frac{\mu H}{kT} > 1$, which is the case here. So in order to obtain the value of μ, magnetization curves must be approximated by the complete Langevin function. When computing, there arises a difficulty, namely, that the value of μ is unknown, while the values of $\frac{\sigma}{\sigma_\infty}$, H and T are known. With these data it is impossible to solve the above equation for μ. Therefore, in order to find μ, a method of successive approximation was used. For this purpose, to determine the points of the magnetization curve, known values of $\frac{\sigma}{\sigma_\infty}$ were substituted in the equation

$$\frac{\sigma}{\sigma_\infty} = \coth \frac{\mu H}{kT} - \frac{kT}{\mu H}$$

while for the value of the argument coth the zero approximation $\frac{\mu H}{kT} \approx 3 \frac{\sigma}{\sigma_\infty}$ was substituted at first. In the expression $\frac{kT}{\mu H}$ μ was treated as unknown. The value of μ computed from this equation was substituted in the function $\cot \frac{\mu H}{kT}$, and the expression $\frac{kT}{\mu H}$ was again treated as unknown. By repeating this operation several times successively more accurate values of μ were obtained. Finally, the difference between successive values was so small that they could be regarded as accurate. Similar accuracy of results was attained by graphical solution of the Langevin equation for μ.

The Langevin function, based on μ values calculated in this manner, cannot, however, exactly express the whole magnetization curve, because nickel particles of different sizes will have different values of μ. In order to determine these values, μ should be calculated for other, possibly distant, points on the magnetization curve using the same Langevin function. For this purpose, the value of μ was calculated for other limiting values of $\dfrac{\sigma}{\sigma_\infty}$ obtained at a field intensity $H = 6500$ Oe. In Fig. 2 diagrams of the Langevin function calculated for both the values of μ are presented, together with experimental magnetization curves for comparison. From these diagrams it can be seen that, in the range of magnetic fields from 1000 to 6000 Oe, the Langevin curves are a good approximation to the experimental magnetization curves of the contacts examined.

Dividing the value of μ by 0.61 Bohr magnetons, the atomic moment of ferromagnetic Ni gives 5.6×10^{-21} e.s.u. From this figure the number of nickel atoms in a single crystallite, and thus the approximate size of a crystallite, can be easily calculated. In the above example, the number of atoms in a crystal is $\dfrac{6.06 \times 10^{-17}}{5.6 \times 10^{-21}} = 10,800.$

Assuming a spherical shape, the diameter of a crystal can be computed. The volume occupied by one atom of nickel in the metal is 11 Å^3, and the volume of a crystal is $10,800 \times 11 = 119,000$ Å^3:

$$r = 0.620 \sqrt[3]{V} = 0.620 \sqrt[3]{0.119} \times 10^2 \,\text{Å} = 30.5 \,\text{Å}; \ d = 61 \,\text{Å}$$

In Table 4 the results of calculations of the diameters of nickel crystallites for reduced contact samples within different periods and at different temperatures are presented. These values have been calculated on the basis of limiting points of the magnetization curve, corresponding to field intensities of $H = 1050$ Oe and $H = 6500$ Oe.

It should be added that the above calculations are based on apparent magnetization curves of contacts. In expressing the dependence of magnetization on the intensity of the external field, the demagnetizing field was ignored. As is known, the demagnetizing field is proportional to the magnetization I (or σ). In this connection, for contacts with the greatest magnetization (20% Ni reduced within 6 hr at 400°C) the internal field was

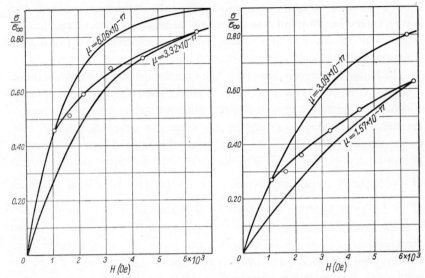

Fig. 2a. Comparison of experimental magnetization curve with Langevin curves drawn on the basis of moments computed from limiting points of the experimental curve regarding contact I (20% Ni) reduced within 6 hr at temperature 400°C.

Fig. 2b. Comparison of experimental magnetization curve with Langevin curves drawn on the basis of moments computed from limiting points of the experimental curve regarding contact II (10% Ni) reduced within 6 hr at temperature 350°C.

estimated by assuming a demagnetization coefficient of $4\pi/3$, corresponding to a spherical shape of the sample (samples of contacts for magnetization measurements had approximately spherical shape). The corrected magnetization curve thus obtained was somewhat different, but the diameters of the crystallites computed on this basis differed only by about 5–6% from diameters obtained on the basis of apparent magnetization curves. Values computed from magnetization curves corrected in this way are shown in parentheses in the first line of Table 4.

At lower concentrations of Ni, the contacts have a correspondingly lower magnetization, and so the demagnetizing field diminishes, with the result that the difference between the real and apparent magnetization curves also decreases, so that finally the dimensions of crystallites differ only insignificantly. Therefore, in the case of the remaining contacts with lower concentrations of nickel these differences have not been taken into consideration and are not shown in Table 4.

The above results are based on an approximation, but it seems that they correspond to the dimensions of the crystals. For nickel contacts on carriers, the computed values of diameters are in agreement with those reported by other investigators, whose results were obtained from X-ray measurements or from measurements of the surface of the metal. For example, for the contact Ni/Al_2O_3 Rubinshtein (10) gives the dimensions of crystals as varying from 40 to 130 Å, depending on the manner of preparation of the contact. Similar results (40–80 Å) were obtained by Dupont and Piganiol (11) for primary crystals of skeletal nickel.

The X-ray diagrams obtained for a contact containing 14% of metallic Ni with a total Ni concentration of 20% showed a remarkable diffusion of the diffraction lines of Ni. This qualitatively confirms the above results. In these diagrams only the first four lines of Ni, corresponding to the planes (111, 200, 220 and 311), and the two most intense lines of γ-Al_2O_3,

TABLE 4
DIMENSIONS OF Ni CRYSTALLITES (DIAMETERS IN Å)

Time and temperature of reduction		1050 Oe	6500 Oe	Mean
hr	°C			
		contacts with 20% Ni concentration		
6	400	61 (66)	50 (53)	55.5 (59.5)
2	400	68	56.5	62
6	350	57.5	47	52
2	350	67.5	52	60
6	300	72.5	65	69
2	300	78	66.5	72
		contacts with 10% Ni concentration		
6	400	57.5	47.5	50.5
2	400	51	41	46
6	350	48	39	43.5
6	350	50	40	45
2	350	56	45	50.5
2	350	49	41	45
6	300	57	48	52.5
2	300	61.5	50.5	56
		contacts with 5% Ni concentration		
6	400	53.5	43.5	48.5
6	400	56.5	48	52
		contacts with 2% Ni concentration		
6	400	52	44	48
6	400	58	47	52

corresponding to interplanar distances of 2.39 and 1.39 Å, were visible. At smaller concentrations of Ni the X-ray pictures were illegible.

The determination of the sizes of metallic grains in catalysts by the above magnetic method can be used as well for the examination of cobalt contacts. In the case of cobalt supported on active carbon results have been obtained (12) confirming the similarity between the diameters of cobalt grains and those of nickel catalysts. Also, the reduction process of cobalt oxides on carbon proceeds more easily than on γ-Al$_2$O$_3$. This is undoubtedly connected with the fact that the carrier does not possess the ability to form chemical compounds with metallic oxides.

REFERENCES

1. Selwood P. W., *Advances in Catalysis*, **3**, 28 (1951); *ibid.*, **8**, 93 (1957).
2. Hüttig G. F.: Handbuch der Katalyse. G. M. Schwab. Vol. VI. Wien, 1943.
3. Kobozev N. I., Evdokimov V. B., Zubovich I. A., Maltsev A. N., *Zh. Fiz. Khim.* **26**, 1349 (1952).
4. Trzebiatowski W., Kubicka H., Śliwa A., *Roczn. Chem.*, **31**, 497 (1957).
5. Trzebiatowski W., Kubicka H., *Bull Acad. Polon. Sci.*, *Classe III*, **5**, 429 (1957).
6. Trzebiatowski W., Kubicka H., *Roczn. Chem.*, **32**, 3 (1958).
7. Suhrmann R., Schulz K.: *Z. Phys. Chem.*, **1**, 69 (1954).
8. Trzebiatowski W., Romanowski W., *Roczn. Chem.*, **31**, 1123 (1957).
9. Heukelom W., Broeder I. I., van Reijen L. L., *J. Chim. Phys.*, **51**, 474 (1954).
10. Rubinshtein A. M., *Izv. Akad. Nauk SSSR*, 815 (1938).
11. Dupont G., Piganiol P., *Bull. Soc. Chim. France, Ser. V*, **6**, 322 (1939).
12. Romanowski W., *Roczn. Chem.*, **34**, 239 (1960).

XI. THE USE OF CATALYTIC REACTIONS INVOLVING HYDROGEN PEROXIDE IN THE STUDY OF THE FORMATION OF COMPLEXES AND IN THE DEVELOPMENT OF VERY SENSITIVE ANALYTICAL METHODS

K. B. YATSIMIRSKII

For many years the author has been investigating catalytic reactions involving hydrogen peroxide and occurring in acidic media. One of these is the oxidation of an iodide by hydrogen peroxide in an acidic medium according to the empirical equation:

$$H_2O_2 + 2I^- + 2H^+ = 2H_2O + I_2 \tag{1}$$

The kinetics of this reaction has been studied by many scientists (1,2), who have found that the rate of evolution of iodine is expressed by the equation:

$$\frac{d[I_2]}{dt} = k[H_2O_2][I^-] \tag{2}$$

The value of the rate constant, k, depends on the pH of the solution and at a pH of 0.8 it equals 3.7.

Reaction (1) is catalysed by compounds of iron(III), elements of the middle group of the Periodic System, such as Zr, Nb, Mo, Ta and W, and also, apparently, by hafnium compounds.

The author, together with L. P. Raizman, V. I. Rigin and G. A. Karacheva, has studied the kinetics of catalytic reactions of type (1) involving compounds of the elements mentioned above* and has found that, if compounds of molybdenum, tungsten, tantalum and iron are used, the rate of reaction (1) may be expressed by the equation:

$$\frac{d[I_2]}{dt} = \varkappa' C_M [H_2O_2][I^-] \tag{3}$$

---

* A part of this work has been published in *Zh. Anal. Khim.* and in *Zh. Neorgan. Khim.*

[201]

where:

C_M = over-all concentration of compounds of the metals mentioned above, and

$\varkappa'$ = catalytic coefficient.

The values of the catalytic coefficient, $\varkappa'$, expressed in mole$^{-2}\cdot$litre$^{-2}\cdot$minute^{-1}, for a molybdenate, tungstate, and tantalum and iron salts are 1.4×10^3, 1.0×10^8, 0.8×10^7 and 1.1×10^6, respectively, in a solution of pH = 0.8. The rate of the reaction (1) in the presence of zirconium compounds (zirconium chloride) may be expressed by the equation:

$$\frac{d[I_2]}{dt} = \varkappa C_{Zr}[I^-] \qquad (4)$$

The value of $\varkappa$ is equal to 4×10^3 mole$^{-1}\cdot$litre$\cdot$minute^{-1}.

It follows from Eqs. (3) and (4) that the rate of the reaction (1) in the presence of catalysts depends linearly on their concentrations. The rate of reaction (1) may easily be measured by following the changes in the optical density of an iodine–starch solution. The measurements may be carried out by means of a photoelectric colorimeter or a Pulfrich photometer.

The optical density of a solution containing hydrogen peroxide (0.001 mole per litre), potassium iodide (2×10^{-4} mole per litre), hydrochloric acid (approximately 0.1 mole) and starch, may in the presence of catalysts undergo considerable changes even after the first 10 minutes. Since the molar coefficient of adsorption of iodized starch is quite considerable, the rate of reaction (1) may be measured for very slight changes in concentrations of starting substances, and therefore the linear dependence of optical density on time may be followed. Tangents of the angles of the slopes of optical density vs. time curves are proportional to the rate of reaction (1), and therefore proportional to the concentrations of compounds of elements—catalysts—in solution.

The author has used this dependence in the development of new, very sensitive, methods for the determination of molybdenum (3), tungsten (4), iron (5), tantalum and zirconium. Determinations are carried out by means of a very simple calibrated graph: tangent of the angle of the slopes of an optical density vs. time curve—axis of ordinates; and concentration of the ion being determined—axis of abscissae. This method permits the determination of concentrations of molybdenum and tungsten of the order of 10^{-8} mole per litre, tantalum 10^{-7} mole per litre, and iron and zirconium 10^{-7} mole per litre.

In the presence of a large excess of phosphate, arsenate, oxalate and tartrate, the catalytic action of molybdic acid disappears completely. It is known that the anions mentioned above form complex compounds with molybdic acid. As these compounds show no catalytic activity, it has been possible to study the formation of complexes in solutions of molybdic acid. This section of the work has been carried out in collaboration with I. I. Alekseeva (6).

The over-all concentration of molybdic acid in a solution is known from analytical data. The concentration of the free molybdic acid is determined from the graph mentioned above. The difference between the over-all concentration of molybdic acid and the concentration of the free acid is the total concentration of complex compounds. If the ratio of the over-all concentration of the acid to the concentration of the free acid is determined in the presence of varying concentrations of a co-ordinate group such as phosphate, arsenate, etc., the concentration of the complexes formed and their stability may be determined. In this way, we have proved that compounds of the composition $MoO_2C_2O_4$, $MoO_2C_4H_4O_6$, $HMoO_2AsO_4$, $HMoO_2PO_4$ and $H_4MoO_2PO_4$ exist in solution.

The author and G. A. Karacheva, using a similar method, have studied complex compounds of iron(III) with ethylenediaminetetraacetate ($Edta^{4-}$). The formation of the compound $FeEdta^-$ has been detected and its lability constant determined.

Molybdic acid does not form complex compounds with ethylenediaminetetraacetate at a pH of 1. This fact has been used by the author and I. I. Alekseeva to develop a method for the determination of small amounts of molybdenum in iron alloys.

Catalytic activities of various hydrolytic products of compounds of the same element are different. This may be found for zirconium compounds, the hydrolysis of which is very slow, and, therefore, at a pH of 1 the rate of the catalytic reaction (1) in solution is dependent on the acidity at which these compounds were maintained before hydrolysis.

In complete agreement with data found in the literature, we obtained the same catalytic coefficient for all the solutions of zirconium salts, which withstood the action of hydrochloric acid solutions of concentrations above 1 mole per litre. For solutions of zirconium salts in hydrochloric acid of concentrations lower than 1 mole per litre, the catalytic coefficient decreased accordingly. Consequently, in the case of zirconium salts not only the over-all zirconium content but also the contents of their various hydrolytic products may be determined by means of a kinetic method.

The data thus obtained have enabled us to draw certain conclusions concerning the mechanism of the catalytic oxidation of iodide by hydrogen peroxide. The equations given above support the view that the first stage of the catalytic oxidation involves the formation of a complex between hydrogen peroxide and a catalyst fragment:

$$M + H_2O_2 \rightleftarrows MH_2O_2 \tag{5}$$

where:

M = catalyst fragment predominant in the solution (MoO_2^{2+}, ZrO^{2+}, Fe^{3+}, etc.).

The concentration of the complex MH_2O_2 is related to the over-all concentration of fragments $M(C_M)$ by means of the following simple equation:

$$[MH_2O_2] = C_M \frac{\beta \cdot [H_2O_2]}{1 + \beta[H_2O_2]} \tag{6}$$

where:

β = equilibrium constant for reaction (5) (stability constant for the complex MH_2O_2).

If the product $\beta \cdot [H_2O_2]$ is large (high H_2O_2 concentration, stable MH_2O_2 complex), then $\beta \cdot [H_2O_2] \gg 1$ and

$$[MH_2O_2] = C_M \tag{6a}$$

If, however, the product $\beta \cdot [H_2O_2]$ is small (low H_2O_2 concentration, labile MH_2O_2 complex), then $\beta \cdot [H_2O_2] \ll 1$ and

$$[MH_2O_2] = C_M \cdot \beta[H_2O_2] \tag{6b}$$

Relation (6a) has been observed by us for zirconium salts; on the other hand, relation (6b) holds true for reactions involving molybdic and tungstic acids, and iron(III) and tantalum compounds.

In Eq. (4) $\varkappa$ expresses the actual rate constant and in Eq. (3) the conditional rate constant

$$\varkappa' = \varkappa \cdot \beta \tag{7}$$

Since all the catalysts mentioned are substances with marked acidic properties, their affinity for OH^- is large and, consequently, the dissociation of hydrogen peroxide in the complex MH_2O_2 is facilitated according to the equation:

$$H_2O_2 = OH^- + OH^+ \tag{8}$$

OH$^+$ ions formed immediately react with the iodide according to the equation:

$$I^- + OH^+ = IOH \tag{9}$$

IOH may immediately oxidize the next iodide molecule or initiate a series of reactions:

$$IOH + H^+ = I^+ + H_2O \tag{10}$$

$$I^+ + H_2O_2 = IOH + OH^+ \tag{11}$$

$$OH^+ + I^- = IOH \tag{9}$$

Chain termination may result from the direct interaction of I$^+$ and I$^-$ ions.

The chain mechanism is also supported by very large values of the catalytic coefficient, $\varkappa$, in Eq. (3).

In addition to reaction (1), the author and E. F. Naryshkina have investigated the kinetics of the catalytic oxidation of thiosulphate to sulphate in acetic acid. This reaction takes place according to the empirical equation:

$$4H_2O_2 + S_2O_3^{2-} = 3H_2O + 2SO_4^{2-} + 2H^+ \tag{12}$$

The rate of the reaction, catalysed by many elements (7) situated in the middle of the Periodic System, may be measured by a phototurbidimetric method. Barium chloride and gelatine are added to the solution containing thiosulphate, hydrogen peroxide and acetic acid, the gelatine being added to stabilize the suspension of BaSO$_4$. A detailed description of the method of measurement has been published (8).

The catalysis of reaction (12) involving tungsten, vanadium and molybdenum compounds has been studied and it was found that, in a very general case, the rate of reaction (12) may be expressed by the equation:

$$\frac{d[SO_4^{2-}]}{dt} = \varkappa \frac{\beta \cdot [H_2O_2]}{1 + \beta \cdot [H_2O_2]} \cdot C_M \cdot C_{S_2O_3^{2-}} \tag{13}$$

Similarly, as before, the values of the catalytic coefficient, $\varkappa$, are large, but the mechanism of the oxidation of thiosulphate differs from that of the oxidation of iodide. This is evidenced by the fact that reaction (12) is catalysed by titanium and vanadium compounds which show no catalytic activity for reaction (1).

It follows from Eq. (13), however, that in this case as well a complex compound between the catalyst and a molecule of hydrogen peroxide is formed.

The appli cation of reaction (12) provides a quantitative determination of molybdenum, tungsten and vanadium at concentrations of the order of 10^{-8} mole. However, the reproducibility of results is less reliable than the previous method, due to defects in the phototurbidimetric method used.

REFERENCES

1. Noyes A. A., Scott W. O., *J. Phys. Chem.*, **18**, 118 (1895).
2. Bell F., Jill R., *J. Phys. Colloid. Chem.*, **55**, 874 (1951).
3. Yatsimirskii K. B., Afanas'eva L. P., *Zh. Anal. Khim.*, **11**, 319 (1956).
4. Yatsimirskii K. B., Rigin V. I., *Zh. Anal. Khim.*, **13**, 112 (1958).
5. Yatsimirskii K. B., Karacheva G. A., *Zh. Neorgan. Khim.*, **3**, 352 (1956).
6. Yatsimirskii K. B., Alekseeva I. I., *Zh. Neorgan. Khim.*, **1**, 952 (1956).
7. Komarovskii A. S., Shapiro M. I., *Microchim. Acta*, **3**, 144 (1938).
8. Yatsimirskii K. B., Naryshkina E. F., *Zh. Neorgan. Khim.*, **3**, 346 (1958).

XII. FORMATION AND SIGNIFICANCE OF SOLID PHASE NUCLEI IN THERMAL DISSOCIATION PROCESSES

S. Bretsznajder

Many catalysts used in industrial contact processes are obtained by the thermal dissociation of solid compounds, e.g. by the decomposition of carbonates, hydroxides, oxalates, sulphates, sulphites, hydrated salts, etc. The nature of the dissociation process determines the structure and also the catalytic properties of the product obtained.

Therefore, the knowledge of the mechanism of a reaction of the type

$$A(s) \rightleftarrows B(s) + C(g)$$

where (s) is a solid and (g) is a gas, is very important in understanding the origin and the action of many solid catalysts (1).

The start of a reaction of the type considered is the formation of nuclei of a new solid phase (product) in the solid phase of a reactant. The mechanism of formation of the nuclei of a new phase is known only for the simple cases of formation of liquid drops in a vapour and vapour bubbles in a liquid, and crystallization from alloys and solutions.

In the case considered, the formation of nuclei involving the transformation of a solid crystalline phase into another solid phase, associated with a rearrangement of the crystal lattice, the mechanism is very complex. By the use of statistical physics interesting attempts have been made to treat the problem mathematically (2).

Unfortunately, insufficient experimental evidence was available at the time to evaluate the results based on simplified assumptions.

A few years ago, during the Bunsengesellschaft Meeting held in 1952 and during the Industrial Engineering Chemistry Symposium held in 1959, both dedicated to the problems of nuclei formation in new phases, the lecturers stated that, even in the simplest cases of topochemical reactions of the type

$$A(s) \rightleftarrows B(s)$$

(recrystallizations and polymorphic transformations), the mechanism of nuclei formation was unknown (3).

[207]

In an analysis of the extensive experimental material relating to the kinetics of thermal dissociation reactions and reverse reactions, reported in past work conducted jointly with Professor J. Zawadzki and also in later publications by the author, an interesting regularity has been observed, which may suggest the mechanism of solid nuclei formation in reactions involving solid reactants and products, such as the reactions of polymorphic transformations, thermal dissociation, reduction, etc.

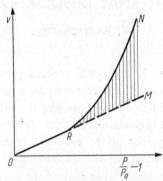

Fig. 1. Dependence of the rate, v, of a reaction of the type: $A(s) \rightleftarrows B(s) + C(g)$ on the distance from the equilibrium position $(P/P_0 - 1)$. The relation for the rate of the reaction occurring on the interface between solid phases A and B is expressed by the straight line OM. The hatched area MNR corresponds to the increase in rate due to the formation of nuclei of a new phase.

Thus, in analysing the shapes of curves for the dependence of reaction rates on the distance from the equilibrium point (Fig. 1), the assumption has been made that a formed nucleus of a new phase always increases to a definite size and then (due to the difference in sizes of elementary cells of the lattices of the reactant and the product) a separation of a small crystal of the product from the lattice of the reactant follows. After splitting off, the crystal stops functioning as a nucleus, the process of the nucleus formation starts again and the reaction rate observed should be proportional to the rate, i.e. the frequency of formation, J, of nuclei.

The analysis of results from experiments performed according to this assumption led to the establishment of the important fact (4,5) that the logarithm of J, i.e. the number of crystalline nuclei of the solid phase product formed from a solid phase reactant per unit time, was proportional to the reciprocal of the square of the logarithm of supersaturation (Fig. 2)

$$\log J' = -A \frac{1}{\log^2 \frac{P}{P_0}}$$

It appears, therefore, that this very complex case of nuclei formation, accompanied simultaneously by a transformation of crystalline lattice belonging to different types and differing by the size of elementary cells, is governed by the same simple laws which are valid in the formation of a nucleus as a minute drop during the condensation of supersaturated

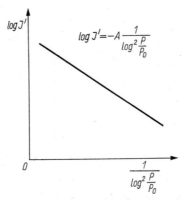

Fig. 2. Dependence of the rate of formation, J, of nuclei on the degree of supersaturation, $\dfrac{P}{P_0}$.

steam. But in this simple case, the cause of nucleus formation is known, namely, the existence of random density fluctuations resulting in the accumulation, in certain parts of the system, of a number of particles (molecules) sufficiently large to form nuclei. Consequently, a new and important conclusion may be drawn to the effect that, also in this general case of a reaction of the type ·

$$A(s) + C(g) \rightleftarrows B(s) + D(g) + \cdots$$

the formation of a nucleus of a new solid phase is determined by random fluctuations resulting in the accumulation, in certain parts of a solid phase reactant, of a number of particles sufficiently large to form a crystalline nucleus of the product. It is reasonable and justified to base the conclusion on the analogy furnished by the case quoted.

The next step was to determine which particles of the crystalline lattice of the reactant are mobile and, due to fluctuations, may accumulate in certain parts of the lattice to give rise to conditions favouring the transformation of a part of the reactant lattice into a nucleus—a crystal of the product lattice.

Certain observations mentioned previously in the work reported jointly with Professor Zawadzki (6,7) proved useful in providing a solution to this problem. In systems of the type under consideration, consisting of two solid phases (reactant and product) and a gaseous phase, the system is univariant, i.e. according to the phase rule, a definite and unvarying decomposition pressure of gas corresponds to a definite temperature.

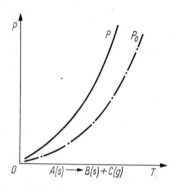

Fig. 3. Decomposition pressures, P, in the initial stage of the thermal dissociation of reactant A when a very small amount of gas C (pressure curve P is above equilibrium pressure curve P_0) is evolved.

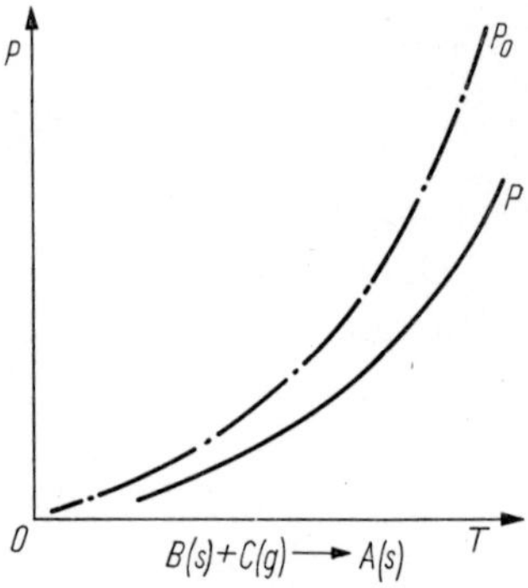

Fig. 4. Decomposition pressures, P, in the initial stage of a reaction reverse to thermal decomposition, when a very small amount of gas is absorbed (pressure curve P is below equilibrium pressure curve P_0).

It has been found that in the initial stage of a dissociation reaction, when a small amount of gas, corresponding to a surface covering of the reactant with several layers of gas molecules, is evolved (or bound in the case of a reverse reaction) and when nuclei of a new solid phase product are no longer formed, constant equilibrium pressures are observed. In dissociations they are higher than the usual equilibrium pressures (Fig. 3), and lower when reverse reactions occur (Fig. 4).

This behaviour is typical of systems where solid solutions of limited solubility appear; therefore, by simplification it might be assumed that the stage preceding the formation of a new solid phase, in processes under consideration, is the formation of solid solutions of a very limited solubility of the product in the reactant. This, however, lacks precision. (The behaviour described is typical, for example, of a CaO–CaCO$_3$ system where, according to accurate studies recently conducted, no formation of solid solutions (8) has been observed.)

Taking account of the fact that abnormal pressures are observed only when the amount of the gas evolved (or bound) is barely sufficient to cover

the surface with one or two layers of gas molecules, it should be assumed
that this is the superficial formation of solid solutions by chemisorption
involving the penetration (Fig. 5) of gas molecules into one or, at the
most, some upper layers of the crystal lattice in the case of the reaction

$$B(s) + C(g) \rightarrow A(s)$$

or (Fig. 6) the vacating of some cells of the reactant lattice by molecules C
in the case of the reaction

$$A(s) \rightarrow B(s) + C(g)$$

This process has been illustrated in Figs. 5 and 6 by reaction
$CaO + CO_2 \rightleftarrows CaCO_3$.

In no case do lattice transformations occur, since nuclei of a new
solid phase have not yet been formed.

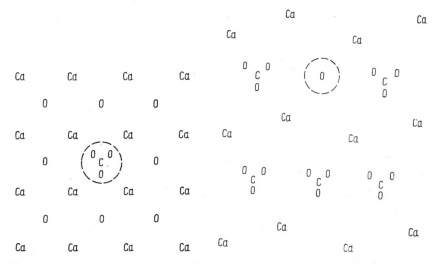

Fig. 5. Lattice microdefect: CO_2 in the   Fig. 6. Lattice microdefect: CO_2 has
CaO lattice.   vacated one of the elementary cells of the
CaCO_3 lattice.

Crystals with elementary cells containing foreign ions or atoms, or,
conversely, crystals with some vacant lattice points, are well known. These
irregularities, called lattice microdefects, appear very frequently in crystals.
It should be assumed that the formation of lattice microdefects is an essential stage in the formation of the nuclei of a new crystalline solid phase

It is known that, due to thermal vibrations of ions or atoms in lattice
points, microdefects are mobile (especially in the range of thermal dissoc-

iation) and readily shift their positions in the lattice. Therefore, fluctuations are also possible, i.e. temporary random accumulation of microdefects in some areas of the surface of a crystal. Based on the analogy with known simple phenomena of nuclei formation, it should be assumed that the condition for nucleus formation of a new crystalline phase of the product from a crystalline phase of the reactant is the accumulation, in a certain area of the surface of the reactant, of a sufficiently large number of microdefects having the composition of the product.

The number of microdefects should be sufficient to allow the energy, liberated due to the transformation of the reactant lattice into the product lattice, to be capable of equilibrating the work used in producing strains resulting from the differences in the dimensions of elementary cells of the reactant and the product (Fig. 7).

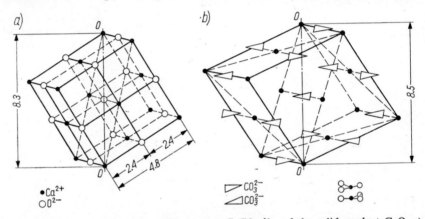

Fig. 7. Elementary cells of the solid reactant $CaCO_3$ b) and the solid product CaO a) in the reaction of thermal dissociation of $CaCO_3$.

Due to the presence of these mechanical strains in a lattice (sometimes, due to certain analogies and tendencies to excessive simplification of the phenomena, erroneously called "surface tension of the nucleus") and due to the small sizes of nuclei, the decomposition pressure of a system containing nuclei differs from the usual decomposition pressure of the system.

As has been found in investigations performed together with Professor Zawadzki (6,7), the pressure of such a system containing nuclei is lower during a thermal decomposition than the usual equilibrium pressure (Fig. 8), and, conversely, it is higher during a reverse reaction (Fig. 9). The differences may be enormous and approach several dozens per cent of the usual values; they decrease with time as the system recrystasllizes (e.g. within several dozens of hours), tending to the usual values of the decomposition pressures.

Langmuir (9) has shown that the reactions under consideration proceed most readily at the interface of a solid reactant and a solid product. Therefore, after a nucleus is formed, it first of all would build up, since the free energy of change for the formation of new nuclei is many times higher than the free energy of change for the same amount of the reactant at the interface.

However, as the small crystal formed builds up in the bulky reactant crystal, mechanical strains resulting from the differences in lattice sizes increase, so that, on having built up to a definite limiting size, the small crystal must split off from the reactant crystal (according to Dankov (10), the lattice deformation due to strains may not exceed 9–10%).

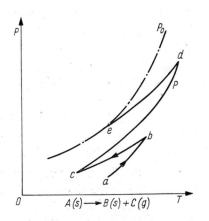

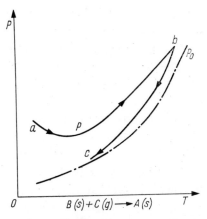

Fig. 8. Decomposition pressures, P, over a system subjected to thermal dissociation and containing a large number of nuclei of a solid phase product on heating ($a \to b$), ($c \to d$) and on cooling ($b \to c$), ($d \to e$) the system. The pressure curve, P, is below the equilibrium pressure curve, P_0, and slowly approaches the latter.

Fig. 9. Decomposition pressures, P, over a system where the reaction reverse to thermal dissociation occurs when the system contains a large number of nuclei of a solid product. The pressure curve, P, is above the equilibrium pressure curve, P_0, and during heating ($a \to b$) and cooling ($b \to c$) it approaches the latter.

After splitting off, the almost catalytic action of the reactant–product interface disappears and the process begins anew with the formation of a new nucleus and a new small crystal.

The acceptance of the mechanism of the process discussed here has led to formulating the above-mentioned general dependence of the rate of formation of nuclei on the logarithm of supersaturation. This also leads to the explanation of the origin of a well-known mosaic structure of some crystals built of a large number of small crystals—basic units.

Lack of space does not permit a more detailed discussion of a large number of observations, made during investigations on the kinetics of reactions involving solid reactants and products, which are in favour of the acceptance of the discussed mechanism for the formation of solid phase nuclei. Thus, for example, it has been found that in large, single well-developed crystals or systems, subjected for a long time to recrystal-lization (favouring lattice orientation), the rate of formation of nuclei is very slow. When the surfaces of large single crystals were damaged mechanically to form macrodefects, the nuclei of a new phase formed readily (already at slight supersaturations).

The rate of formation of solid phase nuclei determines the shape of the kinetic dissociation curve; the reaction rate vs. conversion curve may assume various shapes.

In extreme cases, where nuclei are readily formed, the curve corresponds to a first-order reaction and, when the formation of nuclei occurs only at considerable supersaturations, the curves of autocatalytic reaction are observed.

It has been found that thermal dissociation reactions (when the size of the elementary cell of the reactant lattice is larger than the correspon-ding size for the product lattice) usually occur in the kinetic region.

Reactions reverse to dissociation (the size of the elementary cell of the product is larger than that of the reactant cell) occur in the diffusion region, since, due to the formation of product crystals from nuclei on the surface (a process associated with an increase in the volume of the solid phase), the reactant crystal becomes surrounded with a tight layer of the product which makes the diffusion of a gas to the reaction zone more difficult.

Particularly convincing evidence is provided by the work of Roginskii, Shmuk and Kushnerov (11) and Cremer (12), and they deserve to be men-tioned; they were concerned with investigations of thermal dissociation by means of an electron microscope used for the direct observation of the formation of minute crystals of the product on the surface of a reactant crystal being decomposed.

In spite of many gaps, the concepts discussed here may be considered as an introduction to formulating a general theory of nuclei formation in transformations involving crystalline phases.

REFERENCES

1. Bretsznajder S.: Zagadnienie kinetyki reakcji kontaktowych (Collective work—Kataliza i katalizatory). PWT, Warsaw, 1952.
2. Frenkel I. I., *Izv. Sektora Fiz.-Khim. Analiza, Inst. Obshch. Neorgan. Khim., Akad. Nauk SSSR*, **16**, No. 1, 82 (1943).
3. Symposium poświęcone zagadnieniom tworzenia się zarodków nowych faz. *Ind. Eng. Chem.*, **44**, 1207 (1952).
4. Bretsznajder S., *Congr. Intern. Chim. Pure Appl. 16^e, Paris*, 1957; *Mem. Sect. Chim. Minerale*, 603 (1957).
5. Bretsznajder S., *Roczniki Chem.*, **31**, 1255 (1957).
6. Bretsznajder S., *Roczniki Chem.*, **12**, 551 (1932).
7. Zawadzki J., Bretsznajder S., *Z. Phys. Chem.*, **B22**, 60 (1933); *Zh. Elektrokhem.*, **41**, 215 (1935).
8. Geld P. V., Pashilev A. I., Chuchmarev S. K., *Dokl. Akad. Nauk SSSR*, **91**, 1115 (1953).
9. Langmuir I., *J. Am. Chem. Soc.*, **38**, 2263 (1916).
10. Dankov P. D., *Zh. Fiz. Khim.*, **20**, 853 (1946).
11. Roginskii S. Z., Shmuk E. J., Kushnerov M. I., *Izv. Akad. Nauk SSSR., Otd. Khim. Nauk*, 573 (1950); Roginskii S. Z., *Geterogennyi Kataliz* VI (1949).
12. Cremer E., Bachman L., *Z. Elektrochem.*, **59**, 407 (1955).

XIII. MECHANISM AND KINETICS
OF CERTAIN REDOX SYSTEMS IN SOLUTIONS

B. Jeżowska-Trzebiatowska

For quite a long time now we have been investigating the mechanism and kinetics of the redox systems.

Our main problem was to determine whether the reduction proceeds by direct exchange of one or more electrons, or by the transfer of an atom or groups of atoms.

We also attempted to explain the part played by the temporary complexes in separating the intermediary products of reaction in investigating the radical character of this reaction, and in finding its kinetic equation.

Every redox process passes through some intermediate states of energy, higher than the average: the activated molecules, free radicals or active complexes. Usually there are successive reactions in the system, resulting in several stages of the process. The kinetics of the given reaction throws light on its mechanism.

1. REDUCTIONS OF OXYANIONS BY HYDROXYIONS

Suitable for the kinetic investigations are primarily the reactions between molecules or ions and molecules, or between ions of the same sign.

Reactions between ions of the same sign proceed with difficulty, usually in one of two ways: (1) tunnelling of an electron (1), (2) formation of the intermediate compounds—bridge complexes—facilitating the electron transfer, or transfer of an atomic group (2).

Typical reactions investigated by us were those between oxyanions of high oxidation potential and OH$^-$ ions playing an unusual, for them, part of reducing agents.

Oxyanions of transition metals with a high oxidation potential may be considered as possible oxidizing agents of hydroxide ions. Oxyanions of elements belonging to the main series of the Periodic System, such as bismuthates, periodates, iodates, etc., in spite of their considerable oxidation potential are not reduced by hydroxide ions. This is because the reducing action of OH^- ions depends not only on the oxidation potential of the oxidizing agent but also on the presence of the available d-orbitals, due to which they are electronic pair acceptors.

The oxyanions of manganese and iron—elements occurring in several oxidation states—constitute a particularly interesting object of investigation of the reduction mechanism.

a. Reduction of oxyanions of manganese

For a long time the reducing properties of hydroxyl ions were unknown.

The phenomenon of reduction in alkaline solution of such strong oxidizing agents as permanganates was known, but it was understood as a spontaneous decomposition of permanganate. For a long time the opinion prevailed that the organic substances are active in the reduction.

The transformations occurring in the permanganate in alkaline solutions may easily be traced by the characteristic changes of colour from magenta to navy blue and eventually to green. This phenomenon has been described already by Mendeleev, and hence is derived the name "inorganic chameleon".

These transformations are accompanied by the liberation of oxygen. The over-all reaction may be expressed by the formula:

$$4MnO_4^- + 4OH^- \rightarrow 4MnO_4^{2-} + 2H_2O + O_2$$

Holluta (3), one of the first who investigated this reaction, considered it as a reversible process:

$$2MnO_4^- + 2OH^- \rightleftarrows 2MnO_4^{2-} + O + H_2O$$

Later Fergusson (4) concluded that the rate of reaction increases with the growing pH of the solution, while Stamm (5) expressed an ambiguous idea that in an alkaline solution of permanganate stabilization of equilibrium occurs:

$$MnO_4^- + OH^- \rightleftarrows MnO_4^{2-} + OH$$

Nevertheless there exists a general conviction that the reducing agent enters the solution from the outside. Maximov (6) and later Clark and Coe (7) assumed that peroxides resulting from the interaction of air oxygen with hydroxyl ions participate in the reaction.

Somewhat different was a more recent concept of Duke (8), who attributed the role of actual reducing agent to water molecules in the reversible reaction:

$$MnO_4^- + H_2O \rightleftarrows MnO_4^{2-} + OH + H^+$$

His assumption, however, did not explain the reduction of permanganate in an anhydrous medium such as fused alkali (9). Some new developments as to the reducing action of hydroxides on the oxyanions, and particularly the manganese oxyanions, came with the extensive investigations after 1950.

As a result of these researches it was assumed that the hydroxyl ion is the reducing agent.

Already in the first investigations we established (Jeżowska-Trzebiatowska, Nawojska, and Wrońska) that the rate of reaction increases with the concentration of hydroxyl ions (10), and that in molten alkali the reaction is instantaneous (9). Furthermore, our investigations demonstrated that the reduction of permanganate by concentrated solutions of alkalis represents an example of a successive reaction, running through stages, manganate, hypomanganate, etc., down to MnO_2 (10, 11, 12):

$$MnO_4^- \rightarrow MnO_4^{2-} \rightarrow MnO_4^{3-} \rightarrow MnO_2$$

We succeeded in demonstrating experimentally the radical character of the reaction, as hydroxyl radicals were liberated. Symons (13, 14), who at the same time investigated the kinetics of permanganate reduction in sodium hydroxide solution, also ascribed the role of reducing agents to hydroxyl ions.

In further researches we succeeded in establishing that ferrates(VI) (15, 16) are also reduced by hydroxyl ions, with the formation of ferrates(IV) as intermediate products. Symons pointed out (17) simultaneously that chromates(VI) may also be reduced in favourable conditions (high temperature, high alkaline concentration, etc.) by OH^- ions to chromates(V). Systematic investigations proved that the rate of oxyanion reduction is proportional to the concentration of hydroxyl ions (9, 12, 18, 19). This discovery proved the direct participation of OH^- ions in the reaction, and upset Duke's hypothesis (8), according to which water molecules played the role of reducing agent.

In alkaline solutions the molar concentration of OH^- ions may be of the same order as the concentration of water molecules. In NaOH and KOH solutions of concentrations exceeding 10 M the probability of collision of an oxyanion with a hydroxyl ion is only a few times smaller than with a water molecule. The energy required for splitting a water molecule into radicals H and OH amounts to about 120 kcal, and the electron affinity of the radical OH equals 48 kcal. In consequence there exists a greater possibility of transition of an electron to the given oxyanion from the OH^- ion than from the water molecule. This transition is facilitated by the formation of the intermediate complexes of the oxidizing agent with the reducing agent (kinetic complexes).

The reduction by means of diluted solutions of hydroxyl ions (about 1M) is more complicated. The redox potential of such solutions is more positive; the reducing properties are, therefore, weaker. At the same time the probability of active collision of hydroxyl ions with oxyanions decreases. The consequence of such an alteration of conditions is a considerable fall of reaction rate as well as the formation of the more stable complexes of the oxidizing agent with the reducing agent.

In alkaline solutions of permanganate two competing reactions occur, the reduction and the disproportionation of lower oxidation states of manganese. In concentrated OH^- solutions reduction predominates, in contrast to the diluted solutions, which favour the reaction of disproportionation.

In highly diluted alkali hydroxide solutions, of concentrations below 0.01M KOH, disproportionation of the resulting manganate occurs according to the formula:

$$3MnO_4^{2-} + 2H_2O \rightleftarrows 2MnO_4^- + MnO_2 + 4OH^-$$

and it is only the permanganate ion that undergoes reduction. Evidence for this is that the magenta colour of the solution remains unchanged till the end of the reaction.

The disproportionation stability of the manganate increases with the growing hydroxyl ions concentration. The hypomanganate, which appears at a sufficiently high KOH concentration as would result from the reduction of manganate, disproportionates according to the formula:

$$2MnO_4^{3-} + 2H_2O \rightleftarrows MnO_4^{2-} + MnO_2 + 2OH^-$$

The green colour of the solution remains unchanged till the end of the reaction, i.e. until the complete precipitation of MnO_2.

The further increase of OH^- ions concentration results in very considerable limitation of the reaction of hypomanganate disproportionation, and under these conditions a practically pure reduction process occurs. The rate of the disproportionation reaction increases with the growth of oxyanions concentration in the second power, and affects the course of the reduction.

As the first stage of the reduction of oxyanions of transition metals by OH^- ions, one must consider the formation of the complex $MeO_4^{x-} \cdot OH^-$ which decomposes in the next stage as follows:

$$MeO_4^{x-} + OH^- \rightleftarrows [MeO_4^{x-} \cdot OH^-] \rightleftarrows MeO_4^{(x+1)-} + OH$$

In this reaction the radicals OH are liberated.

The radicals OH in the presence of hydroxyl ions in excess may still reduce the strong oxidizing agents such as permanganates and ferrates (VI), due to the reaction:

$$OH + OH^- \rightleftarrows O^- + H_2O$$

which lowers their oxidation potential.

The formation of an active complex is possible only when d-orbitals of the oxidizing agent overlap the p_x and p_y orbitals of hydroxyl ions, which is the case with transition elements.

The reduction of oxyanions of transition elements need not involve changes in the ion structure, but may consist in acceptance of an electron by the metal atom and not in splitting-off of oxygen. The structure MeO_4 is then maintained and only during the formation of intermediate complexes may d-orbitals be engaged.

KINETIC INVESTIGATIONS

Our kinetic researches confirmed that the reduction reaction of oxyanions is of the first order in respect to the oxyanion concentration (10, 11, 12, 18). Products of the reaction, as a rule, inhibit the further course of the reaction; the order of the reaction is, therefore, lowered. These facts may be represented by the kinetic equation:

$$\text{rate} = k \frac{[MeO_4^{x-}][OH^-]}{[MeO_4^{(x+1)-}]^n} \qquad n = 0-1$$

Concentrated alkali solutions enable the following of the reduction process of transition elements oxyanions, undisturbed by the reaction of disproportionation of these elements. Only these solutions have a sufficiently high reducing power to allow the observation of the particular stages of permanganate reduction (9, 10, 11, 12).

Owing to the application of 10–15M KOH solutions, we have been able to obtain all the consecutive stages of manganese oxidation from Mn(VII) to Mn(IV). Up to now, the final stage of reduction was missed by all the investigators, who thought that the reduction ended on manganate.

We succeeded in confirming that the reaction proceeds in several stages due to isolation in solid state of intermediately occurring potassium manganate K_2MnO_4, barium manganate $BaMnO_4$, sodium hypomanganate $Na_3MnO_4 \cdot 10H_2O$, and also due to final precipitation of MnO_2 (9, 12).

One can limit the reduction to monoelectronic stages

$$MnO_4^- + e = MnO_4^{2-}, \quad MnO_4^{2-} + e = MnO_4^{3-}$$

by the appropriate choice of the reaction temperature. The lowering of temperature to $-30°C$ or even to $-20°C$ results in that reduction in a concentrated solution of alkali scarcely passes the manganate stage. In the temperature range from -18 to $0°C$ the conversion of hypomanganate to MnO_2 proceeds at a very slow rate. We found higher temperatures, i.e. from $+20$ to $+30°C$, more suitable for that reaction.

The kinetics of the first stage, $MnO_4^- \rightarrow MnO_4^{2-}$, at practically constant KOH concentration (13–15M) during the reaction may be expressed by the equation:

$$- \frac{d[MnO_4^-]}{dt} = k \frac{[MnO_4^-]}{[MnO_4^{2-}]^{\frac{1}{2}}}$$

It is also possible to limit the reduction of permanganate to the first monoelectronic stage by lowering the alkali concentration. Already in solutions of KOH concentration lower than 5M the manganate is not apparently reduced to hypomanganate, and at still lower KOH concentrations (*ca.* 1M) manganate may be considered as the ultimate stage of reduction. In these conditions permanganate decomposes by a zero-order mechanism (in respect to manganate).

When only the elementary reactions of electron transfer are taken into consideration, the following mechanism may be suggested (12) for the reduction of permanganate:

1. $MnO_4^- + OH^- \rightleftarrows MnO_4^-OH^- \rightleftarrows MnO_4^{2-} + OH$
2. $OH + OH^- \rightarrow H_2O + O^-$
3. $MnO_4^- + O^- + OH^- \rightarrow MnO_4^{2-} + HO_2^-$
4. $MnO_4^- + HO_2^- + OH^- \rightarrow MnO_4^{2-} + O_2^- + H_2O$
5. $MnO_4^- + O_2^- \rightarrow MnO_4^{2-} + O_2$

The irreversibility of reaction 4 is also confirmed by experiments carried out in the presence of H_2O_2, which causes prompt and complete reduction of permanganate to MnO_2. Similarly we confirmed the irreversibility of reaction 5 while conducting the reaction in an autoclave under oxygen pressure of 30 atm. The lack of influence of molecular oxygen on the rate of the reaction is contradictory to earlier theories, assuming the formation of peroxides under the action of air oxygen.

On the basis of the steady-state theory applied to all radicals and intermediate species, the reaction rate may be expressed by the formula:

$$\text{rate} = \frac{4k_1k_2[MnO_4{}^-]\,[OH^-]^2}{k_{-1}[MnO_4{}^{2-}]+k_2[OH^-]}$$

This equation is essentially in agreement with the equation found experimentally. This applies to the reaction order in respect to both permanganate and hydroxyl ions; it does not, however, represent the variability of the inhibitor order, which depends on the concentration of hydroxyl ions.

The mechanism represented above involves the formation of radicals in reaction. We succeeded in demonstrating experimentally (9, 12) that the action of permanganate in concentrated alkali solution involves hydroxyl radicals which cause dimerization of benzene to diphenyl:

$$C_6H_6 + OH \rightarrow C_6H_5 + H_2O$$
$$2C_6H_5 \rightarrow (C_6H_5)_2$$

and polymerization of acrylonitrile.

Kenyon and Symons (20) also assumed that permanganate in NaOH solutions of higher concentration than 3M reacts more easily with hydroxyl ions than with the organic molecules. The hydroxyl ions are subsequently the main oxidizing agents.

The reduction of manganate in concentrated solutions of alkali proceeds to hypomanganate also in the monoelectronic reaction: $Mn(VI)+e = Mn(V)$. The mechanism of this reaction is similar to that of permanganate reduction and is expressed by the same kinetic equation (11, 12):

$$-\frac{d[MnO_4{}^{3-}]}{dt} = k\frac{d[MnO_4{}^{2-}]}{d[MnO_4{}^{3-}]^{1/2}}$$

However, the rate of this reaction is considerably lower (about 100 times) than that of the first stage of reaction, i.e. the reduction of permanganate.

It may seem odd to attribute reducing properties to the hydroxyl radical, since it is known that it has a very high oxidation potential $E = 2V$, while the oxidation potential of permanganate is $E_{MnO_4^-/MnO_4{}^{2-}} = 0.58$ V. Nevertheless, in view of the considerable excess of OH^- ions, the permanganate potential may become higher than the OH potential owing to the reaction $OH + OH^- = H_2O + O^-$. It seems, however, less probable that OH radicals could play such a role in respect to manganate, which has a lower oxidation potential than permanganate. In this case their oxidizing action $MnO_4{}^{3-} + OH = MnO_4{}^{2-} + OH^-$ may cause inhibition by a lower oxidation state of manganese.

There is no experimental evidence for the formation of OH radicals at moderate concentrations of alkali solutions (below 3M NaOH). The reason for this may be the tendency of radicals to dimerization to $(OH)_2$ $((OH)_2 \rightarrow H_2O_2)$. The investigations of reactions of oxidation of organic compounds by permanganate gave grounds for the conclusion that the oxidizing agent in these conditions is MnO_4^- ion and not the OH radical (21, 22, 23). We also established (18) that a 1M KOH solution does not release hydroxyl radicals in the presence of permanganate, as dimerization of benzene does not occur. The reduction of permanganate by KOH of this concentration scarcely passes the manganate stage. Obviously in these conditions the mechanism of reduction must be different than that in concentrated OH^- solution. The lower concentration of these ions is connected with their higher redox potential, which allows the formation of more stable complexes with manganese oxyanions (18).

The rate of reduction of permanganate to manganate in 1M KOH solution can be expressed by a zero-order equation in respect to manganate and by the first-order equation in respect to OH^-

$$- \frac{d[MnO_4^-]}{dt} = k \frac{[MnO_4^-][OH^-]}{[MnO_4^{2-}]}$$

The mechanism of this reaction takes into consideration both the results of kinetic investigations and the fact that in this case the free radicals do not appear(18):

1. $MnO_4^- + OH^- \rightarrow (MnO_4OH)^{2-}$
2. $(MnO_4OH)^{2-} + MnO_4^- \rightarrow (MnO_4OHMnO_4)^{3-}$
3. $(MnO_4OHMnO_4)^{3-} + OH^- \rightarrow 2(MnO_4OH)^{2-}$
4. $(MnO_4OHMnO_4)^{3-} + MnO_4^- + OH^- \rightarrow 2MnO_4^{2-} + MnO_4^- + H_2O_2$
5. $(MnO_4OHMnO_4)^{3-} + MnO_4^{2-} + OH^- \rightarrow 3MnO_4^{2-} + H_2O_2$
6. $MnO_4^- + OH^- + H_2O_2 \rightarrow MnO_4^{2-} + HO_2 + H_2O$
7. $MnO_4^- + HO_2 \rightarrow MnO_4^{2-} + H^+ + O_2$

The formation of the bridge complexes facilitates the transfer of the electron between the permanganate ion and OH^- ion.

The complex $[MnO_4OH]^{2-}$, sufficiently stable in these conditions, can interact with MnO_4^-, forming the bridge complex (reaction 2), which under the influence of OH^- ions re-forms the two molecules of the initial complex. Reactions 4 and 5 then may possibly have an intermediate stage in which MnO_4^- or MnO_4^{2-} links to the hydrogen of the hydroxyl bridge. The polarization brought about in this manner may result in the transfer of an electron from the bridge to Mn^{7+} and the release of the OH^+

radical, which reacts immediately with the OH^- ion, forming H_2O_2. By application of the steady-state theory to all radicals and intermediate complexes the following formula may be derived:

$$-\frac{d[MnO_4^-]}{dt} = k_1[MnO_4^-][OH^-] + \frac{k_1k_3[MnO_4^-][OH^-]}{k_4[MnO_4^-]+k_5[MnO_4^{2-}]}$$

Assuming that $k_1 < \dfrac{k_1k_3}{k_5}$, $k_3 > k_5$, we get the final equation identical with the one derived experimentally:

$$-\frac{d[MnO_4^-]}{dt} = \frac{k_1k_3[MnO_4^-][OH^-]}{k_5[MnO_4^{2-}]}$$

The higher rate of reaction 3 in comparison with reaction 5 ($k_3 > k_5$) is due to the fact that reaction 3 is bimolecular while reaction 5 is a trimolecular one. The first order of reaction in respect to concentration of hydroxyl ions, resulting from the reaction mechanism, is in agreement with the results obtained by Issa and Khalafalla (19) in their experimental research.

As the concentration of hydroxyl ions decreases, the reduction rate diminishes, while the rate of disproportionation of manganate increases. To learn the mechanism of the disproportionation reaction:

$$3MnO_4^{2-}+2H_2O \rightleftarrows 2MnO_4^-+MnO_2+4OH^-$$

the author and J. Kaleciński investigated its kinetics (24), controlling the concentration in such a way as to be able to ignore the reduction of permanganate. These conditions occurred in KOH solutions of concentrations below 0.1 mole/litre. In such diluted alkali solutions the rate of disproportionation of manganate is sufficiently high and suitable for kinetic measurements.

We have established experimentally that the rate of disproportionation is directly proportional to the square of manganate concentration and inversely proportional to the square of hydroxyl ions concentration:

$$\text{rate} = k\,\frac{[MnO_4^{2-}]^2}{[OH^-]^2}$$

In the accepted mechanism we took into consideration the formation of active bridge complexes $O_3Mn...O...MnO_3$, allowing internal redox process consisting in oxygen transfer. The intermediately occurring Mn(V) in the form of a protonated complex $H_2MnO_4^{2-}$ exchanges an electron with the manganate, probably also as a result of formation of a bridge complex:

1. $2MnO_4^{2-} + H_2O \rightleftarrows Mn_2O_7^{2-} + 2OH^-$
2. $Mn_2O_7^{2-} + H_2O \rightleftarrows MnO_4^- + H_2MnO_4^-$
3. $H_2MnO_4^- + MnO_4^{2-} \rightleftarrows H_2MnO_4^{2-} + MnO_4^-$
4. $H_2MnO_4^{2-} \rightleftarrows MnO_2 + 2OH^-$

On the basis of the steady-state theory a rate equation was derived, which agreed with the experimental results:

$$-\frac{d[MnO_4^-]}{dt} = \frac{2k_1k_2[MnO_4^{2-}]}{k_1[OH^-]^2 + k_2}$$

The disproportionation reaction is also specific for the hypomanganate ions (25), which even in concentrated alkaline solutions undergo inner oxidation and reduction. This is why this reaction plays a fundamental part in the third stage of permanganate reduction in which hypomanganate passes into manganese dioxide, $MnO_4^{3-} \rightarrow MnO_4^{4-}$ (MnO_2). It is rather doubtful whether the reduction of hypomanganate plays a part in this process. These conclusions are based on results of our recent investigations (the author and J. Nawojska (25)) on the kinetics of reaction of hypomanganate in 8–10M alkali solution. In the reaction of disproportionation of MnO_4^{3-} the species MnO_4^{2-} and $Mn(IV)$ are formed. The spectrophotometric methods permitted tracing at the same time the disappearance of MnO_4^- and the increase in MnO_4^{2-} content, as well as plotting the curve of the growth of MnO_2 content in the solution. The manganate ions are reduced by OH^- ions giving MnO_4^{3-} ions. When the concentration of hypomanganate is sufficiently high the manganate reduction is inhibited to such an extent that it can be neglected.

These investigations confirmed the fact that the rate of manganate reduction is inversely dependent on its concentration. The hypomanganate is not reduced by OH^- ions, but instead it disproportionates according to the reaction:

$$2MnO_4^{3-} + 2H_2O = MnO_4^{2-} + MnO_2 + 4OH^-$$

We established furthermore that this is actually a reaction of the second order in respect to hypomanganate and about -2 order in respect to OH^- ions. This means that the reaction rate is directly proportional to the square of hypomanganate concentration and inversely proportional to the square of hydroxyl ions activity. Two mechanisms may be ascribed to the hypomanganate disproportionation reaction, which both are in agreement with the results of our experiments.

The hypomanganate disproportionation may be accomplished, exactly as is the case with manganate, by help of a binuclear complex with an oxygen bridge. This complex decomposes in reaction with water into a manganate ion and the protonated manganate ion (the transfer of an oxygen atom):

1. $2MnO_4^{3-} + H_2O \underset{k_{-1}}{\overset{k_1}{\rightleftharpoons}} Mn_2O_7^{4-} + 2OH^-$

2. $Mn_2O_7^{4-} + H_2O \overset{k_2}{\rightleftharpoons} MnO_4^{2-} + H_2MnO_4^{2-}$
3. $H_2MnO_4^{2-} \rightleftharpoons MnO_2 + 2OH^-$

The application of the steady-state theory to this mechanism leads to the equation:

$$-\frac{d[MnO_4^{3-}]}{dt} = k_2 \frac{k_1}{k_{-1}} \frac{[MnO_4^{3-}]^2}{[OH^-]^2}$$

Alternatively, it may be assumed that the protonated and unprotonated ions may also form a binuclear complex linked by means of a hydrogen bridge:

1. $MnO_4^{3-} + 2H_2O \underset{k_{-1}}{\overset{k_1}{\rightleftharpoons}} H_2MnO_4^- + 2OH^-$

2. $H_2MnO_4^- + MnO_4^{3-} = [HMnO_4HO_4Mn]^{4-}$
3. $[HMnO_4HO_4Mn]^{4-} = H_2MnO_4^{2-} + MnO_4^{2-}$
4. $H_2MnO_4^{2-} = MnO_2 + 2OH^-$

Assuming the transitional equilibria, we may calculate the concentration of the protonated ion and obtain on this basis the final rate expression:

$$-\frac{d[MnO_4^{3-}]}{dt} = k_3 \frac{k_1 k_2}{k_{-1} k_{-2}} = \frac{[MnO_4^{3-}]^2}{[OH^-]^2}$$

It is therefore right to suppose that in the hypomanganate disproportionation both these mechanisms are equally probable.

In this stage the reaction is complicated by the catalytic activity of the freshly precipitated MnO_2. It is, therefore, necessary to take into consideration the possibility of the heterogeneous reactions.

They may consist in the regeneration of Mn(V) from MnO_2 and manganate:

$$MnO_4^{2-} + MnO_2 + 2H_2O \rightleftharpoons 2H_2MnO_4^-$$

or in the oxidation of surface MnO_2 molecules by active oxygen or the OH radical accompanied in the first case by the formation of intermediate peroxide radical compounds of Mn(IV):

1. $MnO_2 + OH \rightleftharpoons MnO_2OH$
2. $MnO_2OH + 3OH^- \rightarrow MnO_4^{3-} + 2H_2O$

or in the second case by the formation of an active complex with the OH radical:

$$OMnO + OH \rightarrow OMnO...HO \rightarrow MnO_2^+ + OH^-$$
$$MnO_2^+ + 2OH^- = H_2MnO_4^-$$

The investigations of kinetics and equilibrium together with the chemical investigations give a general view on the reactions and species occurring in an alkali solution of oxyanions of manganese.

In the $MnO_4^- - MnO_4^{2-} - OH^-$ system two competing reactions occur: (a) reduction of permanganate under the action of hydroxyl ions, and (b) reaction of disproportionation of manganate. While the rate of reduction increases proportionally to the first power of hydroxyl ions concentration, the rate of disproportionation decreases proportionally to its square. On this basis it is clear why in diluted alkaline solutions the reaction of disproportionation proceeds more easily than the reduction reaction.

In the $MnO_4^{2-} - MnO_4^{3-} - OH^-$ system in concentrated alkali solutions two competitive reactions occur: (a) reduction of manganate, (b) disproportionation of hypomanganate.

In this case the reduction rate increases as before proportionally to the first power of hydroxyl ions concentration and the rate of disproportionation decreases proportionally to its square. The reactions in both systems lead to the transformation of the whole manganese in the solution into MnO_2.

b. Reduction of ferrates(VI)

Another type of oxyanion thoroughly investigated by the present author and M. Wrońska (15, 16, 26, 27) was the ferrate(VI). Up to now it did not occur to the earlier investigators that FeO_4^{2-} can be reduced by OH^- ions. On the other hand, it was a known fact that the stability of ferrate(VI) increases with the increasing alkali concentration in the solution. Our investigations demonstrated that the concentration of ferrates(VI) in solutions decreases in the course of two processes:

(1) decomposition

$$2FeO_4^{2-} + 2H_2O \rightarrow 2FeOOH + O_2 + 4OH^-$$

(2) reduction by the hydroxyl ions

$$2FeO_4^{2-} + 3OH^- \rightarrow 2FeO_4^{5-} + 3O + 3H^+$$

The decomposition of ferrates(VI) is inhibited by the hydroxyl ions (26, 27), while the reduction is accelerated in their presence (15, 16).

The first-order reaction of ferrates(VI) reduction has not been thus far detected by the investigators, because of the more rapid second-order reaction of their decomposition. Only by applying very diluted 10^{-4} – 10^{-5}M solutions of ferrates and a considerable KOH concentration of 7–10 mole/litre was it possible to detect the reaction of the reduction and subsequently to investigate its mechanism.

The ferrate(VI) reduction proceeds eventually to ferrates(III). The rate of reaction is expressed by the formula:

$$v = k[FeO_4{}^{2-}]$$

After the product of solubility $Fe(OH)_3$ is exceeded, the order of the kinetic equation decreases, as a result of the inhibiting action of the reaction occurring on the surface of the freshly precipitated active $Fe(OH)_3$. As an intermediate stage in this reduction, Fe(IV) appears in the form of potassium ferrate, K_2FeO_3. We succeeded in isolating the ferrate(IV) in the form of a black precipitate during the reaction of very concentrated ferrate(VI) solutions. It is a very unstable compound, decomposing in a few minutes with the evolution of oxygen and the formation of $Fe(OH)_3$ (15, 16).

As it was impossible to detect even the intermediate formation of ferrate(V), it has to be assumed that the reduction of the ferrate proceeds in two stages: first stage—bielectronic reduction to ferrate(IV); second stage—monoelectronic reduction of ferrate(IV) to ferrate(III). For both these stages a radical mechanism of the reduction by hydroxyl ions may be accepted, valid up to the point where the $Fe(OH)_3$ solubility product is exceeded.

First stage:

1. $FeO_4{}^{2-} + 2OH^- \rightleftarrows FeO_4{}^{2-} \cdot (OH^-)_2$ (active complex)
2. $FeO_4{}^{2-} \cdot (OH^-)_2 \rightarrow FeO_4{}^{4-} + (OH)_2$
3. $(OH)_2 + OH^- \rightarrow HO_2^- + H_2O$
4. $FeO_4{}^{2-} + HO_2^- + OH^- \rightleftarrows FeO_4{}^{4-} + H_2O + O_2$
5. $FeO_4{}^{4-} + H_2O \rightleftarrows FeO_3{}^{2-} + 2OH^-$

Second stage:

1. $FeO_3{}^{2-} + OH^- \rightleftarrows FeO_3{}^{2-} \cdot OH^- \rightleftarrows FeO_3{}^{3-} + OH$
2. $OH + OH^- \rightleftarrows O^- + H_2O$
3. $FeO_3{}^{2-} + O^- + OH^- \rightleftarrows FeO_3{}^{3-} + HO_2^-$
4. $FeO_3{}^{2-} + HO_2^- + OH^- \rightleftarrows FeO_3{}^{3-} + H_2O + O_2^-$
5. $FeO_3{}^{2-} + O_2^- \rightleftarrows FeO_3{}^{3-} + O_2$

6. $FeO_3^{3-}+H_2O \rightleftarrows FeO_2^-+2OH^-$

7. $FeO_2^-+H_2O \rightleftarrows FeO(OH)+OH^-$

The decomposition of ferrate(VI) is in some ways analogous to the disproportionation of oxyanions of manganese(VI) and (V). Its rate increases proportionally to the square of ferrate(IV) concentration and decreases proportionally to the first power of activity of the hydroxyl ion. The experimental equation for the reaction rate is:

$$\text{rate} = \frac{[FeO_4^{2-}]^2}{[OH^-]}$$

The reaction mechanism in this stage may be represented by the formulae:

$$2FeO_4^{2-} \rightarrow \left[\begin{array}{cc} O & O \\ OFe \diagdown{}^{O}_{O} \diagup FeO \\ O & O \end{array} \right]^{4-}$$

$$[FeO_4FeO_4]^{4-}+H_2O \rightleftarrows 2FeO_2^-+2OH^-+3O$$

$$FeO_2^-+H_2O \rightarrow FeO(OH)+OH^-$$

$$2O \rightarrow O_2$$

The appearance of the $Fe(OH)_3$ precipitate results in a change of order of the decomposition reaction and in an increase of its rate because of the positive surface catalysis. In the presence of the complexing agents, such as phosphates, these reactions preserve the original mechanism till the end (27).

c. Thermodynamics of reaction in alkaline solutions of oxyanions

The thermodynamic equilibrium constant we determined for permanganate in alkali solutions, corresponding to the reaction:

$$3MnO_4^{2-}+2H_2O \rightleftarrows 2MnO_4^-+MnO_2+4OH^-$$

amounts to

$$K_r = 4.3\pm0.5$$

and the free energy of the reaction of disproportionation of manganate $F = -0.865$ kcal (28). Accepting the values of the free energy of the other components according to Latimer (29), we calculated the free energy of manganate as $F = -120\,68$ kcal and the oxidation potential of permanganate:

$$E_{MnO_4^-/MnO_4^{2-}} = 0.576 \text{ V}$$

The value of the potential thus agrees with the result obtained by Rogers and Miller (30) by the polarographic method: ($E = +0.58$ V). The determination of the equilibrium constant, permitted the selection of a concentration of OH^- ions for permanganate reduction in which the reaction of disproportionation of manganate could be excluded.

From the expression for the equilibrium constant:

$$k = \frac{[MnO_4^-]^2[OH^-]^4}{[MnO_4^{2-}]^3}$$

it was easy to calculate that in solutions of about 1M KOH concentration the reaction of disproportionation occurs only after the reduction of 95% of permanganate to manganate. As a result the reaction of disproportionation disturbs only the final stage of reduction. In connection with this conclusion we chose the concentration of hydroxyl ions of about 1 mole/litre for the investigation of the reduction mechanism.

The reduction of manganese oxyanions by the OH^- ions proceeds with small activation energy: (a) 8.12 – 9.3 kcal for the first stage of the reduction of permanganate to manganate; (b) 11.2 kcal for the second stage of reduction of manganate to hypomanganate. The activation energy in the last stage is considerably higher, as compared with the hypomanganate transition in a complex reaction (disproportionation of hypomanganate and reduction of manganate) in MnO_2. It amounts to about 24 kcal (11, 12, 18).

The reduction of ferrate(VI) has a similar activation energy to that of the first stage of permanganate reduction, amounting to 8.6 kcal (15,16).

The entropy of activation in the 1M KOH solution, calculated for the monoelectronic reduction of permanganate, has an extremely high negative value, equal to -61.7 entropy units (cal/°K), while the free energy of activation in these conditions equals 25.73 kcal (18).

The Arrhenius coefficient is particularly small for the monoelectronic transition $MnO_4^- + e \rightarrow MnO_4^{2-}$ and equals $A = 2.76 \times 10^{-1}$. The considerable negative value of the entropy of activation and the small frequency factor are the principal characteristics of these reactions between ions of the same sign.

Should we consider from the same point of view the reaction of manganate disproportionation, which is also a reaction between ions of the same sign, it will appear that the activation energy is also small and amounts to 7.65 kcal, the entropy of activation being considerable (-30 e.u.). At the same time the frequency factor is also large and amounts to 1.26 $\times 10^6$ (24).

The significant negative entropy of activation of this process in more diluted alkaline solutions may be the result of the formation of the active bi- and polynuclear complexes.

The entropy of activation of the disproportionation reaction of manganate is also negative, however, less than in the reduction process. In this case the number of molecules diminishes also in the activation process.

The activation energy of ferrate(VI) decomposition, which is a reaction similar to disproportionation, but accompanied by liberation of oxygen, is correspondingly greater and amounts to 12.7 kcal/mole (27).

d. The role of cations in the reduction of oxyanions

The mechanism and the reducing properties of hydroxide ions depend not only on their concentration, but also on the nature of the cation of the alkali metal. The reducing power of hydroxides increases in the follow -ing order: LiOH < NaOH < KOH < CsOH. The growing reducing power results in the increase of the specific rate of reduction. This increase at the same concentration of various alkalis is much greater than the simultaneous increase of activity coefficients. While the activity of a 5M KOH solution is about 1.5 times larger than the activity of a 5M NaOH solution, the specific rate of reduction of the oxyanions is about 50 times higher. Undoubtedly in this case a certain part must be attributed to catalysis of the reaction occurring between negative ions by positive ions of the alkali metals (12, 15, 16, 26, 27). This action may consist in the formation of complexes with the cationic bridges, thus facilitating the drawing closer of the negative ions and in consequence the electron transfer:

$$MeO_4^- \ldots K^+ \ldots OH^- \rightarrow MeO_4^- \ldots K \ldots OH \rightarrow MeO_4^{2-} + K^+ + OH$$

The increase of the catalytic action of the cation with the growing ion radius can be explained by the simultaneously diminishing hydration shell.

The addition of the Na^+ cation to the potassium hydroxide solution reduces the rate of the process of oxyanion reduction, while the addition of Rb^+ or Cs^+ accelerates it (15, 16, 26).

It is characteristic that amphoteric cations such as Al^{3+}, Fe^{3+} in alkali solutions, appearing as oxy- or hydroxyanions, do not act as catalysts in the reduction process.

M. Wrońska established (27) that the cation bridges also play a role in the decomposition of ferrates(VI), which is a reaction between negative ions, the rate coefficients being about 10 times higher in the reaction with potassium ions than with sodium ions.

The cation bridges between negative ions are analogous to anion bridges between the reacting cations. Marcus, Zwoliński, Eyring (1) and, above all, Taube (2, 31, 32) attributed the essential part in the redox reactions between the cations to those bridges.

It is doubtful, however, if the catalysis involving cation bridges can fully account for such significant differences in the reducing action of alkali hydroxides. The specific action of alkalis as reducing agents will be an object of further investigations.

2. PEROXY COMPLEXES AS INTERMEDIATE STAGES OF OXIDATION

Another redox problem which we investigated was the process of binding oxygen by the complex compounds with the formation of peroxy compounds. Such compounds may appear as intermediate stages of oxidation. All the valency electrons of the metal ion remain in this case intact and the acceptor able to receive them (O_2^{2-}) is firmly bound in the complex. The metal atom may be oxidized through the loss of electrons contained in the oxygen bond.

The reaction of the reversible binding of oxygen by the binuclear complex of rhenium(IV), i.e. the oxochlororhenate $(ReOCl_{10})^{4-}$, discovered by us (the author and H. Przywarska), was a suitable model for studying the composed mechanism of such reactions (33, 34). The reversible binding of oxygen is well known in the natural complex compounds of iron(II) (haemoglobin), copper(I) (haemocyanin), and cobalt(III) (vitamin B_{12a}). Similarly the cobalt complexes with salicylic aldehyde and ethylenediamine, synthetized by Tsumaki (35) and by Calvin with co-workers (36–42), subsequently obtained by Hearon and Burk with histidine (46,47), bind reversibly oxygen-forming binuclear peroxygen complexes. Recently complexes of this type with nickel, iron and manganese have been discovered.

The oxochlororhenate constituting a new type of strictly inorganic compound binding oxygen (33) in the above-mentioned way further widens this group of complexes. It binds oxygen in the acid solutions forming a blood-red peroxy complex. Hydrogen peroxide, and cation or oxyanion oxidizing agents as Fe^{3+}, Ce^{4+}, and IO_3^-, BrO_3^-, $Cr_2O_7^{2-}$, etc. may play the role of oxygen donors (48, 49). The molecular oxygen is bound into peroxy complexes only in the presence of catalysts.

The reactions of binding oxygen from cationic or anionic oxidizing agents are instantaneous and therefore available for investigations only in the state of equilibrium. Only the molecular oxidizing agents such as hydrogen peroxide and molecular oxygen acted slowly enough to permit the kinetic investigations (50, 51).

The blood-red peroxy complex of rhenium(IV) occurs as an intermediate stage in the oxidation of chlororhenate to perrhenate. The formation of this complex under the action of cationic oxidizing agents points to the radical character of the oxidation process. The mechanism involving water radicals may be attributed to the reaction:

$$
\begin{array}{c}
\overset{|}{\underset{|}{Re}} \quad \overset{\boxed{\;\;|\;\;}}{e \downarrow} \quad \overset{|}{\underset{|}{Re}} \\
\overset{|}{\underset{|}{O}} + \quad \begin{array}{c} OH\ H + Ce^{4+} \\ OH\ H + Ce^{4+} \end{array} \quad \longrightarrow \quad \overset{|}{\underset{|}{O{:}\ddot{O}{:}}} + 2Ce^{3+} + 2H^+ + H_2O \\
\overset{|}{\underset{|}{Re}} \quad \underset{\boxed{\;e \uparrow\;}}{} \quad \overset{|}{\underset{|}{Re}}
\end{array}
$$

Oxyanions with a high oxidation potential can act similarly or else, possessing the ability to split off the oxygen atom as periodates, iodates, bromates, etc., may transfer their own oxygen atom to the oxygen bridge (48, 49).

$$
\begin{array}{ccc}
\overset{|}{\underset{|}{Re}}\ \overset{(-)}{O} & \overset{|}{\underset{|}{Re}}\ \overset{(-)}{O} & \overset{|}{\underset{|}{Re}} \\
\overset{|}{\underset{|}{O}} + O{=}I & \overset{|}{\underset{|}{O{:}O{=}I}} & \overset{|}{\underset{|}{O{:}OH^+}} + IO_2^- \\
\overset{|}{\underset{|}{Re}}\ \overset{\parallel}{O} & \overset{|}{\underset{|}{Re}}\ \overset{\parallel}{O} & \overset{|}{\underset{|}{Re}}
\end{array}
$$

with arrows: $\longrightarrow$ and $\xrightarrow{+H^+}$

The reaction of binding oxygen from hydrogen peroxide has been investigated in the equilibrium state (50). The investigations by optical methods demonstrated that first a complex of the oxidizing agents (H_2O_2) with the reducing agent (oxochlororhenate(IV)) in a stoichiometric ratio, oxo : $H_2O_2 = 1 : 3$, is formed, the amount of the bonded oxidizing agent being exactly the amount necessary for complete oxidation of Re(IV) to Re(VII).

We followed the progress of the reaction to the state of equilibrium. On the basis of kinetic investigations we obtained the following formula for the specific rate of the reaction:

$$
\text{rate} = k\,\frac{[H_2O_2]^2}{[H_2O_2]_{\frac{1}{2}}}
$$

where $[H_2O_2]_{\frac{1}{2}}$ represents the excess of hydrogen peroxide in the half-time. It should be underlined that the inhibiting action of the excess of the substrate has been established.

In the first stage of the reaction a complex of oxochlororhenate(IV) with two molecules of H_2O_2 may be formed. At the same time the co-ordination number of rhenium increases to 7 in $[Re_2OCl_{10} \cdot 2H_2O_2]^{4-}$. This intermediate complex reacts with a third molecule of H_2O_2 yielding a peroxy complex. Since the properties of the peroxy complex point to a vertical bridge $-\overset{\overset{\textstyle O}{|}}{O}-$ rather than a horizontal one $-O-O-$, the participation of ion radicals OH^+ in the bridge formation is possible, since the reaction proceeds in an acid solution:

$$H_2O_2 + H^+ \rightarrow OH^+ + H_2O$$

$$[Re_2OCl_{10} \cdot 2H_2O_2]^{4-} + OH^+ \rightarrow \left[Cl_5Re\overset{\overset{\textstyle OH^+}{|}}{O}ReCl_5 \right]^{4-} \cdot 2H_2O_2$$

The inhibiting role played by the substrate, expressed by zero order in respect to chlororhenate, is a result of secondary reactions of the substrate with the active complex and the peroxy complex, due to which these complexes decompose.

The peroxy complex is quite stable in the solid state, i.e. in the form of quinoline ((quin H)$_4$[Re$_2$O$_2$Cl$_{10}$]), caesium (Cs$_3$H[Re$_2$O$_2$Cl$_{10}$]) or rubidium salts. At room temperature it decomposes slowly, losing oxygen, and the rate of decomposition increases with the growth of temperature.

The peroxy complex decomposes in a first-order reaction, and its rate is given by the expression:

$$\text{rate} = k[Re_2Cl_{10}O_2]^{4-}$$

The initial complex of rhenium(IV) is reformed and oxygen released:

$$[\overset{\text{IV}}{Re_2O_2Cl_{10}}]^{4-} \rightarrow [\overset{\text{IV}}{Re_2OCl_{10}}]^{4-} + O$$

The reactions of peroxygen complex formation and decomposition possess similar, and quite considerable, activation energies equalling 18.22 and 16.05 kcal, respectively. The oxochlororhenate formed in the decomposition reaction has the property of repeated binding of oxygen and reforming the peroxy complex. There occurs, however, a certain irreversibility in this reaction, as the liberated oxygen partly oxidates Re(IV) to perrhenate.

The reversibility of the oxygen absorption is more distinct in the reaction of oxochlororhenate with molecular oxygen (51). It is a typical catalytic reaction, since the oxygen atom may be transferred from the O_2 molecule to the oxygen bridge only in the presence of a catalyst. As catalyst nitrites or nitrates in acid solution may be used. A similar case of nitrate-catalysed reaction has been observed by Merton-Bingham and Posner (52), i.e. the oxidation of HBr by molecular oxygen. The rate of catalytic formation of the peroxy complex under constant pressure of molecular oxygen is proportional to the catalyst concentration, and may be expressed by the equation:

$$\text{rate} = k[\text{nitrate}] \ \sqrt{[\text{oxo}] [\text{peroxo}]}$$

where [oxo] represents the concentration of oxochlororhenate and [peroxo] the concentration of peroxychlororhenate.

The activation energy of the catalytic reaction of oxygen-binding amounts to 10.62 kcal, which is lower than the activation energy of the reaction with hydrogen peroxide.

The short induction period of the reaction may indicate that during it the traces of nitrogen oxides contained in the nitrate initiate the chain reaction. The mechanism of this reaction in accordance with its kinetics may be expressed as follows:

1. $NO + O_2 \xrightarrow{k_1} NO_3$

2. $NO_3 + [\text{oxo}] \xrightarrow{k_2} [\text{peroxo } NO_2]$

3. $[\text{peroxo } NO_2] + [\text{oxo}] \xrightarrow{k_3} 2[\text{peroxo}] + NO$

4. $NO + [\text{peroxo}] \underset{k_4}{\overset{k_4}{\rightleftarrows}} [\text{peroxo } NO]$

5. $[\text{oxo}] + 2HNO_3 \underset{k_5}{\overset{k_5}{\rightleftarrows}} [\text{oxo } 2HNO_3]$

6. $[\text{oxo } 2HNO_3] + [\text{peroxo } NO] \underset{k_6}{\overset{k_6}{\rightleftarrows}} 2[\text{oxo } HNO_3] + NO_2$

7. $NO_2 + [\text{peroxo}] \xrightarrow{k_7} [\text{peroxo } NO_2]$

8. $[\text{oxo } HNO_3] + H_2O + O_2 \xrightarrow{k_8} [\text{peroxo}] + HNO_3 + 2OH$

9. $[\text{oxo } HNO_3] + 2OH \xrightarrow{k_9} [\text{peroxo}] + HNO_3 + H_2O$

In fact not only the nitrogen oxides act as a catalyst, their role being limited to the induction period, but also the nitrate or nitric acid, forming an active complex with oxochlororhenate (oxo $2HNO_3$). As in the case of hydrogen peroxide (oxo $2H_2O_2$), the co-ordination number of rhenium atoms in this active complex of the oxidizing agent with the reducing agent would increase to 7. The oxidation potential of nitric acid is, however, too low in these conditions, so it cannot become in turn an oxygen donor, to form a peroxy complex. The active complex passes into an even more active one (oxo HNO_3) in which the NO_3^- group can play the part of a bridge between rhenium atoms .... $Re\overset{\displaystyle NO_3}{\underset{\displaystyle O}{\diamondsuit}}Re$ .... This complex

easily reacts with O_2, yielding a peroxy complex ...ReO_2Re... Only oxygen is consumed in this reaction, and the nitrate remains unchanged.

The steady-state theory leads to an equation agreeing well with the experimental results:

$$\frac{d[\text{peroxo}]}{dt} = 2k_8\sqrt{K_6K_5K_4}\,[NO_3^-]\sqrt{[\text{oxo}][\text{peroxo}]}$$

The reversibility of reaction of oxygen absorption by the binuclear rhenium complex becomes obvious when oxygen and nitrogen in turn are passed through the acid solution with a small amount of nitrate. The blood-red colour occurring under the influence of oxygen disappears when instead of oxygen nitrogen is introduced. The red solution returns to its original yellowish-green colour as a result of oxochlororhenate re-forming. Introduction of gaseous oxygen into this solution changes its colour once more to the blood-red characteristic of the peroxy complex. In this case also the reaction is characterized by a certain irreversibility as a result of partial oxidation of rhenium(IV) by active oxygen to perrhenate.

The peroxy complex of rhenium(IV) may be considered as an intermediate stage in the process of oxidation to perrhenate. It is particularly apparent in the case of molecular oxidizing agents which form intermediate complexes with such amounts of oxidizing agent (H_2O_2, HNO_3) as are required to complete the oxidation of rhenium.

The electronic structure of rhenium in oxochlororhenate $d^2d^1d^0$ renders possible the momentary increase of the co-ordination number of rhenium to 7.

We also succeeded in obtaining a stable complex compound with the co-ordination number 7. Both oxochlororhenate and peroxochlororhenate pass into a lemon-yellow u-ol-oxochlororhenate $\left[Cl_5Re\overset{\displaystyle OH}{\underset{\displaystyle}{-}O-}ReCl_5\right]^{5-}$. However, while the peroxochlororhenate gives this reaction under the influence of strong alkali (KOH, NaOH) and ammonia, the oxochlororhenate undergoes transformation already under gentle action of ammonia solutions. The alkalis produce immediate and total hydrolysis.

The lemon-yellow ol-complex has no more the property of binding oxygen to give a peroxy complex, which is the result of filling up all d-orbitals and obtaining a $d^2d^1D^3SP^3$ structure.

It remains to be explained in what manner the oxygen absorbed is bound to the molecule of oxochlororhenate. The analogy between the rhenium(IV) complex binding oxygen and other oxygen-carrying complexes is superficial. There exists an essential difference in the process of oxygen binding by the complexes of iron and cobalt, which react directly with the oxygen molecule. The rhenium complexes—owing to their bridge structure—only absorb the oxygen atom from the oxidizing agent by means of a radical reaction or from molecular oxygen in a catalytic chain reaction. The peroxygen group does not form an ordinary horizontal bridge —O—O—, as in H_2O_2, but a vertical one in which either one oxygen atom (Ia) or both atoms (Ib) are bound with rhenium atoms (Ia)

$$\text{(Ia)} \quad -\text{Re}-\overset{..}{\underset{..}{\text{O}}}-\text{Re}- \rightleftarrows \text{(Ib)} -\text{Re} \underset{\underset{..}{\text{O}}}{\overset{\overset{..}{\text{O}}}{|}} \text{Re}-$$

:Ö: ·H+

Blood-red in   Reddish in solid
acid solution   state

A bridge similar to (Ib) was accepted by Hearon (43–47) for cobalt(II) complex with histidine $-\text{Co}\underset{\text{O}}{\overset{\text{O}}{\diagup\!\!\diagdown}}\text{Co}-$. The original oxochlororhenate(IV) $[Cl_5Re-O-ReCl_5]^{4-}$ is diamagnetic. The diamagnetism is caused by the antiparallel arrangement of electronic spins (53, 54) in both rhenium atoms which may be named "the intermolecular antiparamagnetism". It seems that because of the splitting of levels t_{2g} in the field of symmetry D_{4h} the configuration $b_{1g}^2 e_g^1$ occurs. The electrons e_g^1 have antiparallel spins. A configuration leaving one of the orbits e_g free permits the formation of complexes with d^3sp^3 configuration. The addition of a new oxygen atom may cause some increase of distance of both the rhenium atoms, owing to which the complete quenching of magnetic moment is now impossible. Accordingly, the peroxy complex is paramagnetic and has an effective moment equal to about 3β, corresponding approximately to two unpaired electrons.

Paramagnetism of the peroxy complex may be also explained by the assumption that both the unpaired electrons are located in the peroxy bridge. As a result the bridge would obtain the structure similar to the molecular oxygen ion $O_2 + 2e \rightarrow \overset{..}{\underset{..}{:O:}}\,^{2-}$, where one unpaired electron would be included into the three-electron bond.

The reversible bonding of oxygen by rhenium complexes establishes in a way a new model of an inorganic oxygen carrier, which transfers the oxygen atom.

REFERENCES

1. Marcus R. J., Zwoliński B. J., Wyring H., *J. Phys. Chem.*, **58**, 438 (1954).
2. Taube H., King B. L., *J. Am. Chem. Soc.*, **76**, 4053 (1954).
3. Holluta J., *J. Am. Phys. Chem.*, **102**, 276 (1922).
4. Fergusson R. H., Lerch W., Day J. E., *J. Am. Chem. Soc.*, **53**, 126 (1931).
5. Stamm J., *Z. Angew. Chem.*, **47**, 791 (1934).
6. Maximov A., *Z. Anorg. Chem.*, **163**, 49 (1927).
7. Clark G. Coe S., *J. Chem. Phys.*, **5**, 97 (1937).
8. Duke F. R., *J. Am. Chem. Sec.*, **69**, 2885 (1947).
9. Jeżowska-Trzebiatowska B., Nawojska J., Wrońska M., *Roczniki Chem.*, **25**, 405 (1951).
10. Jeżowska-Trzebiatowska B., Nawojska J., Wrońska M., *Bull. Acad. Polon. Sci.*, *Classe III*, **1**. 311 (1954).
11. Jeżowska-Trzebiatowska B., Nawojska J., Wrońska M., *Bull. Acad. Polon. Sci.*, *Classe III*, **2**, 4447 (1954).
12. Jeżowska-Trzebiatowska B., Wrońska M., Nawojska J., *Roczniki Chem.*, **29**, 259 (1956).
13. Symons M. C. R., *J. Chem. Soc.*, 1953 (1956).
14. Symons M. C. R., *Research*, **6**, 55 (1953).
15. Jeżowska-Trzebiatowska B., Wrońska M., *Bull. Acad. Polon. Sci.*, *Classe III.*, **5** 659 (1957).
16. Jeżowska-Trzebiatowska B., Wrońska M., *Congr. Intern. Chim. Pure Appl.*, *16ᵉ*, *Paris, 1957.*
17. Bailey N., Symons M. C. R., *J. Chem. Soc.*, **1957**, 203.
18. Jeżowska-Trzebiatowska B., Kaleciński J., *Bull. Acad. Polon. Sci.*, *Ser. Sci. Chim.*, No 6 (1959).
19. Issa I. M., Khalafalla S. E., Issa R. M., *J. Am. Chem. Soc.*, **77**, 5503 (1955).
20. Kenyon J., Symons M. C. R., *J. Chem. Soc.*, 3580 (1953).
21. Landbury J. W., Cullis C. F., *Chem. Rev.*, **58**, 403 (1958).
22. Drumond A. Y., Waters A. W., *J. Chem. Soc.*, 435 (1953).
23. Merz J. H., Waters W. A., *Discussions Faraday Soc.*, **2**, 179 (1951).
24. Jeżowska-Trzebiatowska B., Kaleciński J., *Bull. Acad. Polon. Sci.*, 290.
25. Jeżowska-Trzebiatowska B., Nawojska J., *Bull. Acad. Polon. Sci.*, *Ser. Sci. Chim.* (in press).
26. Wrońska M.: Dissertation. Wrocław, 1957.

27. Wrońska M., *Bull. Acad. Polon. Sci., Ser. Sci. Chim.*, **6**, 3 (1959).
28. Jeżowska-Trzebiatowska B., Kaleciński J., *Bull. Acad. Polon. Sci., Ser. Sci. Chim.*, **6**, 411 (1959).
29. Latimer W. M.: Oxidation Potentials. Prentice-Hall. New York, 1953.
30. Miller H. H., Rogers L. B., *Science*, **109**, 61 (1949).
31. Taube H., Myers H., Rich K. R., *J. Am. Chem. Soc.*, **75**, 4118 (1953).
32. Taube H., Myers H., *J. Am. Chem. Soc.*, **76**, 2103 (1954).
33. Jeżowska-Trzebiatowska B., *Trav. Soc. Sci. Lettres Wroclaw, Ser. B*, No. 39 (1953).
34. Jeżowska-Trzebiatowska B., Przywarska H., *Bull. Acad. Polon. Sci., Classe III*, **3**, 429 (1955).
35. Tsumaki M., *Bull. Chem. Soc. Japan*, **13**, 252 (1938).
36. Calvin M., *Trans. Faraday Soc.*, **34**, 1181 (1938).
37. Calvin M., *J. Am. Chem. Soc.*, **61**, 2230 (1939).
38. Calvin M., Bailes R. H., Wiemarth W. K., *J. Am. Chem. Soc.*, **68**, 2254 (1946).
39. Wilmarth W. K., Aranoff, Calvin M., *J. Am. Chem. Soc.*, **68**, 2263 (1946).
40. Harle R., Calvin M., *J. Am. Chem. Soc.*, **68**, 2612 (1946).
41. Bailes R. H., Calvin M., *J. Am. Chem. Soc.*, **69**, 1886 (1947).
42. Hughes Z. C., Wilmarth W. K., Calvin M., *J. Am. Chem. Soc.*, **68**, 2273 (1946).
43. Burk D., Hearon J. Z., Schade A. L., *J. Biol. Chem.*, **165**, 72 (1946).
44. Hearon J. Z., Schade A. L., Levy J., Burk D., *Cancer Res.*, **7**, 713 (1947).
45. Hearon J. Z., *J. Natl. Cancer Inst.*, **9**, 1 (1948).
46. Hearon J. Z., Burk D., Schade A. L., *J. Natl. Cancer Inst.*, **9**, 337 (1949).
47. Hearon J. Z., Burk D., *J. Natl. Cancer Inst.*, **9**, 337 (1949).
48. Jeżowska-Trzebiatowska B., Przywarska H., *Congr. Intern. Chim. Pure et Appl., 16e , Paris, 1957*.
49. Jeżowska-Trzebiatowska B., Przywarska H., *Bull. Acad. Polon. Sci., Ser. Chim.*, **6** 345 (1958).
50. Jeżowska-Trzebiatowska B., Przywarska H., *Bull. Acad. Polon. Sci., Ser. Chim.*, **6**, 349 (1958).
51. Jeżowska-Trzebiatowska B., Przywarska H., *Bull. Acad. Polon. Sci., Ser. Chim.*, **6** 611 (1958).
52. Merton-Bingham B. E., Posner A. M., *J. Am. Chem. Soc.*, **77**, 2634 (1955).
53. Jeżowska-Trzebiatowska B., Wajda St., *Bull. Acad. Polon. Sci., Classe III*, **2**, 249 (1954).
54. Jeżowska-Trzebiatowska B., Wajda St., *Bull. Acad. Polon. Sci., Classe III*, **2**, 451 (1954).

XIV. KINETICS OF REACTION AT THE INTERFACE LIQUID–LIQUID OR LIQUID–GAS

E. Józefowicz

Classical kinetics comprises almost exclusively the reactions in homogeneous systems either gaseous or liquid. Among reactions proceeding at the interface the most important industrially are the contact reactions proceeding on the surface of solid catalysts. Information concerning these reactions is recorded in the literature and a detailed discussion would exceed the scope of this report. As is well known, adsorption of reagents on the surface of contact plays an important part in these reactions.

Reactions of solid substances with those in solutions were first examined by J. J. Boguski in 1875. According to the theory of Noyes and Whitney (1), as developed by Nernst (2) and his followers, the rate of these reactions is determined by diffusion of the substance in solution towards the solid phase surface through a motionless layer of liquid adjacent to this surface. Centnerszwer and Heller (3), as a result of their investigations on the solution of metals in acids, developed a theory, completed by Basiński (4), that the first stage in these reactions is the adsorption of acid on the surface of metal.

More recently the attention of scientists in the field of kinetics was drawn to reactions proceeding at the boundary of two immiscible liquids, or at the liquid–gas interface. It has been established that substances lowering the surface tension of a solution collect at the interface, where a monomolecular layer is formed. The surface-active substances comprise, among others, organic compounds containing longer or shorter hydrocarbon chains connected with polar groups such as OH, COOH, NH_2, etc. According to Langmuir's (5) theory, confirmed by later investigations, in a monomolecular layer forming for example at the boundary of an aqueous phase with another liquid or gas, individual molecules are directed in a definite way, the polar group being "anchored" in the aqueous phase, while the hydrocarbon chain is directed towards the non-aqueous solvent, or gaseous phase.

This conception of the molecular orientation of surface-active substances at the interface provides an explanation for many facts concerning the kinetics of reactions of these substances with aqueous solutions, e.g. the oxidation of oleic acid and other unsaturated compounds with permanganate, the hydrolysis of esters of higher aliphatic acids, etc. (6).

The reaction mechanism in biphasic systems, in which substances without pronounced superficial activity participate, has not been adequately explained. Some years ago, in the Institute of Inorganic Chemistry at the Technical University, Łódź, investigations on reactions in liquid-liquid and liquid-gas systems were undertaken. Particular attention was paid to chemical changes of elements of the VIth and VIIth groups of the Periodic Table and some of their compounds.

1. REACTION PROCEEDING AT A LIQUID-LIQUID INTERFACE

a. Oxidation of arsenious acid by iodine

The course of this reaction in aqueous solution has been examined frequently, as well as by the author of this report (7). As a result of these investigations, the reaction mechanism is established as a reversible hydrolysis of iodine molecules resulting in formation of hypoiodous acid:

$$I_2 + H_2O \rightleftarrows HIO + H^+ + I^-$$

The latter reacts (also reversibly) with arsenious acid, forming arsenic acid and more hydrogen iodide:

$$H_3AsO_3 + HIO \rightleftarrows H_3AsO_4 + H^+ + I^-$$

This second stage of the reaction is slower than the first and determines the rate of the over-all process.

S. Witekowa (8) has examined this same reaction, however, not in a homogeneous solution, but at the boundary of two liquid phases: an aqueous solution of arsenious acid and a solution of iodine in benzene, carbon tetrachloride, chloroform and bichloroethane. With arsenious acid always present in considerable excess, the reaction rate is proportional to the square root of iodine concentration in the non-aqueous solvent:

$$\frac{dx}{dt} = k\sqrt{[I_2]} \tag{1}$$

Hence, it follows that the reaction proceeds through single iodine atoms formed by dissociation of I_2 molecules:

$$I_2 \rightleftarrows 2I$$

In connection with the dependence of the reaction rate on the arsenious acid concentration in the aqueous phase, an increase in concentration is accompanied by an increase of reaction rate until a limiting value is reached, and beyond this point a further concentration increase of arsenious acid does not bring about a further acceleration of the reaction. Figure 1 presents the dependence of rate constant, k, from equation (1) on the

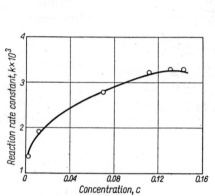

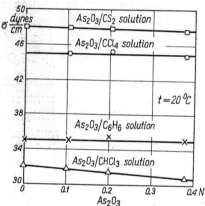

Fig. 1. Rate constant k of the reaction of arsenious acid with iodine versus the concentration of arsenious acid.

Fig. 2. Interface tension versus the concentration of arsenious acid.

concentration of arsenious acid. This dependence can be expressed by an equation analogous to Freundlich's adsorption isotherm:

$$k = A \cdot c^{1/n} \tag{2}$$

This suggests that iodine reacts only with molecules of arsenious acid adsorbed on the boundary surface between the aqueous solution and the organic solvent.

Bogusławski (9) established by direct measurement of the interface tension, applying the stalagmometric method, that, except in systems with chloroform, this tension is probably independent of the arsenious acid concentration in the aqueous phase, thus proving that the adsorption taking place is slight (Fig. 2).

The relatively high temperature coefficient of the rate constant, about 1.6 (corresponding to an apparent activation energy of about 8600 kcal/mole), may be considered as a further proof against the diffusive character of the examined process.

b. Hydrolysis of sulfuryl chloride

R. Sołoniewicz (10, 11) found that adsorption at the boundary layer has a pronounced effect on the hydrolysis of sulfuryl chloride. The experiments were carried out so that the sulfuryl chloride dissolved in carbon tetrachloride underwent hydrolysis at the boundary of its contact with an aqueous phase. The reaction course was followed by determination of the concentration in the aqueous solution of Cl⁻ ions, formed according to the equation:

$$SO_2Cl_2 + 2H_2O = SO_4^{2-} + 2Cl^- + 4H^+$$

The process may be represented by an equation of the first order. The decrease in the rate constant during the initial stages of the reaction was shown by further investigation to be caused by increased acidity of the aqueous phase. The equation of the reaction shows that 4 gram-equi-

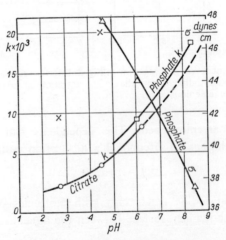

Fig. 3. Rate constant k of hydrolysis of the sulfuryl chloride and the interface tension σ versus the pH of the aqueous phase.

valents of acid are formed by the hydrolysis of 1 mole of SO_2Cl_2. Figure 3 represents the dependence of the constant, k, on the hydrogen ion concentration of this phase, maintained by citrate or phosphate buffers.

It is noteworthy that in the case of phosphate buffers, the increase of pH, with resulting increase of reaction rate constant, is accompanied by a drop of interface tension between the two phases. The interface tension has a significant influence on the reaction rate; this is proved experimentally by introducing variable quantities of surface-active substances, such as

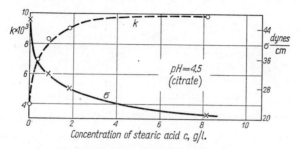

Fig. 4. Rate constant k of the sulfuryl chloride hydrolysis and the interface tension σ versus the concentration of stearic acid.

stearic acid or cetyl alcohol, into the reacting mixture. As is shown in Fig. 4, the rise of the rate constant curve is convergent with the fall of the interface tension curve. A further addition of surface-active substances does not have a further accelerating effect, and may even inhibit the reaction (Figs. 5 and 6).

Addition of cationic detergents, such as Sapamine KW and Zephirol, has a particularly pronounced accelerating action on the reaction. On

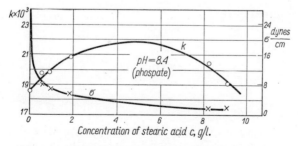

Fig. 5. Rate constant k of the sulfuryl chloride hydrolysis and the interface tension σ versus the concentration of stearic acid.

the other hand, anionic detergents such as sodium stearate and Ultravon W, in spite of a marked drop in interface tension, either have no influence on the rate constant or may even reduce it slightly.

Table 1 gives results of these experiments.

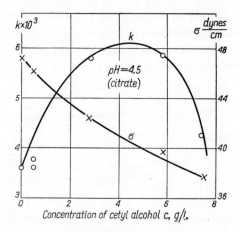

Fig. 6. Rate constant k of the sulfuryl chloride hydrolysis and the interface tension σ versus the concentration of cetyl alcohol.

TABLE 1

EFFECT OF DETERGENTS ON THE SULFURYL CHLORIDE HYDROLYSIS AT 25 °C, $SO_2Cl_2 = 0.1$ MOLE/L., pH = 4.5 (CITRATE BUFFER), STIRRING VELOCITY 140 REV/MIN

Substance added	mg/1000 ml	dyne/cm	$k \times 10^3$
Without addition	—	47.0	3.6
Sapamine KW $[C_{18}H_{35}CO \cdot NH \cdot CH_2 \cdot CH_2 \cdot N(C_2H_5)_3]^+ \cdot [SO_4 \cdot CH_3]^-$	82	35.0	6.8
Zephirol $\left[R_1 - N \begin{smallmatrix} R_2 \\ \\ R_3 \end{smallmatrix} - CH_2 \bigcirc \right]^+ Cl^-$	160	26.0	14.5
Ultravon W $ HO_3S$ with NH, N, $C-(CH_2)_{16}-CH_3$	200	7.6	3.42

The temperature coefficient of the rate constant and the apparent activation energy have about the same values as in the previous reaction, namely, 1.6 and 8600 kcal/mole, respectively.

The above results may be briefly explained as follows.

The factor determining the over-all rate of the process is not the diffusion of sulfuryl chloride towards the interface surface, but the hydrolysis reaction of its molecules adsorbed on the interface of both the liquid phases. This is also supported by the magnitude of the temperature coefficient. The reaction rate is proportional to the number of adsorbed molecules, and, as the adsorption is only slight, it is proportional to the total concentration of SO_2Cl_2 in the carbon tetrachloride. The addition of small quantities of surface-active substances favours penetration of the reacting molecules and their adsorption in the boundary layer. This is verified in a separate experiment: namely, the addition of sulfuryl chloride to a CCl_4–H_2O system lowers the interface tension to a greater degree when this system contains small amounts of stearic acid than when the latter is absent. Larger quantities of detergent make the reaction more difficult because of surface blocking. The ionic charge of the detergent brings about proper orientation of the dipole molecules of SO_2Cl_2 towards the boundary surface. Positive charges collecting on this surface orientate the dipoles towards the negative poles, i.e. the atoms of chlorine, which facilitate the process of hydrolysis. Otherwise the orientation direction of dipoles is reversed and the reaction rate is diminished.

2. REACTION AT A LIQUID–GAS INTERFACE

a. Reaction of sulphur dioxide with iodine

Iodine reacts with sulphur dioxide only in the presence of water, according to the equation:

$$I_2 + SO_4 + 2H_2O = 2HI + H_2SO_4$$

In a homogeneous solution the rate of the reaction cannot be examined kinetically. Fischer's method of determining small quantities of water in non-aqueous liquids is based on this reaction.

S. and T. Witek (12) have proved that the hydrogen iodide formed enters into a reversible reaction with a further quantity of SO_2, forming an unstable complex which gives a yellow colour to the solution:

$$HI + SO_2 \rightleftarrows HI \cdot SO_2$$

In this connection it should be mentioned that conductometric and spectrophotometric investigations made by S. and T. Witek in collaboration with T. Paryjczak et ae. (13) indicate the formation of analogous complexes in solutions containing, besides SO_2, hydrogen bromide or hydrogen chloride.

S. and T. Witek (14) have studied the kinetics of the reaction between iodine dissolved in water or in hydrated alcohols such as methanol, ethanol or isopropanol, and gaseous sulphur dioxide passed over the free surface of the liquid. Under these conditions the rate of the first stage of the reaction appears to be proportional to the square root of the iodine concentration and to the rate of flow of SO_2. Consequently the authors propose the following mechanism for the reaction:

$$SO_2 + I \rightarrow SO_2I$$

$$SO_2I + I \rightarrow SO_2I_2$$

$$SO_2I_2 + 2H_2O \rightarrow H_2SO_4 + 2HI$$

It has also been shown that there is a linear dependence of rate constant on the water content of the ethanolic iodine solution and on the stirring velocity in the liquid phase. Addition of H_2SO_4, KCl, KBr, KI or NaCl to the liquid phase has a definite though slight effect. While H_2SO_4 has a slight inhibiting effect on the reaction, the remaining compounds accelerate it slightly. This action is probably due to primary salt effect, according to Brönsted's theory.

The rate of the second stage of the reaction between sulphur dioxide and hydrogen iodide is proportional to HI concentration as well as to the rate of flow of SO_2. The reaction does not attain complete consumption of hydrogen iodide and the equilibrium established at constant flow speed of SO_2 is independent of the initial HI concentration.

The temperature coefficients of the rate constants in both stages of the reaction are small (1.1–1.2), thus indicating that the reaction takes place in the region of diffusion. The adsorption of SO_2 in the superficial layer was not found to have any effect on the reaction rate.

The kinetics of the same reaction in the system aqueous solution of sulphur dioxide–solution of iodine in carbon tetrachloride was investigated by Witekowa and Lewicki (15). In the presence of constant excess of SO_2 in the aqueous phase the reaction rate is directly proportional to the concentration of molecular iodine in CCl_4, and inversely proportional to the concentration of SO_4^{2-} ions formed:

$$-\frac{d[I_2]}{dt} = k \cdot \frac{[I_2]}{[SO_4^{2-}]}$$

The dependence of the rate constant on the concentration of SO_2 in the aqueous phase can be shown graphically by a curve analogous to that for the reaction with arsenious acid in Fig. 1. The replacement of CCl_4 by chloroform, with almost half the viscosity value, brings about a doubling of the rate constant. Addition of electrolytes and ethanol has a similar effect to that on the liquid–gas system.

The authors propose the following different mechanism for the reaction in liquid biphasic systems:

$$SO_2 + I_2 = SO_2 \cdot I_2$$

$$SO_2 \cdot I_2 + 2H_2O = 4H^+ + 2I^- + SO_4^{2-}$$

The low temperature coefficient of the reaction constant (about 1.2), its linear dependence on the stirring velocity, and the effect of the viscosity of the non-aqueous phase on the reaction rate, suggest that the diffusion of reagents into the boundary layer is the deciding factor determining the rate of the whole process.

Concerning the shape of the curve representing the dependence of the rate constant on the SO_2 concentration in the aqueous phase, it is probable that the SO_2 molecules adsorbed on the interface participate in the reaction with iodine. The inhibitive effect of sulphate ions seems to be in accordance with their partial blocking action on the adsorbing surface.

b. Oxidation of hydrogen iodide by oxygen

W. Kamiński (16) investigated the kinetics of this reaction in solutions of potassium iodide in concentrated hydrochloric acid (over 6 N). The reaction rate is proportional to the square root of the iodide ion concentration, and approximately to the partial pressure of oxygen in the gaseous phase; it also increases with the increase of acid concentration. The reaction is catalysed by even small quantities of Cu^{2+} and Fe^{3+} ions. The independence of the reaction rate of the stirring velocity of the liquid suggests that the reaction rate in solution, being slower than the dissolving of oxygen, controls the rate of the whole process. This is also proved by the high temperature coefficient of the rate constant (1.64). In this case the adsorption at the interface cannot be proved in the preliminary stages of the chemical transformation.

Experimental results, dealing with the reaction course in biphasic systems, are still too scanty to formulate any general conclusions regarding the adsorption of reagents in the interface layer being the preliminary stage in reactions of this type.

Nevertheless, the data suggest that adsorption is of some importance only when substances of unusual surface activity are concerned.

REFERENCES

1. Noyes W. A., *Z. Physik. Chem.*, **18**, 118 (1895).
2. Nernst W., *Z. Physik. Chem.*, **47**, 52 (1904).
3. Centnerszwer M., Heller W., *J. Chim. Phys.*, **34**, 217 (1937).
4. Basiński A., *Roczniki Chem.*, **17**, 567 (1937).
5. Langmuir I., *J. Am. Chem. Soc.*, **39**, 1848 (1917).
6. Davies J., *Advances in Catalysis*, **6**, 1 (1954).
7. Józefowicz E., *Roczniki Chem.*, **12**, 442, 788 (1932).
8. Witekowa S., *Roczniki Chem.*, **25**, 3 (1951).
9. Bogusławski L., Józefowicz E., *Zeszyty Nauk. Politech. Łódz. Chem.*, **II**, 3 (1955).
10. Sołoniewicz R.: Doctor thesis (not published).
11. Józefowicz E., Sołoniewicz R., *Mitteilungsblatt der Chem. Ges. in DDR, Sonderheft,* 215 (1959).
12. Witekowa S., Witek T., *Zeszyty Nauk. Politech. Łódz. Chem. Spożywcza,* **I,** 73 (1955).
13. Witekowa S., Witek T., Paryjczak T., *Zeszyty Nauk. Politech. Łódz. Chem.,* **VII,** 17 (1958).
14. Witekowa S., *Roczniki Chem.*, **31**, 395 (1957); Witekowa S., Witek T., *ibid.*, **31**, 437 (1957).
15. Witekowa S., Lewicki A., *Roczniki Chem.* **37**, 91 (1963).
16. Kamiński W.: Unpublished data.

SUBJECT INDEX